The Optics
of Dipole Magnets

The Optics
of Dipole Magnets

JOHN J. LIVINGOOD

ARGONNE NATIONAL LABORATORY
ARGONNE, ILLINOIS

 1969

ACADEMIC PRESS   New York and London

ACADEMIC PRESS, INC.
111 Fifth Avenue, New York, New York 10003

United Kingdom Edition published by
ACADEMIC PRESS, INC. (LONDON) LTD.
Berkeley Square House, London W.1

LIBRARY OF CONGRESS CATALOG CARD NUMBER: 68-23490

PRINTED IN THE UNITED STATES OF AMERICA

Preface

This book is an introduction to the study of the magnets used to deflect moving charged particles. It is intended to be a clear, systematic, and useful presentation of a subject that is important to those who are involved in the design or use of a particle accelerator. When I was attempting to plan a magnet system some time ago, with very little prior knowledge of the subject, a perusal of the literature seemed to disclose almost as many methods of approach as there were papers. The variables selected as independent usually were different, and most authors treated only the one or two varieties of magnets that were of immediate interest to them, so that comparisons between possibly competing systems were difficult to make. It seemed to me that publication of a single line of attack on the different magnet types and on their uses might be of value. The matrix method has been chosen, in first-order approximation.

Chapter 1 presents the basic physics of the method and the desirable approximations. These lead to results generally accepted as extremely useful, although they cannot yield the precision of higher-order calculations. In Chapter 2 the matrix treatment of radial motion is described, and expressions are developed for the image distance, magnification, dispersion, and resolution. A quick method of converting the matrix coefficients of radial motion into those of the axial mode is presented in Chapter 3, along with the general conditions for the equality of the radial and axial image distances.

Chapter 4 describes eighteen types of magnets used for deflection or momentum analysis. Many charts are displayed, showing the influence of the various parameters, so that a quick appraisal can be made of the different instruments that could be employed.

The resolutions obtained by systems of several magnets, deflecting in the same or in opposite directions, and with intermagnet radial images, are considered in Chapter 5.

Chapter 6 is a tabulation of radial matrix coefficients applicable to a chain of three magnets with arbitrary bending angles, edge angles, and field indices (provided only that the latter lie between zero and plus unity). This tabulation can be of use to the reader who wishes to study magnet types and combinations not specifically treated in this volume. Certain of the coefficients are given in two forms; the first for algebraic solution of certain problems and the second for the numerical calculations involved in finding beam-envelope dimensions. Conversion of the coefficients to the axial form is readily done.

Radial phase-space ellipses and beam envelopes are considered in Chapter 7. An understanding of this subject is highly desirable in obtaining a feeling for what magnets accomplish, and it is necessary if magnets of adequate but not wastefully large apertures are to be chosen. The disadvantages of sequentially calculating the ellipse coefficients are pointed out, and the much quicker method of finding them from the already determined matrix coefficients is described. Axial phase-space ellipses and envelopes are considered in Chapter 8.

Chapter 9 gives a step-by-step procedure to find the necessary axial and radial apertures in one or two magnets of rather general characteristics. This section has been planned to be of use even though the reader may not wish to take time to read all that precedes it.

The general concepts of achromatic (that is, nondispersive) systems are considered in Chapter 10. The distinction is made between doubly achromatic systems, in which both the image and the path slope are independent of momentum, and singly achromatic systems, where only the image does not depend on this property. Chapter 11 demonstrates how the labor of designing a doubly achromatic array is vastly reduced if it has mirror symmetry. Several examples are given.

Systems that give only an achromatic image are treated in Chapters 12–15: many graphs of behavior are presented. Chapter 16 describes how two oppositely bending magnets can be either dispersive or singly achromatic, simply by a change in the positions of the object and image slits.

Certain chromatic aberrations are considered briefly in Chapter 17 to justify approximations made earlier. Although second-order effects lie outside the scope of this book, several methods of correcting one aberration of this character are described, without proof, in Chapter 18.

Since many papers on magnets use the approach of geometrical optics, the calculation of the principal planes and of focal lengths measured from them are given in Chapter 19, with several examples.

Quadrupole magnets receive attention only where they play a role in achromatic systems; analysis of their use in general transport problems is well treated elsewhere.

A bibliography of about 270 items as included. It is divided into categories wherein the entries are arranged chronologically.

I am in debt to Dr. Cyril H. M. Turner and Dr. Tat K. Khoe for interesting discussions on symmetric systems and to Warren G. Ramler for many hours of profitable argumentation. Kenneth W. Johnson has been kind enough to write the programs and to operate the computer by which most of the curves have been obtained.

JOHN J. LIVINGOOD

September, 1968

Contents

4. Dispersive One-Magnet Systems

5. Dispersive Multimagnet Systems

6. Radial Matrix Coefficients for Three Magnets

7. Radial Beam Envelopes

8. Axial Beam Envelopes

9. Routine for Envelopes in One or Two Magnets

10. Achromatic Systems—General Considerations

11. Doubly Achromatic Systems

12. Beam Bending by Two Magnets with Achromatic Image

13. BEAM BENDING BY ONE MAGNET AND TWO QUADRUPLES, WITH ACHROMATIC IMAGE

14. ACHROMATIC SINGLE MAGNETS

15. BEAM TRANSLATION BY TWO MAGNETS WITH ACHROMATIC IMAGE

16. DISPERSED OR ACHROMATIC IMAGE WITH TWO MAGNETS

17. CHROMATIC ABERRATIONS

18. CORRECTION OF CERTAIN ABERRATIONS

Notation

The following are the usual meanings. There are occasional alternative interpretations, but only in circumstances such that there should be no confusion.

$a_j, b_j, \ldots, f_j\,(\bar{a}_j, \bar{b}_j, \ldots, \bar{f}_j)$	Matrix coefficients for radial (axial) motion after passage through jth optic element.
$a^*, b^*, \ldots, f^*$	Radial matrix coefficients at plane of symmetry.
$A, B, \ldots, F$	General matrix elements.
B	Magnetic field strength.
d	Perpendicular distance from pole edge to effective edge.
$D_1, (D_2), (D_{12})$	Dispersion coefficient for first (second, both) magnets.
E	Kinetic energy.
$\Delta E/E$	Energy resolution, with ΔE the FWHM of the transmitted band. Alternatively, the fractional half-energy spread of an accelerator's beam of projectiles.
E_0	Rest mass energy.
f_e	Focal length measured from effective edge.
f_{pp}	Focal length measured from principal plane.
$F_1, (F_2), (F_{12})$	Resolution function, i.e., dispersion coefficient per unit radius and per unit magnification of first (second, both) magnets.
G	Gap height of magnet.
$G = dB_x/dz = dB_z/dx$	Gradient of quadrupole.
H_1, H_2, H_3, H_4	Abbreviations for certain functions.
j	Station number of jth optic element. Used as a subscript.
$K = (G/B_0\,\rho_0)^{1/2}$	Quadrupole constant, where $B_0\,\rho_0$ measures the momentum of the projectile, and G is the gradient.
$L_o = S_0/\rho,\ L_i = S_i/\rho$, etc.	Distance in units of bending radius ρ.
M	General matrix. Also used as abbreviation for M_x.
$M_x\,(M_z)$	Radial (axial) magnification. It is negative for an inverted image.
m	Mass of projectile.
m_1, m_2	First magnet, second magnet.
$n = -r\,dB/(B\,dr)$	Field index of magnet, $1 > n \geqslant 0$.
$N_{\alpha j}, N_{\beta j}, N_{\gamma j}$	Abbreviations for expressions which evaluate the radial ellipse coefficients $\alpha_j, \beta_j, \gamma_j$.
$\bar{N}_{\alpha j}, \bar{N}_{\beta j}, \bar{N}_{\gamma j}$	Abbreviations for expressions which evaluate the axial ellipse coefficients $\bar{\alpha}_j, \bar{\beta}_j, \bar{\gamma}_j$.
$N_1 = \rho_1 x_0'$ $\bar{N}_1 = \rho_1 z_0'$ $N_2 = (x_0/\rho_1 x_0')^2$ $\bar{N}_2 = (z_0/\rho_1 z_0')^2$ $N_3 = \rho_1\,\Delta p/p$	Numerical constants used in evaluation of radial and axial beam envelopes.

p	Reference momentum.
$\Delta p/p$	Momentum resolution, with Δp the FWHM of the transmitted band. Alternatively, the fractional half-momentum spread of the accelerator's beam of projectiles.
$pp_o (pp_i)$	Principal plane in object (image) space.
P	Object distance, measured from principal plane.
q	Charge of projectile.
Q	Image distance, measured from principal plane; also, effective length of quadrupole.
r_e	Effective radius of circular pole.
$R_1 (R_2)$	Effective radius of entrance (exit) cylindrical pole edge.
$R_E = \Delta E/E$	Energy resolution.
$R_m = \Delta m/m$	Mass resolution.
$R_p = \Delta p/p$	Momentum resolution.
s_i	Radial width of slit in image plane.
S	Distance along path.
$S_{0x} (S_{0z})$	Object distance for radial (axial) motion, measured from effective edge; written as S_0 when $S_{0x} = S_{0z}$.
$S_{1x} (S_{1z})$	Image distance for radial (axial) motion, measured from effective edge; written as S_1 when $S_{1x} = S_{1z}$.
S_1	Distance beyond first magnet's effective edge; also, separation between effective edges of first and second magnets.
S_2	Distance beyond second magnet's effective edge; also separation between effective edges of second and third magnets.
S_3	Distance beyond effective edge of third magnet.
$t_1 = \tan u_1, t_2 = \tan u_2$, etc.	
$u_1 (u_2)$	Angle of input (output) edge of first magnet.
$u_3 (u_4)$	Angle of input (output) edge of second magnet.
$u_5 (u_6)$	Angle of input (output) edge of third magnet.
v	Velocity.
$V_o (V_i)$	Distance of object (image) space principal plane from effective edge. It is positive if the principal plane is outside the magnet.
w_o	Radial width of object.
w_i	Radial width of image.
x	Radial displacement with respect to p orbit. It is positive in the direction of increasing ρ in the first magnet.
$x' = dx/dS$	Radial slope of path with respect to p orbit.
$x_0 = w_o/2$	Half radial width of object.
x_0'	Maximum radial slope of path at object.
x_1, x_1'	Radial parameters of arbitrary point of object.
z	Axial displacement with respect to midplane.
$z' = dz/dS$	Axial slope of path with respect to midplane.
z_0	Half axial height of object.
z_0'	Maximum axial slope of path at object.
z_1, z_1'	Axial parameters of arbitrary point of object.
α, β	Coefficients in a series expansion of the magnetic field. (Chapter 18 and Bibliography.)
$\alpha_x (\alpha_z)$	Angular divergence at object; $\tan \alpha_x = x_0'$, $\tan \alpha_z = z_0'$.

$\alpha_J, \beta_J, \gamma_J \, (\bar{\alpha}_J, \bar{\beta}_J, \bar{\gamma}_J)$ Coefficients of radial (axial) phase-space ellipse after passage through jth optic element.

$\delta = (1 - n)^{1/2}$

$\varepsilon = n^{1/2}$

ϵ Emittance = phase-space area$/\pi = x_0 \, x_0' \, (z_0 \quad z_0')$.

ρ Radius of curvature of path with momentum p.

θ Bending angle of path with momentum p.

Θ Net bending angle of two or three magnets.

$\phi = \delta\theta$

$\psi = \varepsilon\theta$

$\sigma_1 = \sin\phi_1, \; \sigma_2 = \sin\phi_2$, etc.

$\kappa_1 = \cos\phi_1, \; \kappa_2 = \cos\phi_2$, etc.

$\tau = KQ$ Angular length of quadrupole.

$\Omega = \theta - u_1 - u_2$ Wedge or sector angle.

1 Purpose and Basis

This book is concerned with the dipole electromagnets used as adjuncts to particle accelerators. The purpose of the magnets may be twofold: either to change the direction of motion, so the projectiles will reach some particular target, or to separate from each other ions of different momenta.

The fundamental equation describing the passage of a particle with mass m, charge q, and velocity v through a uniform magnetic field of strength B is

$$mv^2/\rho = qBv.$$

The left side is the centripetal force required to make the orbit a circle of radius ρ, while the right side is the centripetal force that is available. The radius is determined when the other quantities are fixed. The units may be mks (kilograms, meters, meters/second, coulombs, and webers/square meter) or cgs (grams, centimeters, centimeters per second, electromagnetic units of charge, and gauss). The particles are deflected through the angle θ given by $\theta = $ length of magnet$/\rho$. Since ρ is proportional to mv, as shown by the expression above, the deflection through a given magnet becomes less as the momentum increases.

Hence by the nature of the situation, the two actions of deflection and of momentum separation are necessarily intermixed. Without special elaborations, a beam of particles cannot be deflected without introducing separation of momenta, and separation cannot be achieved without a change in direction. We will examine both of these effects, to observe how one or the other can best be done (perhaps with a diminution of the other), and we will see to what extent the use of more than one magnet can further sever the two actions.

Thus our goal is somewhat limited; except when a change in direction is desired, it does not embrace the general problem of transporting particles over long distances. To do this requires quadrupole magnets to keep the

1

cross section of the beam from growing inordinately. In general, we will emphasize momentum-analyzing and nondispersive deflecting systems that do *not* employ quadrupoles. The function of the latter is to supply auxiliary focusing or defocusing forces in the horizontal and vertical planes, and these forces can be provided alternatively by properly slanted entrance and exit edges of a dipole, which can then be said to have built-in quadrupoles. A system of this sort lacks the flexibility of one that includes separate quadrupoles (although, for a price, dipoles can be obtained with rotatable edges), but flexibility can be an advantage more in name than in practice; magnets are heavy, and aligning them is tedious, so a system once installed generally remains as it is for long periods. Furthermore, no apparatus can be built perfectly, and fewer components give less opportunity for errors in construction and placement. Finally, quadrupoles cost money and so do their supporting mounts, regulated power supplies, controls, and wiring. In simplicity, there is virtue.

Magnet Types

There are two basic structures: " C " magnets and " picture-frame " magnets,* both using iron yokes and poles that are activated by copper or aluminum coils connected to a highly stabilized power supply. Typical cross sections are indicated in Fig. 1-1. The plan views can differ considerably. For

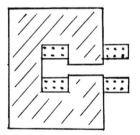 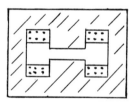

Fig. 1-1. " C " magnet and " picture-frame " magnet.

deflection to the right or left in varying amounts, picture-frame magnets with circular poles are frequently used, so that the magnetized volume of gap is disc shaped. If only one angle of deflection will be used, the poles may be formed to follow the desired path; the yoke also may be curved, or perhaps be

* In this particular field of activity, the word "magnet" generally implies a dipole magnet.

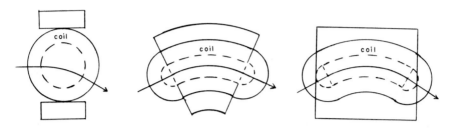

Fig. 1-2. Magnet types; circular pole, sector pole with sector yoke, and sector pole with rectangular yoke. Useful region is bounded by dashed line.

rectangular to reduce machining costs (see Fig. 1-2). Magnets of the latter two types are often called "wedge" or "sector" magnets, since their field regions may be considered as cut from a circle. They are usually of the "C" type to facilitate the introduction of the vacuum chamber.

In all the figures that follow, we shall omit the yoke and coils, indicating only the shape of the region of interest, the field through which the particles pass. To facilitate description, we assume that the plane containing the radius of the curved path is horizontal; the orthogonal axial plane is then vertical.

Magnet iron and machine shop time are both expensive, so it is highly desirable to make the gap's radial width no larger than is necessary. It must be emphasized that since magnetic fields in space do not have abrupt boundaries, the width of the poles must be somewhat larger than the width that is actually used, so that the field in this latter region will indeed be as specified. The gap's height plays a major role in setting the ampere turns needed for a given field strength, and the width is a factor in the length of the windings and in the power. Consequently three chapters of this discussion will be devoted to finding the height and width of the space through which the ions travel so that the gap dimensions can be made just large enough.

APPROXIMATIONS IN FIRST-ORDER THEORY

As is so often the case, it is necessary to make certain approximations in an analysis if it is not to be too cumbersome for ready use. Fortunately, the simplifications required in an examination of magnets are sufficiently close to the truth that results of real value are still obtained, although refinements are possible and indeed necessary if the ultimate in performance is demanded. We will here be concerned only with first-order theory, of which the basis is given in the following paragraphs.

The Effective Edge of a Magnet

When a charged particle enters the gap between the poles of a magnet, it passes through the "fringing field"; this field starts rising from zero at some point outside the magnet and reaches full value, B_0, a short distance inside it. An exact computation of the orbit in the plane of deflection would take into account this region of changing field. Such a procedure is tedious, even if the details of the variation are known, and it is impossible if the magnet has not yet been built. Fortunately, certain aspects of the orbit may be found by assuming that the magnet has "effective edges" where the field abruptly changes from zero to its maximum value. These effective edges lie at small distances outside the true iron edges.

Consider first an ideal "ramp" field B that rises linearly with distance, S, to attain full value B_0 at the edge of the magnet, where $S = S_a$ (Fig. 1-3).

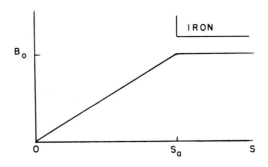

FIG. 1-3. Idealized fringing field.

With K some constant, we have

$$B = KS. \tag{1-1}$$

From the general relation $mv^2/\rho = qBv$, we have

$$\frac{mv}{q}\, d\theta = B\rho\, d\theta = B\, dS = KS\, dS, \tag{1-2}$$

where dS is the path length associated with turning angle $d\theta$. Integrating from $\theta = 0$ to θ' and from $S = 0$ to S_a, we find

$$\theta' = \frac{q}{mv}\frac{KS_a^{2}}{2} = \frac{q}{mv}\frac{B_0 S_a}{2}, \tag{1-3}$$

where θ' is the angle of deflection in the fringing field. Now consider the "effective" or "hard edge" concept as applied to this particular ramp

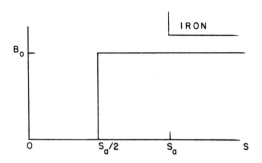

FIG. 1-4. Effective edge of idealized fringing field.

field (Fig. 1-4). B_0 is imagined to extend out to $S_a/2$ from the iron edge and then to fall abruptly to zero. As in Eq. (1-2), we have

$$\frac{mv}{q} \, d\theta = B_0 \, dS, \tag{1-4}$$

where now the field has the constant value B_0. Integrate θ as before, and S from $S_a/2$ to S_a, finding

$$\theta' = \frac{q}{mv} \frac{B_0 \, S_a}{2}. \tag{1-5}$$

This is the same as Eq. (1-3), so the ramp field and the hard-edge field give the same bending angle in the fringing region.

A linear ramp field is an idealization; an actual fringing field will be somewhat as indicated in Fig. 1-5.

Nevertheless, the effective-edge concept may still be applied if this edge is located beyond the iron by a distance d such that area C equals area H.

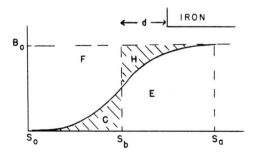

FIG. 1-5. Effective edge of practical fringing field.

This may be seen as follows. For the actual field, we have by Eq. (1-2)

$$\frac{mv}{q} \int_0^{\theta'} d\theta = \int_{S_0}^{S_a} B \, dS,$$

$$\frac{mv}{q} \theta' = C + E.$$

(1-6)

For the hard-edge field,

$$\frac{mv}{q} \int_0^{\theta'} d\theta = B_0 \int_{Sb}^{S_a} dS = B_0(S_a - S_b),$$

$$\frac{mv}{q} \theta' = (C + E + F + H) - (C + F) = E + H.$$

(1-7)

If θ' is to be the same in both cases, then we must have

$$C = H.$$

(1-8)

Hence the actual field and the effective-edge field give the same bend. A plot of the measured fringing field is made and d is located with a planimeter or by "counting squares." Experience shows that d is proportional to the gap height G:

$$d = kG.$$

(1-9)

For most magnets, k lies between 0.5 and 0.7, although in some cases it exceeds unity; the shape and location of the exciting coils are important factors. It should be noted that k generally increases slightly as the field strength is raised; this can be minimized by appropriate rounding of the corners of the iron, so as to reduce saturation.

The use of the effective-edge notion gives a small error in the lateral position of the orbit (Fig. 1-6), since the path is assumed to maintain a constant ρ out to the distance d on leaving the magnet. Actually, ρ increases

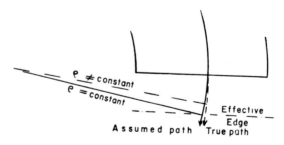

FIG. 1-6. The effective edge concept introduces a small lateral displacement of the orbit.

steadily in the fringing field, so that the real and the "effective-edge" paths are separated. This very small displacement is neglected in first-order theory.

The bending angle of a magnet exceeds the angle between the true edges. This is *not* a small effect and should be taken into account when designing for a given bend of orbit (see Fig. 1-7). A prior knowledge of d is required, to be

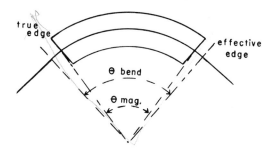

FIG. 1-7. Because of the fringing field, the orbit is deflected through an angle greater than that defined by the iron edges.

obtained from past experience or from consultation with a reliable manufacturer.

Object and image distances and the separation between magnets should be measured from the effective edges. This is assumed in all that follows.

EDGE LENS FOR RADIAL MOTION

A uniform magnetic field acts to converge ions (of a single energy) approaching it on parallel paths, as is indicated in Fig. 1-8(a), where the three initial trajectories are perpendicular to the effective edge. There are three intersection points inside the field, and these get closer together as the separation of the initial paths is smaller and smaller with respect to the radius of curvature. An "image" is said to exist at the region where the envelope of the rays is narrowest, and in first-order theory this narrowest region is considered to be a point. Justification for this will be given later.

Now suppose the edge of the magnet is rotated through the angle u, as in Fig. 1-8(b). (By convention, u is positive for the sense of rotation indicated.) Different distances in the field-free region are traversed by the ions before they reach the effective edge, at which the radii become finite, and it is apparent that the image is formed further downstream; hence the edge may be said to defocus the paths before the body of the magnet focuses them. In Fig. 1-8(c) the edge is rotated in the opposite sense (so that the angle u is negative) and the image occurs further upstream than in Fig. 1-8(a); the edge is focusing.

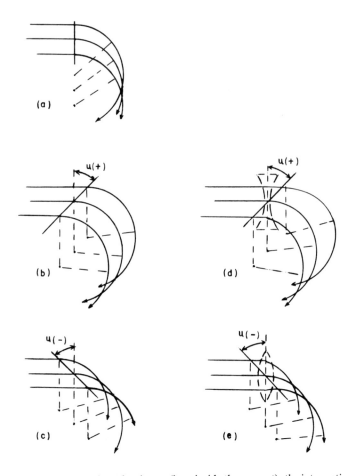

FIG. 1-8. (a) The formation of an image (here inside the magnet); the intersection points get closer together as the separation of the incident particles is reduced. (b) and (c) The defocusing and focusing action of positive and negative edge angles. (d) and (e) The equivalent lenses which may be considered to replace the edge angles. When a line, drawn normal to an edge and extending into the field-free region, lies on the opposite side of the orbit to the center of curvature, then the edge angle u is positive.

Geometrical constructions of this sort are easy to draw, and several analyses of magnets have been made with such figures as a basis for path computations. But an alternative description exists that will be used throughout this volume, since in many respects the resulting analysis is simpler. This is the concept of the equivalent "edge lens," as is shown in Fig. 1-8(d) and (e). All paths are imagined to have the same length in the field-free space and the slanted edge is replaced by a fictitious thin lens that alters the slope of all paths (except the central one) without changing their positions. This lens is located at the intersection of the central ray and the effective edge. Immediately following the lens, all the radii of curvature become finite. It is apparent that the intersection points that locate the image can be made to have the same positions as in the earlier description.

The same concept of an edge lens is employed at the exit surface of a magnet; it is also applicable if the magnetic field is not uniform. It can be shown that the focal length of an edge is given by

$$f = \rho/\tan u, \tag{1-10}$$

this being radially defocusing (focusing) when u is positive (negative).

When $u = 0$ (normal entry or exit), the effective edge lies at a distance d beyond the true iron edge, as described earlier. When $u \neq 0$, the effective edge is still at the perpendicular distance d from the iron, but its distance along the flight path in the field-free region is now

$$d' = d/\cos u, \tag{1-11}$$

as shown in Fig. 1-9. This is important to remember, since the object and

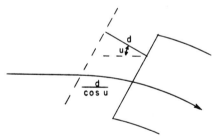

Fig. 1-9. When the perpendicular distance of the effective edge from the iron is d, its distance along the flight path is $d/\cos u$.

image distances and the distance between magnets are measured to the effective edge, along the flight path.

As shown earlier, the bending angle θ is measured from the locations of the input and output effective edges, the radius of curvature being constant between them. This is still true when the edges are rotated. But since the path outside the magnet actually starts bending before the effective edge is reached, the value of u presented to an ion when it reaches the equivalent lens is slightly different than had this early deflection not occurred. However, in the interest of simplicity and in conformity with much current usage, we will neglect this very small correction in what follows, since it cannot be made unless the details of the fringing field are already known.

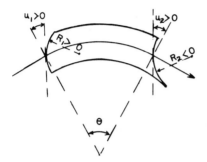

FIG. 1-10. Some magnets have cylindrical edges.

As a further elaboration, edges can be made with cylindrical surfaces of radii R_1 and R_2, as shown in Fig. 1-10. The angle u is then between a normal to the central path and the tangent to the surface, at the intersection of the path with the effective curved edge. The reason for such curved faces will be given in Chapter 18.

Edge Lens for Axial Motion

It is an experimental fact that when $u > 0$, there is not only a horizontal divergence of the beam, but also a vertical convergence (and vice versa if $u < 0$). A moment's consideration shows that no vertical force could be generated if the field really began abruptly, because a purely vertical field can produce only a horizontal force on a charge moving horizontally through it. Hence to explain the vertical force, we must abandon the fiction of an effective edge with its abruptly terminating field and must return to the concept of the fringing field, with lines of force that bulge outward from the iron. At any point not on the midplane in this fringing region, the field B has a vertical component B_z, and a horizontal component B_h that is normal to the edge (see Fig. 1-11). This latter field may be resolved into azimuthal

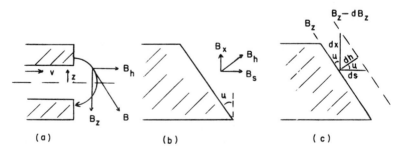

FIG. 1-11. Components of the fringing field. (a) Elevation. (b) Plan at $z > 0$. (c) Plan at $z > 0$.

and radial components B_S and B_x. B_x reacts with the azimuthal velocity v to produce the vertical force. It is qualitatively apparent that since B_x is zero at points well within the magnet and far away from it, the vertical force must have a maximum somewhere near the edge. Quantitatively, we argue as follows. Express B_h as the first term in a Taylor's series:

$$B_h = z \left(\frac{dB_h}{dz} \right)_{z=0} + \cdots . \tag{1-12}$$

Now curl $B = 0$, so

$$\frac{dB_h}{dz} = \frac{dB_z}{dh} . \tag{1-13}$$

Also

$$B_x = B_h \sin u . \tag{1-14}$$

Hence

$$B_x \approx z \frac{dB_z}{dh} \sin u . \tag{1-15}$$

In Fig. 1-11(c), let B_z be the field component at the edge, and let $B_z - dB_z$ be the value at a line parallel to the edge but distant from it by the perpendicular distance dh. Then

$$dh = \cos u \, dS , \tag{1-16}$$

so that

$$B_x \approx z \frac{dB_z}{dS} \tan u . \tag{1-17}$$

(Consideration of the directions of the quantities involved shows that the axial force is focusing if u is positive, and vice versa. This is just contrary to the effect of an edge on radial motion.)

From a curve of measured values of B_z vs. S (the flight path), we may plot dB_z/dS vs. S, somewhat as indicated in Fig. 1-12. Thus the axial force can be seen to peak at some point outside the magnet, for constant z and u.

A rigorous analysis of the z motion through the fringing field should take into account the changes in u (due to radial motion), the changes in z, and in dB_z/dS. This, indeed, can be done, by a detailed step-by-step integration through the particular fringing field, although at the expense of considerable

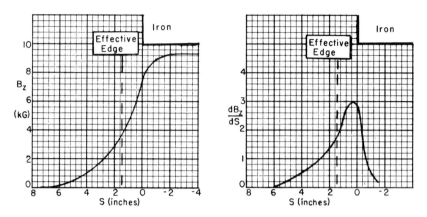

FIG. 1-12. The axial field and its gradient in the fringing region.

labor or by the use of a digital computer. An alternative, though involved, procedure is to assume an "axial" edge lens, not necessarily at the location of the "radial" lens nor at the peak of the dB_z/dS curve nor at its center of gravity (which can be shown to lie at the distance where $B = B_0/2$). Then the bending angle used in the axial equations of motion is not the same angle as is employed in radial motion; furthermore, the axial edge angle can differ from the radial edge angle, since different deflections will have occurred before the axial and radial lenses are encountered. Using some or all of these concepts, determined attempts at handling the axial motion problem, with varying degrees of rigor, may be found in the recent literature.*†

But since there seems to be no simple analytical method for accurately locating an equivalent axial lens, we will adopt a procedure (much used in the theory of particle accelerators and first published by Penner‡ with respect to beam-analyzing magnets) based on the following assumption:

The effect of a rotated edge on both radial and axial motion is to be described by a *single* lens, converging for axial motion and diverging for radial if u is positive, and conversely if u is negative. The lens is taken as located at the junction of the central path and the effective radial edge.

This approximation gives axial image distances that are not quite in accord with experimental values, but for most purposes this is not too serious a matter.

---

* Initial figures indicate the serial number in the bibliography at the end of this book.

† 83, Enge; 40, Wollnik and Ewald; 87, Godlove and Bendel; 41, Wollnik; 20, Steffen; 129, Green *et al.*; 91, Ezoe.

‡ 33, Penner.

VALIDITY OF THE CONCEPT OF A POINT IMAGE

The radial width of the image, when the object is a point, is most readily calculated when the deflection of the central ray is through 180° in a uniform field (see Fig. 1-13). Ions that leave the object, point A, perpendicularly to

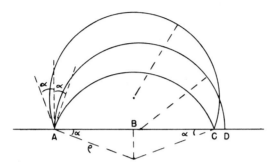

FIG. 1-13. A point object emitting particles with radial divergence angles $\pm\alpha$ will give an image of width CD.

the field edge, will reach the point D. Those that depart with maximum divergence angles $\pm\alpha$ arrive at point C. Now $AB = BC = \rho \cos \alpha$ and $AD = 2\rho$, so the width of the image is $CD = AD - AC = AD - 2AB$;

$$w_i = CD = 2\rho(1 - \cos \alpha). \tag{1-18}$$

For small α, this may be expanded, to give

$$w_i = \rho\alpha^2 = \rho x_0'^2, \tag{1-19}$$

where the radial slope with respect to the central path is written as $x_0' = \tan \alpha \approx \alpha$.

A more general case, for deflection through an arbitrary angle θ and with the object and image remote from the magnet, has been considered by Stephens*; we shall merely quote the result, since the derivation is lengthy.

$$w_i = CD = \frac{\rho}{\sin \zeta} \frac{\alpha^2}{2} \left[\frac{\sin^2 \zeta}{\sin \eta} + \frac{\sin^2 \eta}{\sin \zeta} \right]. \tag{1-20}$$

The symbols are defined in Fig. 1-14.

For $\zeta = \eta = \theta/2$, so that the object and image distances are equal, we find

$$w_i = CD = \rho\alpha^2, \tag{1-21}$$

* 50, Stephens.

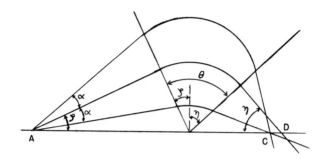

FIG. 1-14. The image width is CD for a point object, when θ is arbitrary.

as in the example above. Expressions more involved than Eq. (1-20) may be found in the literature, for cases where the edge angles u_1 and u_2 are finite.

Thus in all instances the radial image width depends (among other factors) on the square of the divergence angle. This can be of consequence in spectrographs used to analyze the particles from a radioactive material or from a nuclear disintegration, since acceptance of a large radial spread is needed in the interest of intensity. But when the magnet is used to deflect or analyze the beam from an accelerator, where the value of α is only a few milliradians, we are justified in assuming a point image of a point source. (Other aberrations—sources of a widened image—are then generally quite small also.) Nevertheless, there are means of eliminating this so-called α^2 or $x_0'^2$ aberration, and some of them will be discussed in due course.

For somewhat similar reasons, the axial image is never a true point, but it may be considered to be so, in first-order calculations.

FURTHER APPROXIMATIONS

In consonance with the above assumption, several other approximations and postulates are in order:

The same bending angle θ applies to both modes of motion, this angle being determined by the positions of the effective edges, as noted earlier.

The effective edge angles are the same as the true iron edge angles.

The radial divergences from the central path of the trajectories as they approach the magnet are so small that the same value of edge angle may be considered as presented to all rays. This approximation is extremely good for the ions from a particle accelerator, where the divergences are usually measured in milliradians, but it can be of less validity when considering spectrographs, where the disintegration particles emitted from the target can be accepted by the magnet over radial divergences up to several degrees.

The radial displacement of a particle, measured with respect to the central path, is designated as x. The slope (i.e., divergence) in the plane of bending is $x' \equiv dx/dS = \tan \alpha$, where S is the distance along the central orbit. Within the body of a magnet, only the central path is considered as having a constant radius ρ; the path of a noncentral orbit is described as a sinusoidal deviation from the circular central path. (This is not quite the truth, but it is exceedingly close to it.) Such a point of view means that the noncentral orbits are treated as portions of the "radial betatron oscillations" familiar in the theory of orbits used in particle accelerator design.*

In a similar vein, the axial departures of the ions from the midplane of the magnetic field are designated as z, the slope with respect to this plane being $z' \equiv dz/dS$. Nonmidplane orbits are considered as portions of sinusoidal "axial betatron oscillations." *

Furthermore, the matrix treatment of motion through the body of a magnet depends on all of the assumptions inherent in the Kerst–Serber equations† of betatron oscillations; not only that the radial displacement be small compared to the radius of curvature and that all second- and higher-order terms in the equations be negligible, but also (the basic premise) that axial motion occurs at a single radius and that radial motion lies wholly on the midplane, so that the two modes of motion may be considered as not interacting.

Finally, space charge forces are totally neglected. In most present applications, this appears to be justified, but with the strong currents of the next generation of accelerators, the omission of such forces may indeed introduce serious errors.

In spite of this dispiriting list of what is wrong with the fare about to be presented, the results are in complete accord with those derived by others (sometimes using rather different techniques) that have been of immense value to magnet users throughout this century. Roughly speaking, the situation is like this: There are two methods of attack. In one, we are as rigorous as possible in determining the particle's path, and after much tedious computation we arrive at a lengthy and cumbersome expression. Many of the terms (expressing the "aberrations" that contribute to the width or height of the image) have small values, so we disregard them to obtain an approximate equation that displays the main features. In the other approach (here

* 13, Livingood, Chapter 2.
† 25, Kerst and Serber.

used), we assume the validity of the betatron oscillation equations (in the derivation of which all small terms are neglected at the start) and make certain simplifying assumptions about the magnet's edges and the size of the beam's divergences; lo and behold, with practically no effort, we obtain the same approximate result.

One final word of caution. Although the *method* employed in the present analysis is valid no matter what the value of the field index n (see beyond), the *equations* that are displayed are correct *only* if n lies between 0 and $+1$, inclusive. The trigonometric functions of Eq. (2-7) for radial motion would have to be replaced by the corresponding hyperbolic functions if n exceeded $+1$, and the same alterations would be needed in the axial counterpart of Eq. (2-7) if n were negative.

WEDGE ANGLE

Certain authors employ this term (also known as the sector angle), so it may be a convenience to make its meaning clear. It is the angle Ω included between extensions of the effective edges, as indicated in Fig. 1-15.

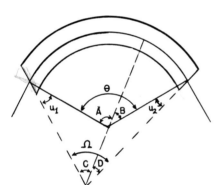

FIG. 1-15. Relations involving the wedge or sector angle Ω.

Since the exterior angle of a triangle is the sum of the opposite interior angles, we have $A = u_1 + C$ and $B = u_2 + D$. Hence

$$A + B = u_1 + u_2 + C + D \quad \text{or} \quad \theta = u_1 + u_2 + \Omega,$$

so

$$\Omega = \theta - u_1 - u_2. \tag{1-22}$$

The use of this concept introduces an extra parameter, so it will not be employed in what follows.

2 Radial Motion in One Magnet

We assume that the magnetic field is plotted in polar coordinates: radius r and azimuth θ. It is then possible and customary to describe any radial dependence of the field B in the form

$$B = K/r^n.$$

Here K is a constant and n is the so-called field index. In a properly designed magnet n also is a constant over a radial width large enough to contain all the particles that pass through it. By differentiation, with K and n fixed, we find that we have

$$n = -\frac{r}{B}\frac{dB}{dr},$$

so that n is proportional to the radial gradient of the field. For a uniform field, we note from either expression that

$$n = 0.$$

For a field that decreases with rising r, the gradient is negative so

$$n > 0,$$

while if the field strengthens as r increases, then

$$n < 0.$$

It is shown in the theory of particle accelerators that an ion's path can exhibit axial oscillations of small amplitude about the midplane of the field only if $n > 0$, and that radial oscillations of small amplitude can occur about a circular orbit only if $n < 1$. Both types of motion are simultaneously possible only if $1 > n > 0$.

Many of the magnets with which we shall be concerned have a uniform field ($n = 0$); consequently radial oscillations can exist (i.e., the body of the

17

magnet acts to focus radially) while axial oscillations do not occur (the body behaves as a field-free region, as far as axial motion is concerned). If axial focusing forces are required, they must be supplied by appropriate edge angles, which then necessarily act to defocus radially, so that the overall radial focusing property of the entire magnet is weakened.

Other magnets to be described have $1 > n > 0$ (in particular, $n = 0.5$). The magnet's body then gives both radial and axial focusing forces, so that finite edge angles are not required, though they may still be employed for special reasons.

THE REQUIRED VALUE OF $B\rho$

We may call to mind the fact that a magnet's field strength B and the radius of curvature ρ of the path through it must be such that their product equals the "rigidity" $B_0 \rho_0$ of the projectile. This is given by

$$B_0 \rho_0 = \frac{1}{kZ} [E^2 + 2EE_0]^{1/2},$$

where Z is the number of electronic charges on the particle, E is its kinetic energy, and E_0 its rest mass energy, both in MeV ($E_0 = 0.511$ MeV for electrons and 938.2 MeV for protons), while k has the values

$k = 300$ for $B_0 \rho_0$ in (webers/m^2)m,
$k = 0.300$ for $B_0 \rho_0$ in kilogauss cm,
$k = 0.762$ for $B_0 \rho_0$ in kilogauss in.

For heavier particles, we may write

$$B_0 \rho_0 = \frac{A}{kZ} \left[\left(\frac{E}{A} \right)^2 + 2 \left(\frac{E}{A} \right) E_{0p} \right]^{1/2},$$

where A is the number of nucleons in the projectile, so that E/A is the kinetic energy (in MeV) per nucleon and E_{0p} is the rest mass energy of a proton.

We now consider the general equations for radial motion.

EQUATIONS OF RADIAL MOTION

When a charged particle of fixed momentum $p + dp$ moves through a magnetic field with index $n < 1$, the equation of radial motion is approximately*

$$\frac{d^2x}{dS^2} + (1 - n) \frac{x}{\rho^2} = \frac{1}{\rho} \frac{dp}{p}, \tag{2-1}$$

---

* For the derivation of this expression and of the matrices to be used in this chapter, see, for example, 13, Livingood; 33, Penner. Originally 25, Kerst and Serber.

where x is the lateral displacement with respect to the circular path of a particle with momentum $p = mv$ and radius ρ. The distance traveled in time t is $S = vt$. The above expression is valid if $x \ll \rho$ so that the radial dependence (if any) of the field B may be given by the first two terms in a Taylor's expansion. For convenience we write

$$\delta \equiv (1 - n)^{1/2} \tag{2-2}$$

and a solution of Eq. (2-1) is

$$x = a \sin(\delta S/\rho) + b \cos(\delta S/\rho) + (\rho/\delta^2)(dp/p), \tag{2-3}$$

where a and b are constants. The radial slope is therefore

$$x' \equiv dx/dS = a(\delta/\rho) \cos(\delta S/\rho) - b(\delta/\rho) \sin(\delta S/\rho). \tag{2-4}$$

As initial conditions, let $x = x_1$ and $x' = x_1'$, when $S = 0$. Then

$$a = \rho x_1'/\delta \quad \text{and} \quad b = x_1 - (\rho/\delta^2) \, dp/p. \tag{2-5}$$

Since the path of the particle with momentum p is curved with radius ρ, we have $S = \rho\eta$, where η is the angle traversed in distance S. Consequently when the entire magnet of effective bending angle θ has been passed, we have $S = \rho\theta$, and the quantity $\delta S/\rho$ may be written as

$$\delta\theta \equiv (1 - n)^{1/2}\theta \equiv \phi. \tag{2-6}$$

Passage through the body of a magnet with a field that is azimuthally constant over the effective angular length θ may therefore be written in the matrix form:

$$\begin{pmatrix} x \\ x' \\ \dfrac{dp}{p} \end{pmatrix} = \begin{pmatrix} \cos\phi & \dfrac{\rho}{\delta}\sin\phi & \dfrac{\rho}{\delta^2}(1 - \cos\phi) \\ -\dfrac{\delta}{\rho}\sin\phi & \cos\phi & \dfrac{1}{\delta}\sin\phi \\ 0 & 0 & 1 \end{pmatrix} \begin{pmatrix} x_1 \\ x_1' \\ \dfrac{dp}{p} \end{pmatrix}. \tag{2-7}$$

Let the input and output faces of the magnet be slanted at the angles u_1 and u_2 with respect to a perpendicular to the p orbit (the orbit with momentum p), the planes of the faces remaining normal to the plane of bending. Then the fringing field at each end has a radial component, and when this is in the direction of increasing ρ we have seen that this field acts approximately as a thin lens that defocuses radially without changing the displacements. The radial transfer matrix through an edge is

$$\begin{pmatrix} 1 & 0 & 0 \\ \dfrac{\tan u}{\rho} & 1 & 0 \\ 0 & 0 & 1 \end{pmatrix},$$

(2-8)

where u is positive for radial defocusing.

Passage through a field-free region of length S (that terminates at the effective edge) leaves the slope unchanged, but the displacement increases in proportion to Sx'. The matrix that transforms across S is therefore

$$\begin{pmatrix} 1 & S & 0 \\ 0 & 1 & 0 \\ 0 & 0 & 1 \end{pmatrix}.$$

(2-9)

Consider a source of ions (perhaps bounded by a slit) of radial width $w_0 = 2x_0$. If the particles originate from an accelerator with internal focusing forces, it will be shown in Chapter 7 that ions which leave the source with maximum slope $\pm x_0'$ have zero radial displacement, while those that start with maximum displacement $\pm x_0$ have zero slope. Thus x_0 and x_0' are *not* associated with the same ion. Let the parameters of an ion that leaves any arbitrary point on the source be x_1 and x_1'. Then the values of x and x' after passage through each of the elements of the system may be found in terms of these initial parameters. These stations are indicated by encircled numbers in the following Fig. 2-1, where the object distance is S_0.

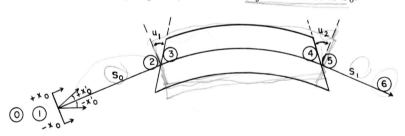

FIG. 2-1. Encircled numbers indicate the stations at which the matrix coefficients change in value. Stations 0 and 1 are at the object; 2 is just outside the entrance effective edge, and 3 is just inside it; 4 and 5 are at the two sides of the exit edge and 6 is at any distance S_1 beyond the magnet.

For convenience we write

$$\boxed{t \equiv \tan u.}$$

(2-10)

Then at any distance S_1 past the magnet we have

$$
\begin{pmatrix} x_6 \\ x_6' \\ dp/p \end{pmatrix} = \begin{pmatrix} 1 & S_1 & 0 \\ 0 & 1 & 0 \\ 0 & 0 & 1 \end{pmatrix} \begin{pmatrix} 1 & 0 & 0 \\ \dfrac{t_2}{\rho} & 1 & 0 \\ 0 & 0 & 1 \end{pmatrix} \begin{pmatrix} \cos\phi & \dfrac{\rho}{\delta}\sin\phi & \dfrac{\rho}{\delta^2}(1-\cos\phi) \\ -\dfrac{\delta}{\rho}\sin\phi & \cos\phi & \dfrac{\sin\phi}{\delta} \\ 0 & 0 & 1 \end{pmatrix}
$$

$$
\times \begin{pmatrix} 1 & 0 & 0 \\ \dfrac{t_1}{\rho} & 1 & 0 \\ 0 & 0 & 1 \end{pmatrix} \begin{pmatrix} 1 & S_0 & 0 \\ 0 & 1 & 0 \\ 0 & 0 & 1 \end{pmatrix} \begin{pmatrix} x_1 \\ x_1' \\ dp/p \end{pmatrix}. \qquad (2\text{-}11)
$$

Thus x_6 and x_6' are of the form

$$x_6 = a_6 x_1 + b_6 x_1' + c_6\, dp/p, \qquad (2\text{-}12)$$

$$x_6' = d_6 x_1 + e_6 x_1' + f_6\, dp/p, \qquad (2\text{-}13)$$

where the coefficients may be evaluated by multiplying out the above matrices. Only the first three are of present interest. They are

$$
a_6 = -\{(S_1/\rho)[\delta\sin\phi - (t_1+t_2)\cos\phi - (t_1 t_2 \sin\phi)/\delta] \\
- \cos\phi - (t_1 \sin\phi)/\delta\}, \qquad (2\text{-}14)
$$

$$
b_6 = (\rho/\delta)\sin\phi + S_0[\cos\phi + (t_1 \sin\phi)/\delta] \\
- S_1\{(S_0/\rho)[\delta\sin\phi - (t_1+t_2)\cos\phi - (t_1 t_2 \sin\phi)/\delta] \\
- \cos\phi - (t_2 \sin\phi)/\delta\}, \qquad (2\text{-}15)
$$

$$c_6 = (\rho/\delta^2)(1-\cos\phi) + S_1[t_2(1-\cos\phi)/\delta^2 + (\sin\phi)/\delta]. \qquad (2\text{-}16)$$

IMAGE DISTANCE

The criterion, in first-order theory, for the formation of an image at some particular value of S_1 is that b_6 should vanish in Eq. (2-12), since an image is characterized by the fact that all particles from any one point on the source, irrespective of the radial slopes of their paths at that point, will have the same displacement at the image (assuming the same momentum for all). Consequently we set

$$b_6 = 0 \qquad (2\text{-}17)$$

in Eq. (2-15) and solve for S_1, which then by definition is the radial image distance S_{ix}. This procedure yields

$$S_{ix} = \frac{S_0[\cos \phi + (t_1 \sin \phi)/\delta] + (\rho \sin \phi)/\delta}{(S_0/\rho)[\delta \sin \phi - (t_1 + t_2) \cos \phi - (t_1 t_2 \sin \phi)/\delta] - \cos \phi - (t_2 \sin \phi)/\delta}$$

(2-18)

Occasionally it is useful to solve this for S_0:

$$S_0 = \frac{S_{ix}[\cos \phi + (t_2 \sin \phi)/\delta] + (\rho \sin \phi)/\delta}{(S_{ix}/\rho)[\delta \sin \phi - (t_1 + t_2)\cos \phi - (t_1 t_2 \sin \phi)/\delta] - \cos \phi - (t_1 \sin \phi)/\delta}.$$

(2-19)

FOCAL DISTANCE

The image distance will be infinite when the object distance is the upstream radial focal distance S_{0xf}, given by

$$S_{0xf} = \frac{\rho[\cos \phi + (t_2 \sin \phi)/\delta]}{\delta \sin \phi - (t_1 + t_2)\cos \phi - (t_1 t_2 \sin \phi)/\delta}.$$

(2-20)

If we divide all terms on the right of Eq. (2-18) by S_0 and then let $S_0 = \infty$, we obtain the downstream focal distance S_{ixf}:

$$S_{ixf} = \frac{\rho[\cos \phi + (t_1 \sin \phi)/\delta]}{\delta \sin \phi - (t_1 + t_2)\cos \phi - (t_1 t_2 \sin \phi)/\delta}.$$

(2-21)

MAGNIFICATION

When evaluated at the image distance (that is, at $S_1 = S_{ix}$), the quantity a_6 is known as the radial magnification M_x for particles of momentum p, since then Eq. (2-12) is simply

$$x_6 = M_x x_1.$$

(2-22)

If we now let the arbitrary displacement x_1 be the object's half-width $x_0 = w_0/2$, where w_0 is the full width, then the full width of the p image is

$$w_i = M_x w_0.$$

(2-23)

A negative value of M_x corresponds to an image that is inverted with respect to its object.

When S_{ix}, as given by Eq. (2-18), is used for S_1 in Eq. (2-14) for a_6, the latter becomes

$$M_x = \frac{-1}{(S_0/\rho)[\delta \sin \phi - (t_1 + t_2) \cos \phi - (t_1 t_2 \sin \phi)/\delta] - \cos \phi - (t_2 \sin \phi)/\delta}$$

(2-24)

Thus M_x equals minus 1 over the denominator of the expression for the radial image distance as given by Eq. (2-18). (The equation for S_{ix} is sometimes seen in the literature after division of all terms by cos ϕ, so that only tan ϕ appears. But then the denominator no longer represents $-1/M_x$, which must often be computed anyway.)

When Eq. (2-24) is solved for the object distance, we find

$$\frac{S_0}{\rho} = \frac{(-1/M_x) + \cos \phi + (t_2 \sin \phi)/\delta}{\delta \sin \phi - (t_1 + t_2)\cos \phi - (t_1 t_2 \sin \phi)/\delta}.$$

(2-25)

Using this in Eq. (2-18) for the image distance we get

$$\frac{S_{ix}}{\rho} = \frac{-M_x + \cos \phi + (t_1 \sin \phi)/\delta}{\delta \sin \phi - (t_1 + t_2)\cos \phi - (t_1 t_2 \sin \phi)/\delta}.$$

(2-26)

These last two expressions are occasionally of convenience.

DISPERSION

When c_6, as given by Eq. (2-16), is evaluated at the image distance, so that S_1 appearing in Eq. (2-16) is replaced by S_{ix} as given in Eq. (2-18), then c_6 is called the dispersion coefficient D, which is found to have the value

$$D = \frac{(\rho/\delta^2)\{(S_0/\rho)[\delta \sin \phi + t_1(1 - \cos \phi)] + 1 - \cos \phi\}}{(S_0/\rho)[\delta \sin \phi - (t_1 + t_2)\cos \phi - (t_1 t_2 \sin \phi)/\delta] - \cos \phi - (t_2 \sin \phi)/\delta}.$$

(2-27)

It will prove convenient to extract from this the denominator and the ρ in the numerator, and to *define* the quantity:

$$F \equiv \frac{1}{\delta^2} \{(S_0/\rho)[\delta \sin \phi + t_1(1 - \cos \phi)] + 1 - \cos \phi\}.$$

(2-28)

Note that this depends on t_1 ($=\tan u_1$) but not on u_2.

Then, using Eq. (2-24) for M_x, the dispersion coefficient may be given as

$$D = -M_x \rho F.$$

(2-29)

Thus F is the dispersion coefficient per unit radial magnification and per unit radius of curvature. For reasons to become apparent later, F may also be called the resolution function.

When $S_0 = \infty$, we find that $F = \infty$ and $M_x = 0$, so that D, as given by Eq. (2-29), is indeterminate. We must then find D by dividing the numerator and denominator of Eq. (2-27) by S_0 before setting it equal to infinity:

$$D = \frac{(\rho/\delta^2)[\delta \sin \phi + t_1(1 - \cos \phi)]}{\delta \sin \phi - (t_1 + t_2) \cos \phi - (t_1 t_2 \sin \phi)/\delta}. \qquad (2\text{-}29a)$$

MOMENTUM RESOLUTION FROM A CONTINUUM

Particle accelerators usually emit a beam of ions with a greater spread in momentum than the experimenter desires. The dispersive property of a magnet can be used to reduce this spread if a narrow slit is placed in the image plane, so that only a small band of momenta is transmitted.

Assume that there is no transverse ordering of momenta in the initial beam. Let the object (perhaps defined by an input aperture) have a radial width $w_0 = 2x_0$. Draw the object as an arrow, so that its ends may be identified, as shown in Fig. 2-2. The object's tip has the displacement $+x_0$, while

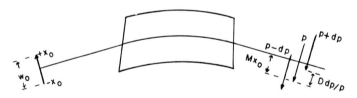

FIG. 2-2. The position of the inverted images of different momenta for a magnet with negative magnification. Not to scale. For clarity, images are separated along the flight path.

its image, for particles of momentum p, has a negative displacement $M_x x_0$ (since M_x is negative for the usual case, where the bending angle θ is less than $180°$). More energetic ions, of momentum $p + dp$ are deflected less and form an image of the tip with less negative displacement, since by Eq. (2-12) at the image distance (where $a_6 = M_x$, $b_6 = 0$, and $c_6 = D$), we have

$$x_6 = M_x x_0 + D \, dp/p. \qquad (2\text{-}30)$$

For a given D and a sufficiently large dp, the tip of the $p + dp$ image moves into the region of positive x, and can even be located beyond the tail of the p image, as is indicated in the following Fig. 2-3.

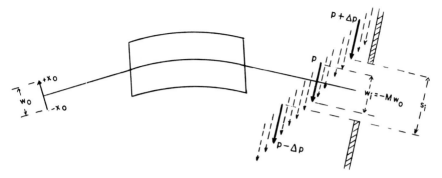

FIG. 2-3. The array of images when there is a continuous distribution of momenta.

In the image plane let there be a slit of width s_i which exceeds the width w_i $(= - M_x w_0)$ of a single image (Fig. 2-3), the slit being centered on the p image. Then in the continuum of images there will be two limiting ones of momenta $p + \Delta p$ and $p - \Delta p$ which *just* fail to be transmitted in any degree at all. This *defines* Δp.

If $s_i > w_i$, not only is the p image entirely transmitted, but so also are some images immediately adjacent. More remote images are only partially passed. Assuming equal populations of all momenta, the ideal plot of percent transmission vs. momentum is trapezoidal, with a base width of 2 Δp. Such a wide slit is useful if high intensity is more important than extreme homogeneity of momentum (Fig. 2-4).

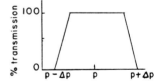

FIG. 2-4. Intensity of transmitted momenta when the slit width exceeds that of one image.

The value of Δp may be related to the magnet's properties as follows.

The displacement, from the optic axis, of the tip of the $p + \Delta p$ image is $x_6 = s_i/2$ and since $x_0 = w_0/2$, we have, from Eq. (2-30),

$$s_i/2 = M_x w_0/2 + D \, \Delta p/p. \qquad (2\text{-}31)$$

The momentum resolution is *defined* as

$$R_p \equiv \frac{\Delta p}{p}, \qquad (2\text{-}32)$$

expressed as a fraction or as a percentage. A small value is wanted. Hence

$$R_p = \frac{\Delta p}{p} = \frac{s_i - M_x w_o}{2D} = \frac{s_i - M_x w_o}{-2M_x \rho F}, \tag{2-33}$$

where F is given in terms of the magnet's parameters by Eq. (2-28). Recall that M_x is negative.

If the image slit has a width s_i just as large as one image ($s_i = w_i = -M_x w_o$), the resolution becomes

$$R_p = \frac{\Delta p}{p} = \frac{-M_x w_o}{D} = \frac{w_o}{\rho F}. \tag{2-34}$$

This choice is almost universally used in momentum analyzing magnets following accelerators, since *only* the wanted ions of momentum p are *fully* transmitted. The intensity plot is triangular, the full width at half maximum (FWHM) being Δp (Fig. 2-5). The total spread is again 2 Δp, but now Δp is smaller than in the previous case.

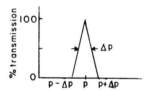

FIG. 2-5. Intensity of transmitted momenta when the slit width just equals that of one image.

Further reduction of s_i is not very profitable, for the intensity falls rapidly with but small improvement in resolution. Thus for s_i (and the intensity) approaching zero, the resolution approaches $R_p = -M_x w_o/(2D) = w_o/(2\rho F)$.

The object slit width w_o is made no larger than the least spot size that can be cast on it by a pair of quadrupoles* located between the accelerator and w_o, which then transmits all of the ions. Improvement in resolution can be effected by reducing w_o, but only at the expense of fewer particles.

When the input beam is of width w_o and is composed of approximately parallel rays, we have $S_0 = \infty$ and $M_x = 0$; then by Eq. (2-30) we find that

$$R_p = \frac{\Delta p}{p} = \frac{x_6}{D} = \frac{w_o}{2D}, \tag{2-34a}$$

where D is given by Eq. (2-29a). Since the output slit, now of width $s_i = w_o$, is finite, it will pass all ions with momentum between $p - \Delta p$ and $p + \Delta p$,

* 13. Livingood, Chapter 15.

but since the images are points (ideally) it is not possible to transmit only a portion of each (as does occur with images of finite size). Consequently a plot of percent transmission vs p theoretically will be a rectangle, rather than having the shape of a truncated triangle such as was shown in Fig. 2-4.

SLIT SCATTERING

From Eq. (2-28), we see that F is proportional to S_0, so by Eq. (2-34) a large object distance improves the resolution. But from Eq. (2-24) it is evident that a large S_0 decreases $|M_x|$, so the image becomes very narrow. This may be satisfactory if the source emits particles of discrete energy, such as the alpha particles from radium, since the images may be recorded directly on a photographic emulsion without the use of an output slit. (See Fig. 2-6.)

But if the magnet is used to take a momentum bite from a continuous distribution, as with the beam from an accelerator, then an output slit is required. As noted earlier, it should be just as wide as the image of a single momentum if all the wanted p ions are to be passed and the best resolution is desired. Scattering at and through the jaws of the output slit will occur,* so if the transmitted beam is not to be too seriously contaminated with particles degraded in energy, the image plane slit must be sufficiently wide that the ratio of open area to scattering area is acceptable. This puts some minimum on the absolute value of radial magnification that can be employed profitably. (We can supply no simple recommendation.)

An alternative method of reducing the background of degraded ions can be employed if funds and floor space are available: The output slit can serve as the object slit for a second magnet and at its image plane a one-jawed "half slit" intercepts the low energy degraded particles.†

When negative ions, such as H^-, are to be analyzed, massive slit jaws may be replaced by thin foils. These convert to H^+ all particles that strike them, so that any subsequent magnet, such as a switch, will bend them away from the highly resolved H^- ions that are transmitted through the slit opening. There is no scattering to degrade the purity of the transmitted beam, so the image and slit can be as narrow as wanted.

ENERGY RESOLUTION

In many cases it is desirable to express the resolution of a magnet in terms of the kinetic energy E and the ΔE, such that the images of energies $E + \Delta E$ and $E - \Delta E$ just fail to be passed by the image plane slit.

---

* 227, Courant; 228, Burge and Smith.
† 229, Yagi.

It can be shown* that the momentum p is related to the kinetic energy E and the rest-mass energy E_0 by the relativistic expression:

$$p = (E^2 + 2EE_0)^{1/2}/c. \qquad (2\text{-}35)$$

(This is in mks units. The energies are in joules and c, the velocity of light, is in meters per second.) From this it follows that the energy resolution R_E is

$$R_E \equiv \frac{\Delta E}{E} = \left(\frac{E + 2E_0}{E + E_0}\right)\frac{\Delta p}{p}. \qquad (2\text{-}36)$$

For nonrelativistic cases, where $E \ll E_0$, this becomes

$$R_E \equiv \frac{\Delta E}{E} = 2\,\frac{\Delta p}{p}, \qquad (2\text{-}37)$$

while for highly relativistic particles, where $E \gg E_0$, we get

$$R_E \equiv \frac{\Delta E}{E} = \frac{\Delta p}{p}. \qquad (2\text{-}38)$$

Certain versatile electron accelerators can operate over both regimes. As the energy is raised, the last two expressions show that although the momentum resolution of a given magnet remains constant, the energy resolution improves, by as much as the factor 2. [Note that Eq. (2-36) is dimensionless; the energies can be in any units.]

ALTERNATIVE DEFINITIONS OF RESOLUTION IN MOMENTUM AND ENERGY

Nomenclature is not standardized, unfortunately, and in about half the literature resolution is defined as

$$R_p \equiv \frac{p}{\Delta p} \quad \text{and} \quad R_E \equiv \frac{E}{\Delta E}. \qquad (2\text{-}39)$$

In these forms, the resolution is a *large* positive number.

SPECTROGRAPHS FOR DISCRETE MASSES OR ENERGIES

The dispersive property may be used to separate beam components that differ in momentum because of a difference in mass, as occurs, for example, in isotope separators. The accelerating voltage V applied after the ionizing source

---

* 13, Livingood, Eqs. (1-2) and (1-36); there kinetic energy is written as T.

is generally so small that nonrelativistic expressions may be used. Assuming the same charge q on all ions and equal distance of travel in the accelerating field, we have,

$$mv^2/2 = qV \quad \text{so that} \quad p = mv = (2qVm)^{1/2}.$$

Hence the mass resolution is

$$R_m \equiv \frac{\Delta m}{m} = 2\,\frac{\Delta p}{p}. \tag{2-40}$$

A similar situation arises when a magnet is used to record on a photographic emulsion the images of particles (say protons) coming from a nuclear disintegration as a result of bombardment (see Fig. 2-6). The particles have

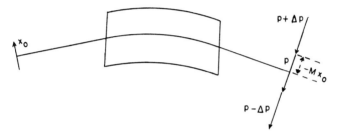

FIG. 2-6. Resolved images of discrete momenta recorded on a photographic emulsion.

the same mass but differ in energy, and as this latter is usually nonrelativistic we have, as before,

$$R_E \equiv \frac{\Delta E}{E} = 2\,\frac{\Delta p}{p}. \tag{2-41}$$

In both these cases, the masses and energies are discrete and are resolved when neighboring images just fail to overlap (except for a vanishingly small gap to allow recognition of their ends). No slit in the image plane is used; consequently, a small magnification, $|M_x| < 1$, is profitable, as will be evident in the following Eq. (2-42).

The tip of the $p + \Delta p$ image has positive displacement $x_6 = -M_x x_0$. Hence

$$-M_x x_0 = M_x x_0 + D\,\Delta p/p,$$

$$\frac{\Delta p}{p} = \frac{-2M_x x_0}{D} = \frac{-M_x w_0}{D},$$

$$R_m = R_E = 2\,\frac{\Delta p}{p} = \frac{-2M_x w_0}{D} = \frac{2w_0}{\rho F}. \tag{2-42}$$

A magnet designed to just resolve masses of, say, $m = 100$ and $m + \Delta m = 101$, will not resolve heavier ions, since their images will overlap. On the other hand, lighter particles will have images that are more than critically resolved.

SPECTROMETERS WITH ELECTRIC RECORDING

Here the electric charges carried by the various images are collected on an electrode behind the image-plane slit, and the resulting current is displayed on an x-y chart recorder. This process introduces a complication that worsens the resolution of a magnet, as compared with the case when the images are directly recorded on an emulsion.

The various discrete images of width w_i $(= -M_x w_o)$ are successively slid past the slit of width s_i by changing the magnetic field. An isolated image will give a triangular or trapezoidal signal on the recorder; the sloping sides are generated as more and more (or less and less) of the image is transmitted by the slit. If there are two or more images of equal intensity that just do not overlap, the signal from one starts to rise as that from the other starts to decline, so the total signal will be of constant intensity.

Some finite separation Δ is required between images to cause a dip in the signal. This means that the dispersion must be greater than if the images were just in contact; i.e., a given magnet will have poorer resolution when used in this manner when Δ must be finite, than when employed in such a way that Δ can be zero.

For images of greatly differing intensity, there can be controversy as to what constitutes identifiable discrete momenta, so it is often arbitrarily demanded that the recorder's signal must drop to zero between completely resolved images. We here adopt this convention, and for simplicity of illustration, we assume equal intensity of the various images.

We now consider several different relations between the image separation Δ, the slit width s_i, and the image width w_i.

Case A. $\Delta > s_i > w_i$

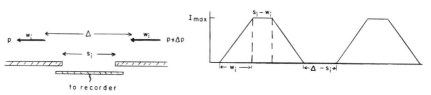

FIG. 2-7. The magnet has better resolution than is needed.

The signals are of maximum intensity I_{max}, but the distance of zero signal, $\Delta - s_i$, is unnecessarily long; i.e., the p and $p + \Delta p$ images are separated by more than is required for the signals to be *just* resolved.

Case B. $\Delta = s_i > w_i$

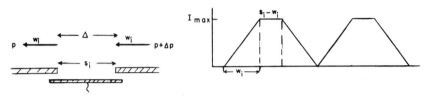

FIG. 2-8. The magnet again has better resolution than is needed.

$I = I_{max}$, the signals are just resolved, but their flat tops result from Δ being larger than necessary.

Case C. $\Delta = s_i = w_i$

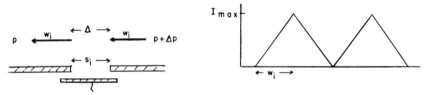

FIG. 2-9. The magnet has just adequate resolution.

$I = I_{max}$, the signals are just resolved, Δ and the dispersion are no larger than is required. This is the ideal arbitrary condition.

Case D. $\Delta = s_i < w_i$

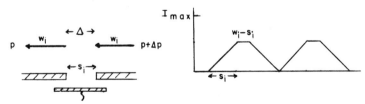

FIG. 2-10. The magnet's resolution is just adequate but not all the ions are recorded.

The signals are just resolved but are of less intensity than I_{max}, being $I = I_{max} s_i / w_i$. How far one can go in making $\Delta = s_i \ll w_i$ will depend on the signal-to-noise ratio of the recording equipment.

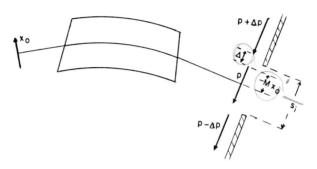

FIG. 2-11. Image positions for an electrically recording spectrometer.

We now compute the resolution. In Fig. 2-11, the displacement of the tip of the $p + \Delta p$ image is $x_6 = -M_x x_0 + \Delta$.

Let $\Delta = s_i$, as in the just-resolved cases B, C, and D. Then

$$-M_x x_0 + s_i = M_x x_0 + D\,\Delta p/p. \qquad (2\text{-}43)$$

Then

$$\frac{\Delta p}{p} = \frac{s_i - 2M_x x_0}{D} = \frac{s_i - M_x w_0}{D}, \qquad (2\text{-}44)$$

and

$$\frac{\Delta m}{m} = \frac{\Delta E}{E} = 2\,\frac{\Delta p}{p} = \frac{2(s_i - M_x w_0)}{D}. \qquad (2\text{-}45)$$

For $\Delta = s_i = w_i = -M_x w_0$ (the "ideal" Case C), this last expression gives

$$\frac{\Delta m}{m} = \frac{\Delta E}{E} = \frac{-4M_x w_0}{D} = \frac{4w_0}{\rho F}. \qquad (2\text{-}46)$$

Note that this resolution is poorer by the factor 2 than that of Eq. (2-42), where the images were recorded on an emulsion, so that the separation Δ of the images could be almost zero. For s_i (and therefore the intensity) approaching zero, we have

$$\frac{\Delta m}{m} = \frac{\Delta E}{E} = \frac{-2M_x w_0}{D} = \frac{2w_0}{\rho F}. \qquad (2\text{-}47)$$

3 Axial Motion in One Magnet

CONVERSION OF RADIAL TO AXIAL COEFFICIENTS

The axial motion of a charged particle in an azimuthally constant field may be described to a good approximation by the expression[*]

$$\frac{d^2z}{dS^2} + \frac{nz}{\rho^2} = 0.$$

Thus the axial "restoring force" is proportional to n, rather than to $1 - n$ as in the radial case of Eq. (2-1). Further, an edge that is radially defocusing is axially focusing, and vice versa. Finally, axial motion is not altered by changes in momentum, to first order. Consequently the expressions for radial motion may be converted to apply to the axial mode by the following steps.

$$\boxed{\begin{aligned}
&\text{Replace } \delta = \sqrt{1 - n} \qquad\qquad \text{by} \quad \varepsilon = \sqrt{n}. \\
&\text{Replace } \phi = \delta\theta = \sqrt{1 - n}\,\theta \quad \text{by} \quad \psi = \varepsilon\theta = \sqrt{n}\,\theta. \\
&\text{Replace } x_0 \text{ and } x_0' \qquad\qquad \text{by} \quad z_0 \text{ and } z_0'. \\
&\text{Change the sign of } t = \tan u. \\
&\text{Set } \Delta p = 0.
\end{aligned}}$$

$$(3\text{-}1)$$

In the *special case* where $n = 0$, so that $\delta = 1$ and $\varepsilon = 0$, these steps lead to

and

$$\boxed{\begin{aligned}
\cos \phi &\to \cos \psi = \cos \varepsilon\theta = 1, \\
\sin \phi &\to \sin \psi = \sin \varepsilon\theta = 0.
\end{aligned}}$$

$$(3\text{-}2)$$

[*] 13, Livingood; 33, Penner. Originally 25, Kerst and Serber.

An indeterminancy then arises in the expression

$$\frac{\sin \psi}{\delta} \to \frac{\sin \psi}{\varepsilon} = \frac{\sin \varepsilon\theta}{\varepsilon} = \frac{\sin 0}{0} = \frac{0}{0}.$$

This may be avoided by first expanding $\sin \psi$:

$$\frac{\sin \psi}{\varepsilon} = \frac{\sin \varepsilon\theta}{\varepsilon} = \frac{\varepsilon\theta}{\varepsilon} = \theta. \tag{3-3}$$

Note that this is not an approximation, since the expansion becomes exact when the angle $\varepsilon\theta$ is zero.

Of particular interest are the expressions for axial magnification and axial image distance, derived by converting Eqs. (2-24) and (2-18):

$$M_z = \frac{-1}{\dfrac{S_{oz}}{\rho}\left[\varepsilon \sin \psi + (t_1 + t_2)\cos \psi - \dfrac{t_1 t_2 \sin \psi}{\varepsilon}\right] - \cos \psi + \dfrac{t_2 \sin \psi}{\varepsilon}} \tag{3-4}$$

$$S_{iz} = -M_z\{S_{oz}[\cos \psi - (t_1 \sin \psi)/\varepsilon] + (\rho \sin \psi)/\varepsilon\}. \tag{3-5}$$

Here we have designated the object distance as S_{oz} to indicate that it may be different from the object distance for radial motion.

For a uniform field ($n = 0$), these give

$$S_{iz} = \frac{S_{oz}(1 - t_1\theta) + \rho\theta}{(S_{oz}/\rho)(t_1 + t_2 - t_1 t_2 \theta) - 1 + t_2 \theta}, \tag{3-6}$$

and if also $t_1 = t_2 = 0$, then

$$M_z = 1 \tag{3-7}$$

and

$$S_{iz} = -(S_{oz} + \rho\theta). \tag{3-8}$$

Since S_{iz} is measured from the exit face, this means that the axial image lies directly on the object, has the same size, and is upright; i.e., the only axial image is the object itself. The upstream focal length occurs when $S_{iz} = \infty$:

$$S_{ozf} = \frac{\rho(1 - t_2 \theta)}{t_1 + t_2 - t_1 t_2 \theta}. \tag{3-9}$$

The downstream focal length is obtained when $S_{0z} = \infty$:

$$S_{izf} = \frac{\rho(1 - t_1\theta)}{t_1 + t_2 - t_1 t_2 \theta}. \tag{3-10}$$

THE TWO MEANINGS OF DOUBLE FOCUSING

When magnet enthusiasts get together, there is often confusion as to the interpretation of the expression "double focusing," because, most unfortunately, it has two separate and distinct senses, depending on the interest of the speaker.

First, in mass spectroscopy, the mass of the particle is to be determined or different masses are to be separated and collected. In apparatus particularly designed for this purpose, a single image is formed of each mass, independent of the velocity of the projectile and of its radial divergence (both within limits) as it leaves the source. When these criteria are fulfilled, the device is said to be double focusing.

Second, in alpha or beta particle spectroscopy and in momentum analysis of ions from an accelerator, the mass is known; what is wanted is a separate image for each momentum. If the image distance is the same in the radial and axial directions, double focusing is said to exist. This condition is also sometimes called "two directional focusing."

In this book, we shall not discuss systems that fall within the first class (except in quoting references in the bibliography), but shall be concerned exclusively with the second group. Hence, *as here used, double focusing means equality of the radial and axial image distances.*

GENERAL CONDITIONS FOR DOUBLE FOCUSING

By equating S_{ix} to S_{iz}, as given by Eqs. (2-18) and (3-5), an expression is found that may be solved for t_1 (as a function of t_2, n, θ, S_{0x}, and S_{0z}) that will cause double focusing; or the expression may be solved for t_2 (as a function of t_1, n, θ, S_{0x}, and S_{0z}) that will give the same result. In many practical cases, there are auxiliary conditions which simplify the expressions for S_{ix} and S_{iz} and hence reduce the complexity of the equations for t_1 and t_2. But as a matter of possible interest, the general expressions will now be given. (In most cases $S_{0x} = S_{0z}$, but situations do exist in which they are different.)

The value of $t_1 \equiv \tan u_1$ needed for double focusing when $t_2 \equiv \tan u_2$ is known is:

$$t_1 = -\frac{B}{2A} \pm \left(\frac{B^2}{4A^2} - \frac{C}{A}\right)^{1/2}, \tag{3-11}$$

where

$$A = \frac{S_{0x}}{\rho} \frac{S_{0z}}{\rho} \left[\frac{\sin \phi}{\delta} \left(\cos \psi - 2t_2 \frac{\sin \psi}{\varepsilon} \right) - \cos \phi \frac{\sin \psi}{\varepsilon} \right], \tag{3-12}$$

$$B = \frac{S_{0x}}{\rho} \frac{S_{0z}}{\rho} \left[2 \cos \phi \left(\cos \psi - t_2 \frac{\sin \psi}{\varepsilon} \right) \right.$$

$$\left. + \sin \phi \left(2t_2 \frac{\cos \psi}{\delta} + \delta \frac{\sin \psi}{\varepsilon} + \varepsilon \frac{\sin \psi}{\delta} \right) \right]$$

$$+ \left(\frac{S_{0x}}{\rho} - \frac{S_{0z}}{\rho} \right) \left[\frac{\sin \phi}{\delta} \left(2t_2 \frac{\sin \psi}{\varepsilon} - \cos \psi \right) + \cos \phi \frac{\sin \psi}{\varepsilon} \right], \tag{3-13}$$

$$C = \frac{S_{0x}}{\rho} \frac{S_{0z}}{\rho} \left[\cos \phi (\varepsilon \sin \psi + 2t_2 \cos \psi) - \delta \sin \phi \cos \psi \right]$$

$$- \left(\frac{S_{0x}}{\rho} - \frac{S_{0z}}{\rho} \right) \cos \phi \cos \psi + \frac{S_{0x}}{\rho} \frac{\sin \psi}{\varepsilon} (2t_2 \cos \phi - \delta \sin \phi)$$

$$+ \frac{S_{0z}}{\rho} \frac{\sin \phi}{\delta} (2t_2 \cos \psi + \varepsilon \sin \psi)$$

$$+ \frac{\sin \phi}{\delta} \left(2t_2 \frac{\sin \psi}{\varepsilon} - \cos \psi \right) + \cos \phi \frac{\sin \psi}{\varepsilon}. \tag{3-14}$$

In the special case where $n = 0$ and $S_{0x} = S_{0z} \equiv S_0$, the value of t_1 required for double focusing is

$$t_1 = \frac{\theta \sin \theta + 2 \cos \theta - 2t_2(\theta \cos \theta - \sin \theta)}{2(\theta \cos \theta - \sin \theta + 2t_2 \theta \sin \theta)}$$

$$\pm \left\{ \frac{[\theta \sin \theta + 2 \cos \theta - 2t_2(\theta \cos \theta - \sin \theta)]^2}{4(\theta \cos \theta - \sin \theta + 2t_2 \theta \sin \theta)^2} \right.$$

$$\left. - \frac{\begin{aligned}\sin \theta(L_o{}^2 + L_o\theta + 1) - \theta \cos \theta \\ - 2t_2[(L_o{}^2 + L_o\theta)\cos \theta + (L_o + \theta)\sin \theta]\end{aligned}}{L_o{}^2(2t_2 \theta \sin \theta + \theta \cos \theta - \sin \theta)} \right\}^{1/2}, \tag{3-15}$$

where $L_o \equiv S_0/\rho$.

The value of t_2 needed for double focusing when t_1 is known is best obtained by a method based on that of Cross.* In Eq. (2-18) for S_{ix}, divide each term by $\cos \phi$; carry out all indicated multiplications and then group the terms so that t_2 is the multiplier of three terms within a parenthesis. Then

---

* 72, Cross.

invert the entire expression; the multiplier of t_2 cancels with the new denominator. Finally divide by L_{ox} $(\equiv S_{0x}/\rho)$. This gives

$$\frac{1}{L_{ix}} = \frac{\delta \tan \phi - (t_1 + 1/L_{ox})}{1 + (1/\delta) \tan \phi(t_1 + 1/L_{ox})} - t_2, \tag{3-16}$$

where $L_{ix} \equiv S_{ix}/\rho$. A similar procedure carried out on Eq. (3-5) for S_{iz} leads to

$$\frac{1}{L_{iz}} = \frac{\varepsilon \tan \psi + (t_1 - 1/L_{oz})}{1 - (1/\varepsilon) \tan \psi(t_1 - 1/L_{oz})} + t_2, \tag{3-17}$$

To obtain the condition for double focusing, we equate these two expressions to find

$$t_2 = \frac{1}{2} \left[\frac{\delta \tan \phi - (t_1 + 1/L_{ox})}{1 + (1/\delta) \tan \phi(t_1 + 1/L_{ox})} - \frac{\varepsilon \tan \psi + (t_1 - 1/L_{oz})}{1 - (1/\varepsilon) \tan \psi(t_1 - 1/L_{oz})} \right],$$

$$\tag{3-18}$$

where, be it remembered, $\phi = \delta\theta = \sqrt{1 - n}\,\theta$ and $\psi = \varepsilon\theta = \sqrt{n}\,\theta$.

For the special case where $n = 0$ and $S_{0x} = S_{0z} = S_0$, we expand $(\tan \psi)/\varepsilon$ into $(\tan \varepsilon\theta)/\varepsilon = \varepsilon\theta/\varepsilon = \theta$ and obtain

$$t_2 = \frac{1}{2} \left[\frac{\tan \theta - (t_1 + 1/L_o)}{1 + \tan \theta(t_1 + 1/L_o)} - \frac{(t_1 - 1/L_o)}{1 - \theta(t_1 - 1/L_o)} \right]. \tag{3-19}$$

If $t_1 = t_2 = 0$ (i.e., if $u_1 = u_2 = 0$) and if $S_{0x} = S_{0z}$, it is readily shown that Eq. (3-18) will be satisfied if $\delta = \varepsilon$, so that also $\phi = \psi$. Since $\delta = (1 - n)^{1/2}$ and $\varepsilon = n^{1/2}$, the field index will then have the value

$$n = 0.5, \tag{3-20}$$

and this requirement is independent of θ. Many magnets are of this type.

It will be shown in Chapter 4, Cases 16 and 17, that double focusing can also be obtained, when $u_1 = u_2 = 0$, with n having other values (between 0 and 1), provided θ has *particular* magnitudes that exceed 180°.

4 Dispersive One-Magnet Systems

Introduction

In this chapter, we will give examples of typical one-magnet dispersive systems. The majority are double focusing. In most cases, charts are included as an aid in rapid evaluation of the various types.

We present first some general conclusions that apply if the magnet is to be used for momentum analysis. For simplicity, we take the usual situation where $S_{0x} = S_{0z} = S_0$, and for convenience we write $S_0/\rho = L_0$, etc.

The output slit should be as wide as one image, in order to pass all the wanted ions. The momentum resolution is then given by Eq. (2-34):

$$R_p = \frac{\Delta p}{p} = \frac{w_0}{\rho F}.$$

For the best resolution, the input slit width w_0 should be as small as is consistent with the intensity requirements; that is, if w_0 is smaller than the minimum width of the beam that can be focused on it by some upstream lens, the resolution will improve but not all of the ions can enter the analyzing system.

Obviously, F should be large, but for a given magnet the larger F is, the smaller becomes the image, so that slit scattering may spoil the purity of the analyzed beam. To continue the discussion, some nominal magnification must be specified, and we choose $M_x = -1$. With this choice, we may summarize the dependence of F on various magnet types.

With a uniform field and with normal entry and exit, it is found that $F = 2$ at all values of θ, for $M_x = -1$. There is no axial focusing.

With a uniform field and either u_1 or u_2 equal to zero but the other with a finite positive value, so as to produce double focusing, we find, for $M_x = -1$, that F ranges from 3.8 to 3.0 as θ varies from 30° to 120°. Double focusing thus improves the resolution, and there is a slight improvement as θ is reduced to small values. On the other hand, the object and image distances are approximately doubled, so that more floor space is needed, and the

38

magnet's gap must be larger in both dimensions, for given divergences of the input beam.

With a uniform field and $\tan u_1 = \tan u_2 = 1/L_0$, only at $M_x = -1$ do we have double focusing, and then $F = 4$ at all θ. L_0 and L_i are, again, about twice the value as with a magnet of $n = u_1 = u_2 = 0$.

With $n = 0.5$ and $u_1 = u_2 = 0$, the magnet is double focusing at all magnifications. For $M_x = -1$, we have $F = 4$ at all θ. The distances are slightly greater than with $n = 0$ and $\tan u_1 = \tan u_2 = 1/L_0$.

At the sacrifice of double focusing, a very substantial increase in F can be obtained if n approaches unity. For example, let $u_1 = u_2 = 0$ and $M_x = -1$; then for $n = 0.9$, we find that $F = 20$. The only relation between θ and n is that their choice determines the value of $L_0 = L_{ix}$.

Double focusing can be retained for high n (with $u_1 = u_2 = 0$ and $M_x = -1$), if θ has a particular value (exceeding 180°) that depends on n. Thus for $n = 0.831$, the bending angle must be $\theta = 270°$ and F has the value 11.8.

Double focusing at high n can also be obtained by the use of finite edge angles. With $n = 0.9$, $\theta = 180°$, $u_1 = 60°$, and $u_2 = -27.8°$, it is found that $F = 26$.

The value of θ has an obvious function in sending the beam into some desired direction and, perhaps more importantly, it determines the floor space required by the analyzing system. For all magnet types, *a larger θ means shorter object and image distances* and hence, in addition, the radial and axial gap dimensions may be less for given beam divergences.

The exit edge angle u_2 contributes to the radial magnification and therefore (although u_2 does not appear explicitly in the expression for F), it does determine the value of F at any given M_x. Thus if u_2 is increased from zero, the same resolution is produced but with greater magnification, so that slit scattering is less serious, or at the same value of M_x the resolution is improved. This effect is most pronounced when $|M_x|$ is in the neighborhood of unity, or greater.

The same remarks apply to u_1, which appears in the expressions both for M_x and for F.

The resolution improves linearly with increasing bending radius ρ. Since the azimuthal length of the magnet is $\rho\theta$, a larger ρ means a longer magnet, but this is the *only* way to better the resolution when the other factors have been exhausted. It is a fallacy to suppose that ρ could be extended profitably to infinity, by omitting the magnet altogether; to obtain resolution the wanted ions must all be in one place and the unwanted ones in others. This means that images must be formed, so that a magnet and a finite ρ are essential.

If the magnet is to be used simply to change the beam's direction, its dispersive property can be a disadvantage. To minimize this, the value of ρ can be reduced by using a stronger magnetic field (here superconductivity may play an important role) or $|M_x|$ can be increased, if this is tolerable with respect to what is to occur further downstream. Deflection without dispersion can be accomplished with one magnet if θ exceeds 180°, or with one magnet and two quadrupoles, or by two or three magnets; these matters will be discussed later.

In most of the following cases, we have expressed all path distances in units of the bending radius in order to reduce the number of curves that need be plotted. Thus:

$$L_o \equiv S_0/\rho, \qquad L_{ix} \equiv S_{ix}/\rho, \qquad L_{iz} \equiv S_{iz}/\rho.$$

This notation is particularly convenient when discussing sector magnets. These are so shaped that the field exists only in the neighborhood of the orbit, so that ρ is a fixed quantity predetermined before manufacture. Therefore when comparing the resolutions of magnets with different θ at a given L_o or M_x, one must keep in mind that the values of F read from the charts are *immediately* indicative of the resolution *only* if ρ is the same.

For simplicity, we have assumed equality of the radial and axial object distances, so that $S_{0x} = S_{0z} \equiv S_0$. Only in rare instances is this not the case in practice.

CASE 1. $n = 0, u_1 = u_2 = 0$

Single Focus

$$M_x = -\frac{1}{L_o \sin \theta - \cos \theta}, \tag{4-1}$$

$$L_{ix} = -M_x(L_0 \cos \theta + \sin \theta), \tag{4-2}$$

$$F = \frac{-D}{\rho M_x} = L_o \sin \theta + 1 - \cos \theta \tag{4-3}$$

$$= 1 - 1/M_x. \tag{4-4}$$

There is no axial focusing. For all θ, F has a fixed value at a given M_x.

For $M_x = -1$, at which $F = 2$, we have $L_o = L_{ix} = \cot(\theta/2)$ (see Table 4-1).

TABLE 4-1

θ (deg)	10	15	20	25	30	45	60	75	90	120	150	180
$L_o = L_{ix}$	11.43	7.60	5.67	4.51	3.73	2.41	1.73	1.30	1.00	0.577	0.268	0

In the following graphs, appropriate for sector magnets of nominally constant ρ, no data are shown for $\theta = 180°$, since the curves have degenerated to points. (See Figs. 4-1 and 4-2.)

Typical Case 1 magnets, with $\theta = 45, 60, 90$, and 180°, are described in papers that will be found in the bibliography.

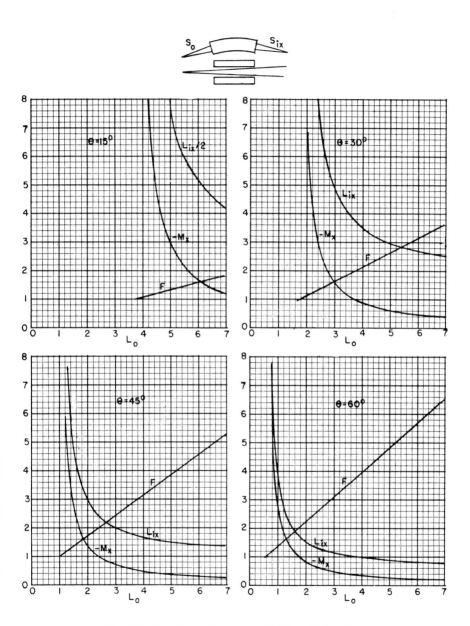

FIG. 4-1. Case 1. $n = 0$, $u_1 = u_2 = 0$. No axial focusing.

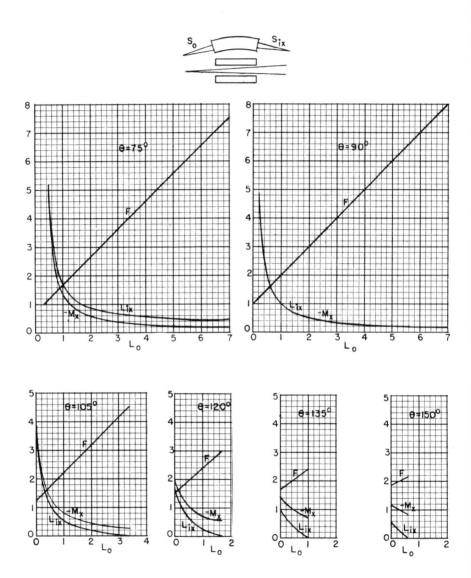

FIG. 4-2. Case 1 cont'd. $n = 0$, $u_1 = u_2 = 0$. No axial focusing.

CASE 2. $n = 0, u_1 = u_2 = 0$

Circular-Pole Switch Magnet. Single Focus

Magnets of this sort are variants of Case 1 and are frequently used as switches to bend the beam of ions through various angles, to the right or left, onto different targets. From the geometry of Fig. 4-3, we see that the effective radius r_e is a constant and that the bending radius ρ depends on the bending angle θ. Thus

$$r_e = \rho \tan \frac{\theta}{2} = \rho \frac{(1 - \cos \theta)}{\sin \theta} = \rho \frac{\sin \theta}{1 + \cos \theta}, \qquad (4\text{-}5)$$

so that

$$\rho = r_e \cot \frac{\theta}{2} = r_e \frac{\sin \theta}{1 - \cos \theta} = r_e \frac{1 + \cos \theta}{\sin \theta}. \qquad (4\text{-}6)$$

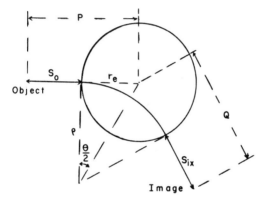

FIG. 4-3. Circular-pole magnet. (See the next section for remarks on P and Q.)

The value of r_e is determined by the maximum momentum $(B_0 \rho_0 q)$ of the incident ions, by the maximum field B_{max} available in the switch magnet, and by the maximum deflection angle θ_{max} that is contemplated. Thus, since $B_{max} \rho = B_0 \rho_0$, we have

$$r_e = \frac{B_0 \rho_0}{B_{max}} \tan \frac{\theta_{max}}{2}. \qquad (4\text{-}7)$$

When r_e has been determined, the characteristics of the system can be found from the equations and curves of Case 1, wherein the normalized distances S/ρ may be converted into the otherwise normalized distances S/r_e through the relation $S/r_e = (S/\rho)\cot(\theta/2)$, Eq. (4-5).

But since the magnet's effective radius r_e is constant while ρ depends on θ, it will be convenient to have equations and curves with distances expressed in terms of r_e rather than ρ. In Eqs. (4-1)–(4-3), we substitute for ρ using Eq. (4-6), to obtain

$$M_x = - \frac{1}{(S_0/r_e)(1 - \cos \theta) - \cos \theta},$$ (4-8)

$$\frac{S_{ix}}{r_e} = -M_x\left(\frac{S_0}{r_e}\cos \theta + 1 + \cos \theta\right),$$ (4-9)

$$F = \left(\frac{S_0}{r_e} + 1\right)(1 - \cos \theta).$$ (4-10)

It will be recalled that for a sector magnet, where ρ is a fixed parameter, the momentum resolution (when the exit slit is as wide as one image) was given by Eq. (2-34) as

$$R_p = \frac{\Delta p}{p} = \frac{w_o}{\rho F},$$

where F is a function of ρ. To obtain a similar expression for R_p with a circular magnet, we express both ρ and F in terms of r_e to find

$$R_p = \frac{\Delta p}{p} = \frac{w_o}{r_e F'}$$ (4-11)

where

$$F' = \left(\frac{S_0}{r_e} + 1\right) \sin \theta.$$ (4-12)

Hence the resolution improves with rising S_0 and increasing θ (up to 90°) as usual. But it should be noted that, for those object distances for which $M_x = -1$, the resolution becomes better as θ is *reduced*, as is shown in Table 4-2.

TABLE 4-2

CIRCULAR POLE MAGNET

θ (deg)	10	15	20	25	30	45	60	75	90
ρ/r_e	11.43	7.60	5.67	4.51	3.73	2.41	1.73	1.30	1.00
At $M_x = -1$:									
$\dfrac{S_0}{r_e} = \dfrac{S_{ix}}{r_e}$	131.	57.7	32.2	20.3	13.9	5.83	3.00	1.70	1.00
F'	22.8	15.2	11.3	9.02	7.46	4.83	3.46	2.61	2.00

Figure 4-4 displays the various parameters as functions of S_0/r_e for large values of θ. (Due to the relative smallness of r_e, the normalized distances at small θ become so great as not to be read meaningfully on a graph of moderate size.)

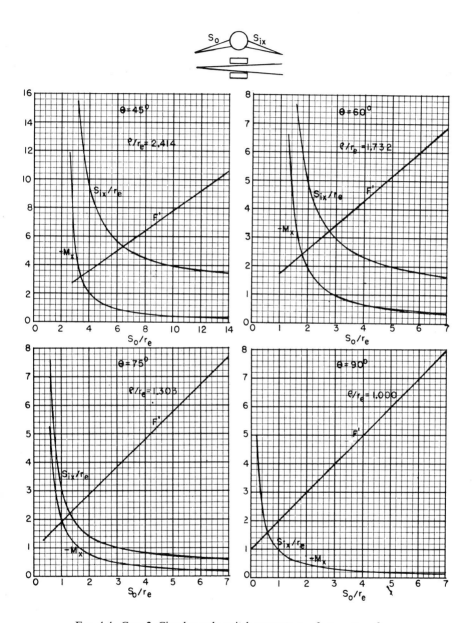

FIG. 4-4. Case 2. Circular-pole switch magnet; $n = 0$, $u_1 = u_2 = 0$.

Circular-Pole Switch Magnet with Parameters P and Q

Manufacturers of circular-pole switch magnets sometimes specify performance in terms of object and image distances P and Q respectively, *these being measured from the center of the magnet*, as was shown in Fig. 4-3. We then have

$$S_0 = P - r_e \tag{4-13}$$

and

$$S_{ix} = Q - r_e. \tag{4-14}$$

The equations of Case 1 may then be expressed in terms of P, Q, and r_e:

$$M_x = -\frac{1}{(P/r_e)(1 - \cos \theta) - 1}, \tag{4-15}$$

$$\frac{Q}{r_e} = \frac{(P/r_e)}{(P/r_e)(1 - \cos \theta) - 1}, \tag{4-16}$$

so that

$$\frac{Q}{r_e} = -M_x \frac{P}{r_e}. \tag{4-17}$$

From this we get

$$\frac{P}{r_e} = \frac{(Q/r_e)}{(Q/r_e)(1 - \cos \theta) - 1}. \tag{4-18}$$

The focal length, measured from the center of the magnet, is the value of Q (or P) when P (or Q) is infinite. It will be shown in Chapter 19 that the principal planes of such a circular pole magnet pass through its center, so we denote the focal length, defined above, as f_{pp}. Hence

$$\frac{f_{pp}}{r_e} = \frac{1}{1 - \cos \theta}. \tag{4-19}$$

Note that f_{pp} exceeds r_e for θ less than 90°.

From Eqs. (4-16) and (4-18) we find that

$$\frac{1}{P} + \frac{1}{Q} = \frac{1}{f_{pp}}. \tag{4-20}$$

This is the usual optical expression, wherein distances are measured from the principal planes of a lens. Finally from Eqs. (4-4) and (4-15) we see that

$$F = -\frac{D}{\rho M_x} = \frac{P}{r_e}(1 - \cos \theta). \tag{4-21}$$

For constant r_e this rises with P and with θ increasing from 0 to 180°. But ρ falls steadily over the same range of θ [see Eq. (4-6)], so we may expect an extremum in the product ρF that appears in the expression for R_p. Thus for an exit slit width s_i that is just as wide as one image (so that $s_i = -M_x w_0$), we have by Eq. (2-34),

$$R_p = \frac{\Delta p}{p} = \frac{w_0}{\rho F} = \frac{w_0}{[r_e \sin \theta/(1- \cos \theta)](P/r_e)(1 - \cos \theta)} = \frac{w_0}{P \sin \theta}. \quad (4\text{-}22)$$

This shows that R_p improves as P is raised, and as θ increases up to 90°; for larger θ, R_p deteriorates. But note that the magnification is not specified in the above expression; from Eq. (4-15) at $M_x = -1$ we get

$$P = \frac{2r_e}{1 - \cos \theta}. \quad (4\text{-}23)$$

Hence Eq. (4-22) becomes (for $M_x = -1$)

$$R_p = \frac{w_0}{2r_e} \tan \frac{\theta}{2}. \quad (4\text{-}24)$$

The best resolution, at $M_x = -1$, occurs at the *smallest* θ, for a magnet with given r_e as was seen earlier when distances were expressed as S/r_e. This is due to the larger ρ associated with smaller θ. The useful length of the magnet is $\rho\theta$; for small θ, we have paid for a long magnet, and for large θ, a short one, as indicated in Fig. 4-5.

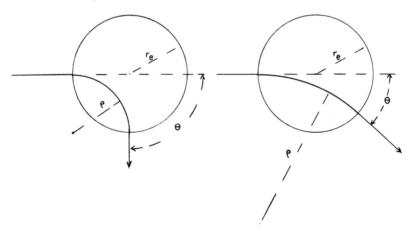

FIG. 4-5. With a given circular pole, a small θ means a large ρ.

A switch magnet usually bends the beam to one of several predetermined angles, the field being altered to suit, for particles of a given energy. Since it is not practical to change the position of the object slit, the images at the various angles have different image distances, and at only one angle can the magnification be unity.

Table 4-3 gives the parameters of interest in an alternative manner. The

TABLE 4-3

CIRCULAR POLE MAGNET[a,b]

θ (deg)	P/r_e	Q/r_e	M_x	$R_p r_e/w_o$	θ (deg)	P/r_e	Q/r_e	M_x	$R_p r_e/w_o$
*15	58.6	58.6	−1.00	0.066	15	4.0	−4.63	1.16	0.966
30	58.6	8.55	−0.146	0.034	30	4.0	−8.62	2.16	0.500
45	58.6	3.63	−0.062	0.024	45	4.0	23.30	−5.82	0.354
60	58.6	2.07	−0.035	0.019	*60	4.0	4.00	−1.00	0.289
75	58.6	1.38	−0.024	0.018	75	4.0	2.03	−0.51	0.259
90	58.6	1.02	−0.017	0.017	90	4.0	1.33	−0.33	0.250
120	58.6	0.67	−0.012	0.019	120	4.0	0.80	−0.20	0.289
15	14.9	−30.4	2.03	0.259	15	2.7	−2.97	1.10	1.43
*30	14.9	14.9	−1.00	0.134	30	2.7	−4.56	1.69	0.74
45	14.9	4.43	−0.29	0.095	45	2.7	−12.86	4.77	0.52
60	14.9	2.31	−0.15	0.077	60	2.7	7.75	−2.81	0.43
75	14.9	1.48	−0.09	0.069	*75	2.7	2.70	−1.00	0.38
90	14.9	1.07	−0.07	0.067	90	2.7	1.59	−0.59	0.37
120	14.9	0.69	−0.04	0.077	120	2.7	0.88	−0.33	0.43
15	6.83	−8.90	1.30	0.560	15	2.0	−2.15	1.07	1.93
30	6.83	−7.71	1.13	0.293	30	2.0	−2.73	1.37	1.00
*45	6.83	6.83	−1.00	0.207	45	2.0	−4.81	2.42	0.71
60	6.83	2.83	−0.41	0.169	60	2.0	∞	∞	0.58
75	6.83	1.68	−0.25	0.152	75	2.0	4.15	−2.07	0.52
90	6.83	1.17	−0.17	0.146	*90	2.0	2.00	−1.00	0.50
120	6.83	0.74	−0.11	0.169	120	2.0	1.00	−0.50	0.58

[a] Object and image distances, P and Q, are measured from the center of the pole of effective radius r_e.
[b] Asterisks indicate values where $M_x = -1$.

object distance is variously chosen so that we have $M_x = -1$ at successively larger values of θ. The best resolution (at unity magnification) occurs at the smallest θ, but the object and images distances are very large. At larger θ, the resolution is poorer but the distances decrease and some images are found inside the magnet. ($Q/r_e < 1$. Q is infinite at $1 - r_e/P = \cos \theta$.) This means that the emergent beam is radially diverging and must be concentrated on the target by an auxiliary quadrupole lens.

Browne–Buechner Spectrograph

This* is of the circular pole type with uniform field, although for economy the iron exists only over the region where the field is actually in use. The object is a radioactive material or a target bombarded by projectiles from an accelerator. The field is held constant so that particles of different momenta take different paths. The object distance is fixed at $S_0 = r_e$, so that $P = S_0 + r_e = 2r_e$. We then see from the lower right hand section of Table 4-3 that at $\theta = 90°$ we have $Q = 2r_e$, $M_x = -1$, and $\Delta p/p = 0.5 \, w_0/r_e$.

From the same part of Table 4-3, we also note that the image lies at the effective edge of the magnet ($Q = r_e$) for $\theta = 120°$ and that $Q = \infty$ for $\theta = 60°$. Hence in the ideal case, images will be formed over this entire range of θ, if the source emits particles of appropriate energies. The limiting radii of curvature, given by Eq. (4-6) as $\rho = r_e \cot(\theta/2)$, then are $\rho_{max} = 1.73 \, r_e$ and $\rho_{min} = 0.57 \, r_e$. A photographic plate lies along the locus of Q; on it are recorded ions that have a range of 3 in momentum and hence of 9 in energy.

In practice, these ranges are more restricted. The plate cannot extend to infinity nor can it reach the effective edge because of mechanical supports. Realistic limiting and central values are given in Table 4-4. The range in

TABLE 4-4

BROWNE—BUECHNER SPECTROGRAPH

θ (deg)	ρ/r_e	Q/r_e	M_x	$R_p r_e/w_0$
85	1.09	2.42	−1.21	0.501
90	1.00	2.00	−1.00	0.500
110	0.70	1.18	−0.59	0.532

momentum is $1.09/0.70 = 1.55$, and in energy it is $(1.55)^2 = 2.42$. Since there is no slit in the image plane, small values of $|M_x|$ cause no trouble. The image widening (aberration) due to a finite value of $x_0'^2$ is automatically removed for ions bent through $\theta = 90°$ (see Chapter 18 for the reason). Since there is no axial focusing, the solid angle of acceptance in the axial plane is limited by the height of the gap. Scattering of particles from the chamber walls next to the poles can be troublesome, unless the angle z_0' is limited by an input slit.

* 101, Browne and Buechner.

CASE 3. $n = 0$, $u_1 = u_2 = 0$

Switch with Least Pole Area. Single Focus

It is clear that with the circular pole magnet of Case 2 only a small fraction of the total magnetized gap is used at any one angle of deflection. A large quantity of iron, long lengths of exciting coils, and much power is employed, most of which is for naught—until the bending angle is changed. To avoid this waste, we need the impossible ideal of a flexible magnet that produces a field only over the curved area that is actually in use.

An ingenious switch has been developed by Hansford* that approaches this ideal. A uniform field is used, with a shape that in plan is a "racetrack" bounded at the ends by two semicircles, each of radius R. A pivot is supplied at the center of the "entrance" semicircle, and for a deflection angle θ the magnet is rotated by $\theta/2$. (See Fig. 4-6.) The vacuum chamber remains fixed

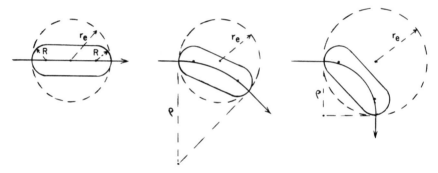

FIG. 4-6. A region of field is rotated to produce different angles of deflection.

in space and is wide enough to accommodate beams of the maximum deflection in both directions. Entry and exit are always normal to the effective edge. As θ increases from zero, the region of "good" field slides around in an imaginary circular field of rising effective radius r_e, while the radius of curvature ρ drops from infinity toward smaller values.

We now calculate the minimum width of magnet required for an ion beam of zero width, zero radial divergence, and of a single momentum. It is clear from Fig. 4-6 that the width is greatest for the greatest bending angle θ_{max}.

Referring to Fig. 4-7, we see that the centers C and C' of the semicircular boundaries of the effective field lie on the lines $\overline{FB}$ and $\overline{BG}$, but with small

* 113, Hansford.

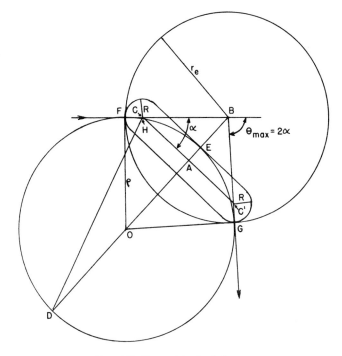

FIG. 4-7. Geometrical relations.

error they may be taken as lying on the orbit; i.e., C and H are almost coincident. The triangles CAE and CAD are similar, so that we have

$$\frac{\overline{DA}}{\overline{AC}} = \frac{\overline{AC}}{\overline{AE}}$$

whence

$$(\overline{AC})^2 = (\overline{DA})(\overline{AE}) = (2\rho - R)R = 2\rho R - R^2. \tag{4-25}$$

Now the effective radius r_e of the equivalent circular field is

$$r_e = (\overline{BC}) + R = \frac{(\overline{AC})}{\cos(\theta_{max}/2)} + R,$$

whence

$$(\overline{AC})^2 = (r_e - R)^2 \cos^2(\theta_{max}/2). \tag{4-26}$$

Equating these two expressions for $(\overline{AC})^2$ gives a quadratic in R, and when we eliminate ρ through the relation of Eq. 4-6, and write $\theta_{max}/2 \equiv \alpha$ for convenience, we find that the solution is

$$R = r_e \left\{ \frac{\cot \alpha + \cos^2 \alpha}{1 + \cos^2 \alpha} - \left[\left(\frac{\cot \alpha + \cos^2 \alpha}{1 + \cos^2 \alpha} \right)^2 - \frac{\cos^2 \alpha}{1 + \cos^2 \alpha} \right]^{1/2} \right\}, \quad (4\text{-}27)$$

where we use the negative sign option. This expression gives the ideal minimum permissible effective radius of the curved ends of the field when $\theta = \theta_{max}$. In practice this ideal value must be increased to some value R', to allow for (a) the finite width of the object, its finite radial divergence, and the extra width needed because of the dispersion of ions with a spread in momentum, and (b) the buffer zone that lies between the region of uniform field and the actual edges of the iron. This latter region is determined by experience; the former's width will be considered in Chapters 7 and 9.

For ions with maximum momentum measured by $B_0 \rho_0$, and with the strongest practical field B_{max}, the bending radius for θ_{max} is

$$\rho = \frac{B_0 \rho_0}{B_{max}}.$$

From this we determine r_e, using $r_e = \rho \tan(\theta_{max}/2)$, Eq. (4-5). With R already calculated, we find $(\overline{AC})$ from

$$(\overline{AC}) = (r_e - R')\cos(\theta_{max}/2). \quad (4\text{-}28)$$

The overall effective length of the magnet is

$$m = 2[R' + (\overline{AC})]. \quad (4\text{-}29)$$

For any angle less than θ_{max}, the sagitta $(\overline{AE})$ is smaller, so the magnet's width will be more than adequate. From Eq. (4-28), we have

$$r_e = \frac{(\overline{AC})}{\cos(\theta/2)} + R',$$

while from Eq. (4-29)

$$(\overline{AC}) = (m/2) - R'.$$

Hence

$$r_e = \frac{(m/2) - R'[1 - \cos(\theta/2)]}{\cos(\theta/2)}, \quad (4\text{-}30)$$

so that r_e rises as θ is increased. But $\rho = r_e \cot(\theta/2)$ by Eq(4-6), so

$$\rho = \frac{(m/2) - R'[1 - \cos(\theta/2)]}{\sin(\theta/2)}, \tag{4-31}$$

and we see that ρ is reduced as θ rises. Since neither r_e nor ρ are constants, it is not practical to plot general performance curves.

CASE 4. $n = 0, u_1 = 0, u_2 > 0$

$$M_x = -\frac{1}{L_0(\sin\theta - \tan u_2 \cos\theta) - \tan u_2 \sin\theta - \cos\theta}, \tag{4-32}$$

$$M_z = -\frac{1}{L_0 \tan u_2 + \theta \tan u_2 - 1}, \tag{4-33}$$

$$L_{ix} = -M_x(L_0 \cos\theta + \sin\theta), \tag{4-34}$$

$$L_{iz} = -M_z(L_0 + \theta), \tag{4-35}$$

$$F = -\frac{D}{\rho M_x} = L_0 \sin\theta + 1 - \cos\theta \tag{4-36}$$

$$= 1 - \frac{1}{M_x} + \tan u_2(L_0 \cos\theta + \sin\theta). \tag{4-37}$$

From Eq. (4-36) we see that F is independent of u_2.
For double focusing we need

$$\tan u_2 = \frac{(L_0^2 + L_0\theta + 1)\sin\theta - \theta\cos\theta}{2(L_0 + \theta)\sin\theta + 2(L_0^2 + L_0\theta)\cos\theta}. \tag{4-38}$$

From the following graphs (Figs. 4-8 and 4-9), we note that u_2 rises with L_0, and that F is not constant for a given M_x at all θ.

This system is inferior to some to be described later, since axial focusing does not occur until the exit edge is reached, so that the gap height must be larger. Compared with the case where $u_2 = 0$, for the same θ we see that M_x is greater for the same resolution, and that the resolution is greater for the same M_x.

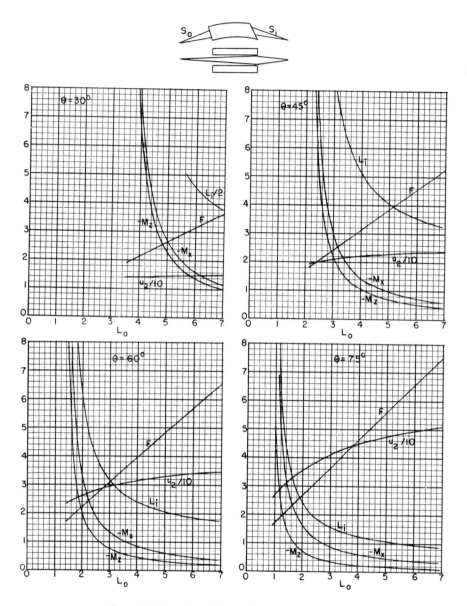

FIG. 4-8. Case 4. $n = 0$, $u_1 = 0$, $u_2 > 0$. Double focus.

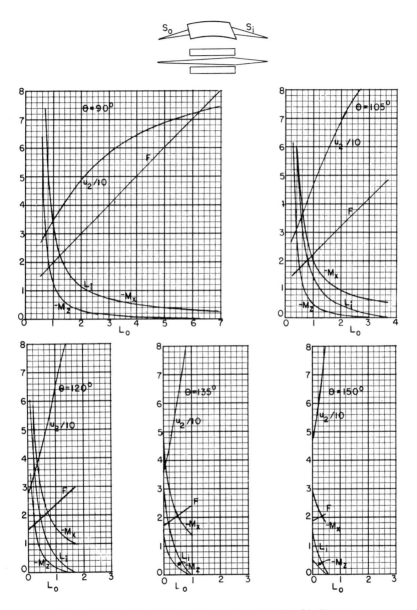

FIG. 4-9. Case 4 cont'd. $n = 0, u_1 = 0, u_2 > 0$. Double Focus.

CASE 5. $n = 0$, $u_1 = 0$, $u_2 > 0$

Semicircular Magnet

A magnet with uniform field, pole radius r, and effective pole radius r_e (where $r_e - r = d$) is bounded on one side by a chord distance d from the effective diameter $2r_e$, so that the field is effectively uniform over a semicircle of radius r_e. An ion entering normal to the flat edge (so that $u_1 = 0$) and passing through the center point O, takes a path of constant radius ρ (centered at C) between O and the exit point A. The line BD is tangent to the effective edge at A, so that angle BAE equals u_2, the angle of the exit face.

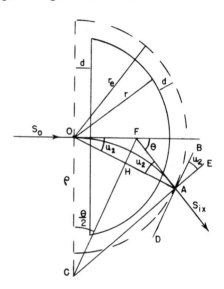

FIG. 4-10. Geometrical relations in a semicircular magnet.

Since OA is perpendicular to AB and FA is perpendicular to AE, then $FAO = BAE = u_2$. By symmetry $FOA = u_2$, so that $OFA = \pi - \theta$. Therefore $2u_2 + (\pi - \theta) = \pi$, and so we have

$$u_2 = \theta/2. \tag{4-39}$$

Therefore

$$\tan u_2 = \tan(\theta/2) = \frac{1 - \cos\theta}{\sin\theta} = \frac{\sin\theta}{1 + \cos\theta}. \tag{4-40}$$

Thus the exit edge angle is prescribed by the bending angle. For each θ, double focusing occurs for particular object and image distances, at which there are certain values of M_x, M_z, and F. These parameters may be found from the graphs of Case 4 (Figs. 4-8 and 4-9) by reading the values at $u_2 = \theta/2$.

But since r_e is constant whereas ρ is not, it is more convenient to describe the magnet's properties in terms of distances measured in units of r_e.

In Fig. 4-10, we note that

$$\sin(\theta/2) = OH/OC = (r_e/2)/\rho, \tag{4-41}$$

so that

$$\rho = r_e/[2\sin(\theta/2)]. \tag{4-42}$$

Note that this is *not* the same expression as for a circular magnet, as in Eq. (4-6). We substitute this value of ρ and the relation $u_2 = \theta/2$ into Eqs. (4-32)–(4-36), using the identities $\tan(\theta/2) = \sin\theta/(1+\cos\theta)$ and $\sin\theta = 2\sin(\theta/2)\cos(\theta/2)$, and obtain

$$M_x = -\frac{1}{(S_0/r_e)2\sin(\theta/2)\tan(\theta/2) - 1}, \tag{4-43}$$

$$M_z = -\frac{1}{(S_0/r_e)2\sin(\theta/2)\tan(\theta/2) - 1 + \theta\tan(\theta/2)}, \tag{4-44}$$

$$\frac{S_{ix}}{r_e} = -M_x\left(\frac{S_0}{r_e}\cos\theta + \cos\frac{\theta}{2}\right) \tag{4-45}$$

$$\frac{S_{iz}}{r_e} = -M_z\left(\frac{S_0}{r_e} + \frac{\theta}{2\sin(\theta/2)}\right), \tag{4-46}$$

$$F = \frac{S_0}{r_e}2\sin\theta\sin\frac{\theta}{2} + 1 - \cos\theta. \tag{4-47}$$

For an output slit as wide as one image, Eq. (2-34) shows that $R_p = \Delta p/p = w_o/\rho F$, where F is a function of ρ. When we express both ρ and F in terms of r_e we obtain, for the semicircular magnet,

$$R_p = \Delta p/p = w_o/r_e F', \tag{4-48}$$

TABLE 4-5. SEMICIRCULAR MAGNET

θ (deg)	10	15	20	25	30	45	60	75	90
ρ/r_e	5.73	3.83	2.88	2.31	1.93	1.31	1.00	0.821	0.707

For $M_x = -1$, we have:

S_0/r_e	131.1	58.2	32.6	20.8	14.4	6.31	3.46	2.14	1.41
S_{ix}/r_e	130.1	57.2	31.7	21.6	13.4	5.38	2.59	1.35	0.71
S_{iz}/r_e	129.9	57.2	31.7	19.2	13.5	5.53	2.81	1.60	0.98
$-M_z$	0.98	0.97	0.94	0.91	0.87	0.76	0.62	0.50	0.39
F'	22.7	15.15	11.38	9.00	7.45	4.85	3.51	2.66	2.12

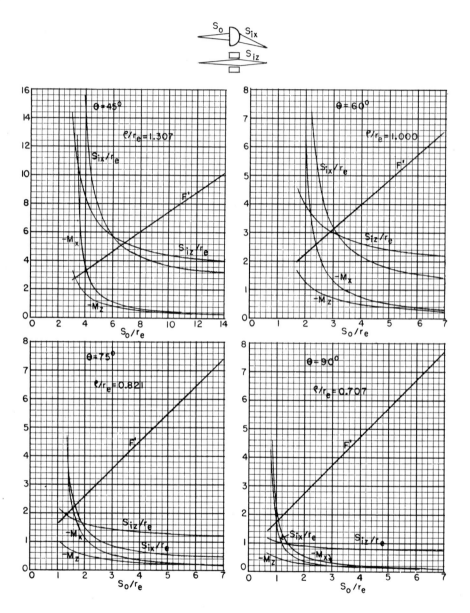

FIG. 4-11. Case 5. Semicircular magnet. $n = 0$, $u_1 = 0$, $u_2 > 0$. Double focus.

where

$$F' = \frac{S_0}{r_e} \sin \theta + \sin \frac{\theta}{2}. \tag{4-49}$$

This shows that the resolution improves with rising θ, but for values of S_0 for which $M_x = -1$, we find the contrary.

The condition for double focusing is obtained by equating S_{ix}/r_e to S_{iz}/r_e. This gives an involved quadratic for the necessary object distance S_0/r_e as a function of trigonometric terms in θ and $\theta/2$. For large θ, this critical object distance for double focusing may be found by inspecting the curves of Fig. 4-11, where it is seen that $M_x \neq -1$. For small θ, we observe from the Table 4-5 (where $M_x = -1$ rather than otherwise) that S_{ix} and S_{iz} are very nearly equal anyway.

The properties of the semicircular magnet also may be treated in terms of the object and image distances measured from the principal planes. This technique is described in Chapter 19.

Comparison of Circular and Semicircular Switch Magnets

We may compare this data for the semicircular magnet with that for the circular one. The ratio ρ/r_e is greater for the circle by a factor that ranges from 2 at $\theta = 10°$ to 1.4 at $\theta = 90°$, so, for a given r_e and field, the circle can handle projectiles of somewhat greater momentum.

With regard to resolution, it is reasonable to make a comparison on the basis of the value of the *effective* radius, r_e, for both magnets; there is then no significant difference in F', at $M_x = -1$, as is seen in Tables 4-2 and 4-5. On the other hand, for the same *bending* radius, ρ, the circle maintains $F = 2$ at all values of θ, at $M_x = -1$, as noted earlier; whereas the semicircle has F values that range from 3.8 at $\theta = 30°$ to 3 at $\theta = 120°$, so that on this basis the semicircle gives the better resolution.

The circle gives no axial focusing, while the semicircle does. Double focusing for the latter exists at each θ for a particular object distance, but then $M_x \neq -1$. If unity magnification is wanted, double focusing must be dispensed with; at small θ, S_{ix} and S_{iz} are almost equal, but at $\theta = 90°$ the discrepancy has grown so that $S_{iz} = 1.38 \, S_{ix}$.

With the circular magnet, the deflected beam apparently comes from the center, no matter what the bending angle. In the semicircular instrument, on the other hand, we see from Fig. 4-10 that $OF = \rho \tan(\theta/2)$, so that the point F, from which the output beam seems to originate, moves about as θ is varied. This is a minor, but important, inconvenience when planning the location of the beam tubes.

CASE 6. $n = 0, u_1 > 0, u_2 = 0$

$$M_x = -\frac{1}{L_o(\sin\theta - \tan u_1 \cos\theta) - \cos\theta},$$ (4-50)

$$M_z = -\frac{1}{L_o \tan u_1 - 1},$$ (4-51)

$$L_{ix} = -M_x[L_o(\cos\theta + \tan u_1 \sin\theta) + \sin\theta],$$ (4-52)

$$L_{iz} = -M_z[L_o(1 - \theta \tan u_1) + \theta],$$ (4-53)

$$F = -\frac{D}{\rho M_x} = L_o[\sin\theta + \tan u_1(1 - \cos\theta)] + 1 - \cos\theta$$ (4-54)

$$= 1 - \frac{1}{M_x} + L_o \tan u_1.$$ (4-55)

From Eq. (4-54) we see that F depends on u_1. For double focusing, it is necessary that we have, by Eq. (3-15),

$$\tan u_1 = \frac{\theta \sin\theta + 2\cos\theta}{2(\theta\cos\theta - \sin\theta)}$$
$$\pm \left\{ \left[\frac{\theta\sin\theta + 2\cos\theta}{2(\theta\cos\theta - \sin\theta)}\right]^2 - \frac{\sin\theta(L_o^2 + L_o\theta + 1) - \theta\cos\theta}{L_o^2(\theta\cos\theta - \sin\theta)} \right\}^{1/2}.$$ (4-56)

Typical data are shown in the accompanying Figs. 4-12 and 4-13. At a given M_x, we see that F is not constant for all θ. Note that u_1 falls as L_o is increased, and that for $\theta > 120°$, the absolute value of M_x is less than unity.

The axial gap need not be as large as in the earlier cases, because axial focusing occurs at the entrance edge.

A spectrograph that is a variant of this type has been built by Green et al.* To increase the axial solid angle, vertical focusing is introduced at the entrance edge (which is cylindrically convex) with $\tan u_1 = \rho_0/S_0$, where S_0 is the fixed object distance and ρ_0 is the bending radius for $\theta = 90°$. Then Eq. (4-52) shows that for these particles we have $S_{ix}/\rho_0 = 2\rho_0/S_0$, so with the choice $S_{ix}/\rho_0 = \sqrt{2}$, it then follows that $S_0/\rho_0 = \sqrt{2}$ also. Consequently $\tan u_1 = 0.707$, so $u_1 = 35.27°$ and $M_x = -0.707$. Ions of greater energy have $\rho > \rho_0$, $\theta < 90°$, $S_{ix} > \sqrt{2}\rho_0$, and u_2 is slightly less than zero; conversely for less energetic ions.

* 129, Green et al.; 131, Feldl et al.

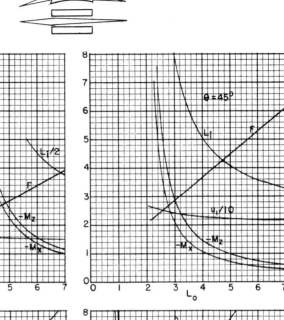

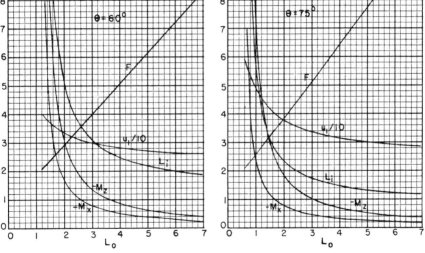

FIG. 4-12. Case 6. $n = 0, u_1 > 0, u_2 = 0$. Double focus.

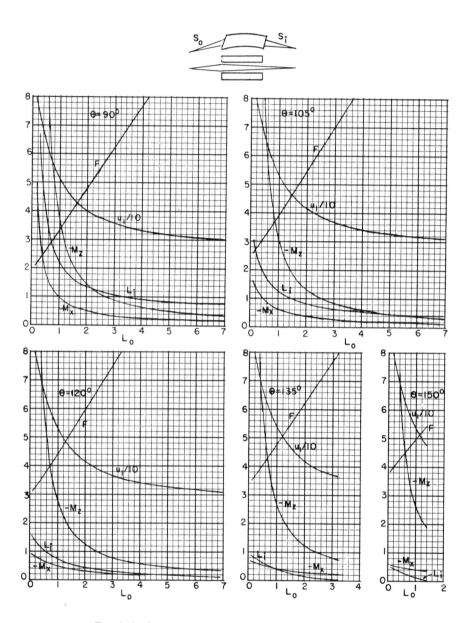

FIG. 4-13. Case 6 cont'd. $n = 0$, $u_1 > 0$, $u_2 = 0$. Double focus.

There is no double focusing; Eq. (4-53) shows that the axial image is at infinity for $\theta = 90°$. The ratio of momenta that can be recorded at a single value of the field is 2.2.

The original paper should be consulted to appreciate the procedure by which the parameters were chosen so as to minimize aberrations.

CASE 7. $n = 0$, $\tan u_1 = \tan u_2 = 1/L_o$

$$M_x = -\frac{1}{L_o \sin \theta - (2/L_o)\sin \theta - 3 \cos \theta}, \tag{4-57}$$

$$M_z = -1, \tag{4-58}$$

$$L_{ix} = -M_x(L_o \cos \theta + 2 \sin \theta) = \frac{L_o^2 + 2L_o \tan \theta}{L_o^2 \tan \theta - 3L_o - 2 \tan \theta}, \tag{4-59}$$

$$L_{iz} = -M_z L_o = L_o, \tag{4-60}$$

$$F = -\frac{D}{\rho M_x} = L_o \sin \theta + 2(1 - \cos \theta) \tag{4-61}$$

$$= 1 - \frac{1}{M_x} + 1 + \frac{2}{L_o} \sin \theta + \cos \theta. \tag{4-62}$$

Relations (4-57)–(4-62) are plotted in Figs. 4-14 and 4-15.

Both u_1 and u_2 are specified, so we equate L_{ix} to L_{iz} to find that the condition for double focusing is that the image and object distances must have the particular values

$$L_o = L_i = 2 \cot(\theta/2), \tag{4-63}$$

for which we have
$$M_x = M_z = -1 \tag{4-64}$$

and
$$F = 4. \tag{4-65}$$

TABLE 4-6. $n = 0$, $\tan u_1 = \tan u_2 = 1/L_o$

θ (deg)	30	45	60	75	90	105	120	135	150
$L_o = L_i$	7.46	4.83	3.46	2.61	2.00	1.53	1.15	0.83	0.54
$u_1 = u_2$ (deg)	7.6	11.7	16.1	21.0	26.6	33.1	40.9	50.4	61.8

This magnet is attractive since both edges supply axial focusing and hence have smaller angles than if only one focuses. This reduces saturation effects at the corners. As will be shown in Eq. (8-34), the axial envelope is greatest at the entrance edge if $\theta < 2L_o$ and at the exit edge if otherwise. The critical angle is $\theta = 123.4°$. This is worth remembering.

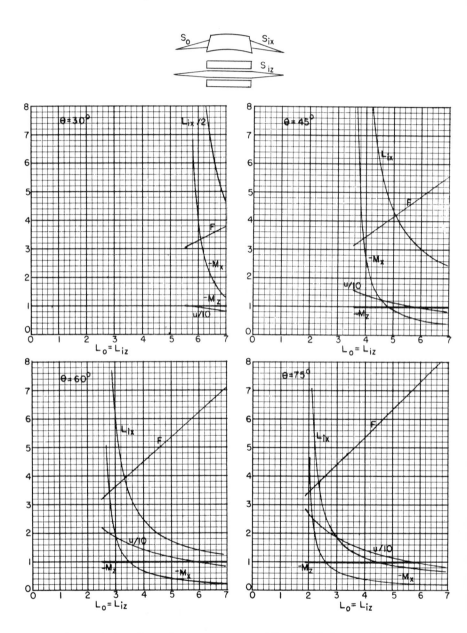

FIG. 4-14. Case 7. $n = 0$, $\tan u_1 = \tan u_2 = 1/L_0$. Double focus at $M_x = -1$.

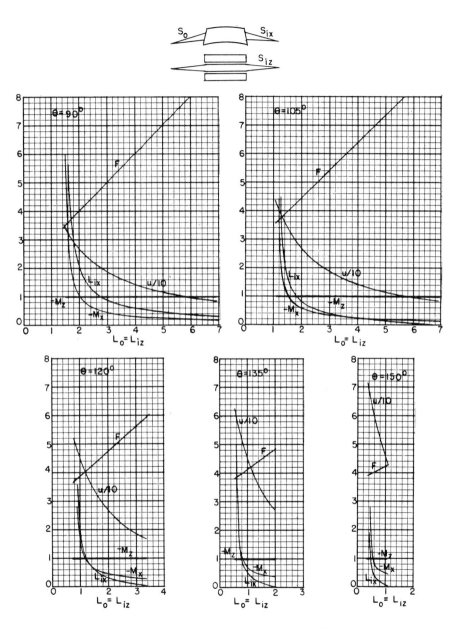

FIG. 4-15. Case 7 cont'd. $n = 0$, $\tan u_1 = \tan u_2 = 1/L_o$. Double focus at $M_x = -1$.

CASE 8. $n = 0$, $u_1 \neq 0$, $u_2 \neq 0$

$$M_x = -\frac{1}{L_o[\sin \theta - (\tan u_1 + \tan u_2)\cos \theta - \tan u_1 \tan u_2 \sin \theta] - \tan u_2 \sin \theta - \cos \theta}, \qquad (4\text{-}66)$$

$$M_z = -\frac{1}{L_o[\tan u_1 + \tan u_2 - \theta \tan u_1 \tan u_2] + \theta \tan u_2 - 1}, \qquad (4\text{-}67)$$

$$L_{ix} = -M_x[L_o(\cos \theta + \tan u_1 \sin \theta) + \sin \theta], \qquad (4\text{-}68)$$

$$L_{iz} = -M_z[L_o(1 - \theta \tan u_1) + \theta], \qquad (4\text{-}69)$$

$$F = -\frac{D}{\rho M_x} = L_o[\sin \theta + \tan u_1(1 - \cos \theta)] + 1 - \cos \theta \qquad (4\text{-}70)$$

$$= 1 - \frac{1}{M_x} + L_o \tan u_1 + \tan u_2[\sin \theta + L_o(\cos \theta + \tan u_1 \sin \theta)]. \qquad (4\text{-}71)$$

For double focusing

if $\tan u_1$ is specified, $\tan u_2$ is found from Eq. (3-19);
if $\tan u_2$ is specified, $\tan u_1$ is found from Eq. (3-15).

Of the infinity of possibilities, a useful sample has been given by Shapiro et al.* This report contains tabular data for $\theta = 20, 22.5, 35, 40$, and $45°$, for each of which the object distance S_0/ρ is 0.5, 1.0, 1.5, ..., 10.5, 20, 30, and 10^6. For each S_0/ρ, the edge angle u_1 has the values 0, 5, 10, ..., $65°$. The double-focusing value of the exit edge angle u_2 is given for each case, as well as the double-focused image distance S_i/ρ and the radial and axial magnifications M_x and M_z.

A magnet with $\theta = 60°$, $u_1 = 46.6°$, and $u_2 = -18.3°$ has been described by Meier et al.†

CASE 9. $n = 0$, $u_1 = u_2 < 0$

Fowler–Hafner Spectrograph

A very interesting variant of Case 8 is found in an early spectrograph (the progenitor of more recent instruments) first described‡ in an abstract by

* 88, Shapiro et al.
† 123, Meier et al.
‡ 117, Hafner et al.; 118, Inglis; 120, Prowse and Gibson; 124, Rout et al.; 130, Barkovsky et al.

Hafner *et al.* in 1949, then briefly by Inglis in 1950, with a little more detail in 1955 by Prowse and Gibson (who credit its origin to Fowler), and quite thoroughly by Rout *et al.* in 1961. We will consider it by the methods developed in this volume.

A uniform field extends, in principle, over a semi-infinite plane. Particles enter and leave through the same straight edge, as indicated in Fig. 4-16.

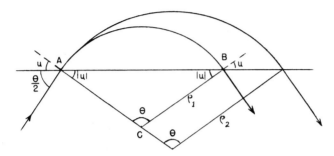

FIG. 4-16. Fowler–Hafner spectrograph.

We note that the edge angles u_1 and u_2 (defined, as usual, as the angles between the effective edges and normals to the beam path outside the magnet) are equal and *negative*. In the triangle ABC for a particle of momentum p_1, radius ρ_1, and bending angle θ, we have $\theta + 2\,|u| = 180°$, so that

$$|u| = 90° - \theta/2, \tag{4-72}$$

and therefore $\tan|u| = \cot(\theta/2) = (1 + \cos\theta)/\sin\theta$. Hence in the expressions that describe the magnet's properties we must write

$$t = \tan u = -\frac{(1 + \cos\theta)}{\sin\theta}, \tag{4-73}$$

since u is negative.

Second, we observe that a more energetic ion, with momentum $p_2 > p_1$ and radius $\rho_2 > \rho_1$, follows the same path in the object space, is subject to the same values of edge angles, and is deflected through the *same* angle θ.

When we use Eq. (4-73) in Eq. (4-66) for the radial magnification, we find that the terms involving L_0 and functions of θ all cancel out, giving us

$$M_x = -1 \tag{4-74}$$

for all bending angles and object distances. This conclusion seems at odds with the usual notion that magnification may be expressed as the ratio of image and object distances. But the latter statement is true only when these distances are measured from the principal planes. It will be shown in Chapter 19 that these planes in the object and image spaces are remote from the effective edges by the distances $V_o = (1 - E)/D$ and $V_i = (1 - A)/D$, where (for $u_1 = u_2 = u$ and $n = 0$) we have $A = E = \tan u \sin \theta + \cos \theta$ and $D = -(\sin \theta - 2 \tan u \cos \theta - \tan^2 u \sin \theta)/\rho$. With $\tan u$ given by Eq. (4-73), we find $A = E = -1$ and $D = 0$, so that $V_o = V_i = \infty$. Hence the object and image distances P and Q are infinite, where P and Q are measured from the principal planes. As will be shown in Eqs. (19-26), with these parameters we have $M_x = -Q/P$, so in the present case we obtain $M_x = -\infty/\infty = -1$, in agreement with the argument given above.

The radial image distance is given by Eq. (4-68), wherein $\tan u$ has the value given above and $M_x = -1$. We find

$$S_{ix} = \rho \sin \theta - S_0. \qquad (4\text{-}75)$$

It is apparent that S_{ix} increases with momentum, for a fixed object distance and a given θ. If both object and image are to lie outside the magnet, S_0 may range from $S_0 = 0$ (when $S_{ix} = \rho \sin \theta$) to $S_{0\,max} = \rho \sin \theta$ (when $S_{ix} = 0$). For $\theta = 180°$, the system degenerates to Case 1, where $n = u_1 = u_2 = 0$, and at this bending angle we have $S_0 = S_{ix} = 0$ and $M_x = -1$, as seen previously.

The location of the images of various momenta may be determined as follows. Choose the object distance such that for an ion of minimum momentum and minimum radius ρ_0, the image lies at the edge of the magnet. Hence, by Eq. (4-75)

$$S_{0\,max} = \rho_0 \sin \theta. \qquad (4\text{-}76)$$

Then the length of magnet edge between entry and exit, for this ion, is

$$q_0 = 2\rho_0 \sin(\theta/2) \qquad (4\text{-}77)$$

as seen in Fig. 4-17.

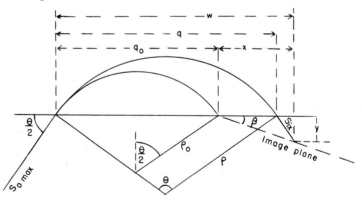

FIG. 4-17. Fowler–Hafner spectrograph.

For a more energetic ion, of radius $\rho > \rho_0$, the corresponding length is

$$q = 2\rho \sin(\theta/2), \tag{4-78}$$

and the image distance is

$$S_{ix} = \rho \sin \theta - S_{0\,max} = (\rho - \rho_0)\sin \theta. \tag{4-79}$$

The distance w is

$$
\begin{aligned}
w &= q + S_{ix} \cos(\theta/2) \\
&= 2\rho \sin(\theta/2) + (\rho - \rho_0)\sin \theta \cos(\theta/2).
\end{aligned}
\tag{4-80}
$$

Then x, the projection along the magnet's edge of the distance between the images for ρ_0 and ρ, is given by

$$
\begin{aligned}
x &= w - q_0 = (\rho - \rho_0)[2 \sin(\theta/2) + \sin \theta \cos(\theta/2)] \\
&= C_1 \, \Delta\rho,
\end{aligned}
\tag{4-81}
$$

where $\Delta\rho = \rho - \rho_0$ and C_1 is a constant for a given θ.

The perpendicular distance from the magnet's edge to the image of ions with radius ρ is

$$
\begin{aligned}
y &= S_{ix} \sin(\theta/2) = (\rho - \rho_0)\sin \theta \sin(\theta/2) \\
&= C_2 \, \Delta\rho,
\end{aligned}
\tag{4-82}
$$

where C_2 is another constant. Eliminating $\Delta\rho$ between these equations for x and y gives

$$y = (C_2/C_1)x. \tag{4-83}$$

This indicates that the images of all momenta lie on a straight line (dashed in Fig. 4-17) and that the tangent of the angle β between this line and the magnet's edge is

$$\tan \beta = \frac{y}{x} = \frac{\sin \theta \sin(\theta/2)}{2 \sin(\theta/2) + \sin \theta \cos(\theta/2)}, \tag{4-84}$$

which can be manipulated into the form

$$\tan \beta = \frac{\sin \theta}{3 + \cos \theta}. \tag{4-85}$$

The resolution function F is given by Eq. (4-70); with $\tan u$ as in Eq. (4-73) we find

$$F = 1 - \cos \theta, \tag{4-86}$$

so that it is profitable to have θ in the second quadrant. Eq. (2-34) shows that

$$\frac{\Delta p}{p} = \frac{w_o}{\rho F},$$

so, as usual, the resolution improves linearly with rising ρ. Unfortunately, particles with large ρ have a long path inside the magnet, and since the entrance edge defocuses axially, the permissible axial divergence at the source falls off as this path increases, thus reducing the number of recorded ions. Furthermore, particles scattered from the top and bottom of the vacuum chamber inside the magnet can cause a disturbing background on the photographic plate.

It has been indicated in Figs. 1-8 and 1-13 that the "image" of a point source is not a point, if the rays from the object have appreciable radial divergence; the "image" actually consists only in a narrowing or waist of the envelope formed by the various trajectories. To record on the focal plane of the spectrograph as many ions of a given momentum as is possible, particles with a considerable radial divergence must be accepted. Hence we enquire if there is any particular deflection angle θ for which the waist is the narrowest. In terms of first-order theory, where a point source is assumed to yield a point image, this is equivalent to asking for that θ for which the distance x in Fig. 4-17 changes the least when θ is varied, as will occur if there is a finite radial divergence at the object. If a plot of x vs. θ shows a minimum at some particular θ, then x will indeed vary least if the change in θ is made from this value.

Since $\sin \theta = 2 \sin(\theta/2)\cos(\theta/2)$, we may write Eq. (4-81) in the form

$$x = \Delta\rho[2 \sin(\theta/2) + 2 \sin(\theta/2)\cos^2(\theta/2)], \tag{4-87}$$

where $\Delta\rho$ is a constant. On calculating $dx/d\tfrac{1}{2}\theta$, and equating it to zero, we find $\sin(\theta/2) = \sqrt{\tfrac{2}{3}} = 0.816$, whence $\theta = 109.4°$. Therefore $u = -35.27°$, the photo plate lies at the angle $\beta = 19.44°$, and the resolution function is $F = 1.94$.

CASE 10. $n = 0$, $u_1 > 0$, $u_2 < 0$

Elbek Spectrograph

This uniform-field instrument* (Fig. 4-18) is similar to that of Fowler and Hafner *et al.* in that θ is the same for all momenta and that u_2 is negative; the

* 125, Borggreen *et al.*

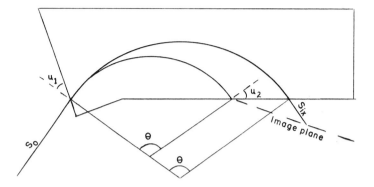

FIG. 4-18. Elbek spectrograph.

distinction is that u_1 is positive (axially focusing), so that particles with a larger axial divergence will pass through the gap. Nevertheless, the defocusing action of the exit edge prevents the formation of an axial image.

The bending angle is $\theta = 107.4°$, so, as in the Fowler–Hafner magnet, there is good focusing of the radial images for moderate radial divergence angles. The edge angles are $u_1 = 35°$ and $u_2 = -36.3°$, and the radial magnification is approximately -0.5. The ratio of momenta that may be recorded at a single field strength is a little over 2.

CASE 11. $n = 0, u_1, u_2, u_3 > 0, u_4 < 0$

Split-Pole Spectrograph

The split-pole spectrograph of Spencer and Enge* is an outgrowth of the Elbek type, which in turn, is an improvement on the Fowler–Hafner instrument. The total bend, for ions of all momenta, is $\theta = 114°$, obtained by the use of two successive magnets (with a common set of coils) that are so close together that no radial image is formed between them (see Fig. 4-19).

The nominal edge angles for midenergy ions are $u_1 = 37°$ and $u_2 = 13.8°$ at the entrance and exit of the first magnet, and $u_3 = 35°$ at the entrance to the second. But due to the large deflection of low energy particles in the first field, the entrance angle of the second magnet is, for them, almost zero, while for the less-deflected highest energy particles it is $55°$. For all projectiles, the final exit angle is $u_4 = -19°$. Further parameters are afforded by the concave surface of the first magnet's entrance edge and by the convex surface at its exit. As a result, approximate double focusing is obtained for all momenta,

* 133, Spencer and Enge; 92, Viswesvariah and Sarma.

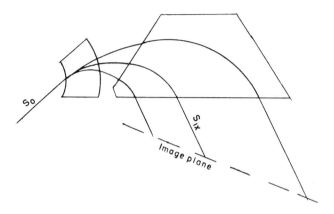

FIG. 4-19. Split-pole spectrograph.

with M_z ranging from -1 to -2.7. The radial magnification is close to -0.35 for all accepted momenta, which have a ratio of 2.7.

With $\rho_{max} = 90$ cm and an object width $w_o = 0.09$ cm, the resolution function is about $F = 5$, so that $\Delta p/p = 1/5000 = 0.02\%$.

The instrument was designed by ray-tracing in steps of a few millimeters with the aid of a digital computer and sophisticated estimates of the fringing fields, until a satisfactory set of parameters was obtained. For the details of this process, the original paper should be consulted. (Note that therein the dispersion is defined as our D divided by ρ.)

CASE 12. $n = 0.5$, $u_1 = u_2 = 0$

$$\delta = \sqrt{1 - n} = \varepsilon = \sqrt{n} = 1/\sqrt{2},$$
$$\phi = \delta\theta = \psi = \varepsilon\theta = \theta/\sqrt{2}.$$

$$M_x = -\frac{1}{(L_{ox}/\sqrt{2})\sin(\theta/\sqrt{2}) - \cos(\theta/\sqrt{2})}, \tag{4-88}$$

$$M_z = -\frac{1}{(L_{oz}/\sqrt{2})\sin(\theta/\sqrt{2}) - \cos(\theta/\sqrt{2})}, \tag{4-89}$$

$$L_{ix} = -M_x[L_{ox}\cos(\theta/\sqrt{2}) + \sqrt{2}\sin(\theta/\sqrt{2})], \tag{4-90}$$

$$L_{iz} = -M_z[L_{oz}\cos(\theta/\sqrt{2}) + \sqrt{2}\sin(\theta/\sqrt{2})], \tag{4-91}$$

$$F = -D/(\rho M_x) = 2[(L_{ox}/\sqrt{2})\sin(\theta/\sqrt{2}) + 1 - \cos(\theta/\sqrt{2})] \tag{4-92}$$

$$= 2(1 - 1/M_x) = (1 - 1/M_x)/(1 - n). \tag{4-93}$$

If $L_{ox} = L_{oz} = L_o$, then $M_x = M_z = M$ and $L_{ix} = L_{iz} = L_i$, so the system is double focusing, and for a given M, we see that F has the same value at all θ. In particular, $F = 4$ at $M = -1$ and the system is then symmetric:

$$L_o = L_i$$

$$= \sqrt{2} \frac{1 + \cos \dfrac{\theta}{\sqrt{2}}}{\sin \dfrac{\theta}{\sqrt{2}}}$$

$$= \sqrt{2} \cot \frac{\theta}{2\sqrt{2}} \tag{4-94}$$

For $M = -1$, Table 4-7 applies.

TABLE 4-7

$n = 0.5, \quad u_1 = u_2 = 0$

θ (deg)	30	45	60	75	90	105	120	135	150	169.7	180	254.5
$L_o = L_i$	7.55	4.96	3.64	2.83	2.28	1.87	1.55	1.29	1.06	0.817	0.700	0

At $\theta = 169.7° = 2\sqrt{2}\,\pi/3$, the aberration (i.e., the increased radial width of image) due to a finite radial divergence at the object is automatically eliminated; see Eq. (18-29).

For $\theta = 254.5° = \pi\sqrt{2}$, we note that the object and image distances are zero. This is sometimes an experimental inconvenience, but, on the other hand, if the object and image are both immersed in a field that extends for more than $\pi\sqrt{2}$ (an extent of 2π is often used) then there are no edge fringing fields to contend with, so the orbits can be calculated with considerable precision in both planes. (More will be said on this subject in Chapter 18.)

For a given M, the $n = 0.5$ magnet gives twice as good a resolution in momentum as does the $n = u_1 = u_2 = 0$ variety. Compared with a magnet with $n = 0$ and $\tan u_1 = \tan u_2 = 1/L_o$, the $n = 0.5$ instrument has a momentum resolution that is superior at $|M| < 1$ and inferior at $|M| > 1$; the resolutions are the same at $M = -1$ but for the $n = 0.5$ type the distances are larger by a factor that ranges from 1.01 at $\theta = 30°$ to 1.97 at $\theta = 150°$.

The behavior is displayed in the following Figs. 4-20–4-22.

Papers describing magnets with $n = 0.5$ may be found in the bibliography.

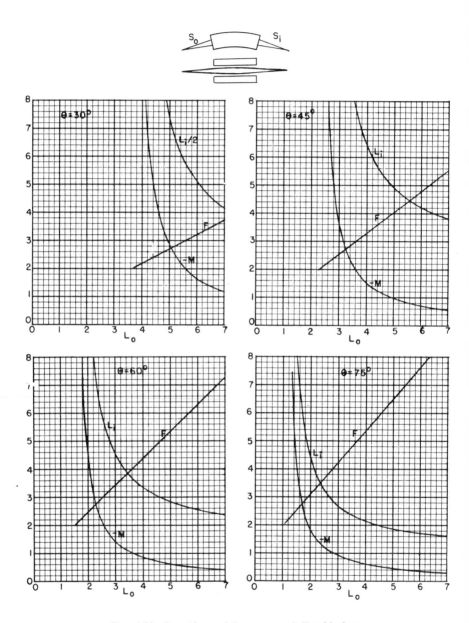

FIG. 4-20. Case 12. $n = 0.5$, $u_1 = u_2 = 0$. Double focus.

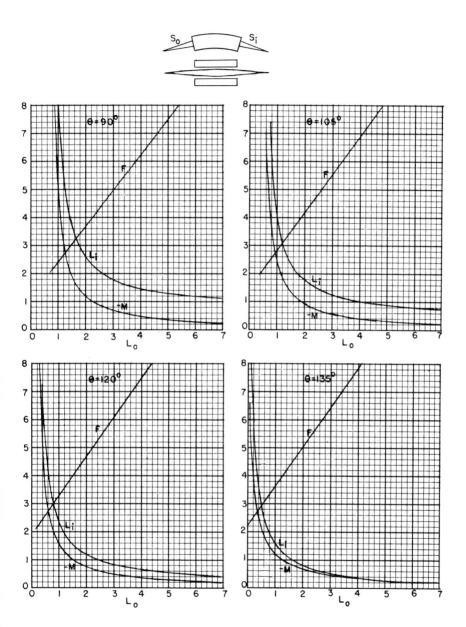

FIG. 4-21. Case 12 cont'd. $n = 0.5$, $u_1 = u_2 = 0$. Double focus.

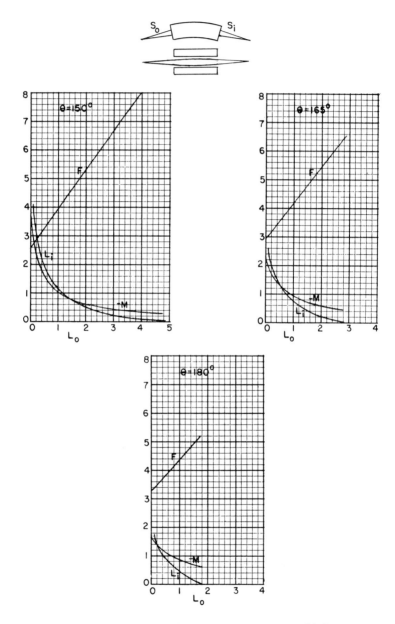

FIG. 4-22. Case 12 cont'd. $n = 0.5$, $u_1 = u_2 = 0$. Double focus.

CASE 13. $n = 0.5$, $u_1 = 0$, $u_2 > 0$

$$M_x = -\frac{1}{L_o[(1/\sqrt{2})\sin(\theta/\sqrt{2}) - \tan u_2 \cos(\theta/\sqrt{2})] - \cos(\theta/\sqrt{2})} - \sqrt{2}\tan u_2 \sin(\theta/\sqrt{2}), \quad (4\text{-}95)$$

$$M_z = -\frac{1}{L_o[(1/\sqrt{2})\sin(\theta/\sqrt{2}) + \tan u_2 \cos(\theta/\sqrt{2})] - \cos(\theta/\sqrt{2})} + \sqrt{2}\tan u_2 \sin(\theta/\sqrt{2}), \quad (4\text{-}96)$$

$$L_{ix} = -M_x[L_o \cos(\theta/\sqrt{2}) + \sqrt{2}\sin(\theta/\sqrt{2})], \quad (4\text{-}97)$$

$$L_{iz} = -M_z[L_o \cos(\theta/\sqrt{2}) + \sqrt{2}\sin(\theta/\sqrt{2})], \quad (4\text{-}98)$$

$$F = -D/(\rho M_x) = 2[(L_o/\sqrt{2})\sin(\theta/\sqrt{2}) + 1 - \cos(\theta/\sqrt{2})]. \quad (4\text{-}99)$$

By comparing Eqs. (4-99) and (4-92), we see that F has not been altered by the finite value of u_2, but Eqs. (4-95) and (4-88) show that $|M_x|$ has been increased.

This unusual magnet affords a reasonable approximation to a system suggested by Hudson and Hicks,* wherein a magnet with $n = 0.5$ and $u_1 = u_2 = 0$ is closely followed by a quadrupole that diverges radially and focuses axially. The above analysis represents the limiting case where there is zero space between the magnet and the quadrupole, for the exit edge performs the same function as the quad.

The virtue of the system is that, for a given θ and L_o, the radial magnification is increased (over its value had the quadrupole been omitted) without changing the resolution. This permits a wider exit slit and hence reduces the bad effects of slit scattering.

For example, assume $\theta = 150°$, so that with $n = 0.5$ and $u_1 = u_2 = 0$ we have $L_o = L_{ix} = L_{iz} = 1.06$, $M_x = M_z = -1$, and $F = 4$, as in Case 12. If we now make $u_2 = 24.8°$ and keep L_o at 1.06, we again have $F = 4$ but now $M_x = -2$, $L_{ix} = 2.12$, and $L_{iz} = 0.715$. Doubling the width of the radial image has entailed only the sacrifice of double focusing. (In Case 12, raising M_x to -2 by reducing L_o to 0.3 would lower F from 4 to 3.)

The focal length of an edge with $u_2 = 24.3°$ ($\tan u_2 = 0.4620$) may be found from Eq. (2-20) or (2-21) by setting $\theta = 0$. We find

$$S_{ixf} = S_{oxf} = -\frac{\rho}{\tan u_2} = -\frac{\rho}{0.4620} = -2.164\rho,$$

where ρ is the radius of curvature of the magnet. A quadrupole of this focal length is not difficult to attain, for reasonable values of ρ.

* 198, Hudson and Hicks.

CASE 14. $n = 0.57$, $u_1 = u_2 = 0$

Tipped Image Spectrograph

When the object is a target being bombarded by projectiles from an accelerator, the energies of the disintegration products vary slightly with the direction of emission, this being measured with respect to the projectiles' line of flight. Small changes in energy will only broaden the image spot of a double focusing spectrometer. If the angle of emission corresponds to the axial divergence angle presented to the analyzing magnet, the resolution of these ions can be brought about by deliberately preventing the magnet from being double focusing; this is done by making n not quite equal to 0.5. Particles of a single energy then produce a line image along the z direction (normal to the plane of bending) and when the energy rises with increasing z_0' the image line will be tipped with respect to the z coordinate, since the faster particles are deflected less than the slower ones. The angle of tipping is a measure of the energy increment. For the details, the original paper* should be consulted.

CASE 15. $n > 0.5$, $u_1 = u_2 = 0$

Single Focusing

When $u_1 = 0$, Eq. (2-28) reads

$$F = \frac{1}{\delta^2} [L_o\, \delta \sin(\delta\theta) + 1 - \cos(\delta\theta)], \qquad (4\text{-}100)$$

and if $u_1 = u_2 = 0$, Eq. (2-24) becomes

$$-\frac{1}{M_x} = L_o\, \delta \sin(\delta\theta) - \cos(\delta\theta). \qquad (4\text{-}101)$$

Hence

$$F = \frac{1}{\delta^2} \left[1 - \frac{1}{M_x} \right] = \frac{1}{1 - n} \left[1 - \frac{1}{M_x} \right]. \qquad (4\text{-}102)$$

In other words, for the same magnification, the quantity $[L_o\delta \sin(\delta\theta) + 1 - \cos(\delta\theta)]$ is independent of δ and hence of n, and so F depends solely on $\delta^2 = 1 - n$. (Compare Eqs. (4-4) and (4-93).) It is consequently very desirable that the value of n should approach unity, as this increases F and so improves the momentum resolution, $\Delta p/p = w_o/(\rho F)$.

On the other hand, since we have seen that double focusing occurs when $n = 0.5$ (with $u_1 = u_2 = 0$), an increase in n will entail the sacrifice of double focusing (except in the special circumstances to be described in Case 16).

* 166, Mileikowsky; 178, Bianchi *et al.*

For $M_x = -1$, we have $L_o = L_{ix}$ and Eq. (2-18) (giving L_{ix} in terms of L_o) becomes

$$L_o = L_{ix} = \frac{1}{\delta} \cot(\delta\theta/2). \tag{4-103}$$

As an example, with $n = 0.89$ (so that $\delta = 0.332$) and with $\theta = 180°$, we find

$$F = 18.2 \quad \text{and} \quad L_o = L_{ix} = 5.24.$$

(Compare this with $F = 4$ and $L_o = L_{ix} = 0.7$ when $n = 0.5$ and $\theta = 180°$, Case 12.)

Magnets with $n = 0.87$ and $n = 0.89$ have been reported by Alekseevsky et al.*

CASE 16. $n > 0.5, u_1 = u_2 = 0$

Double Focusing

With $n = 0.5$ and $u_1 = u_2 = 0$, we have seen that there is double focusing, the one radial and one axial images being coincident. With a larger value of n, better resolution can be obtained, as already seen, and double focusing can be retained if we arrange to have an additional *axial* image at the midpoint of the magnet, as indicated in Fig. 4-23.

Suppose we set $S_0 = S_{ix}$, so that $M_x = -1$. Then, as in the preceding case, we have

$$L_o = L_{ix} = \frac{1}{\delta} \cot(\delta\theta/2). \tag{4-104}$$

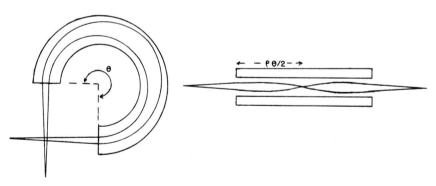

FIG. 4-23. A magnet with one radial and two axial images can be double focusing when $n > 0.5$.

* 200, Alekseevsky et al.

In considering the axial motion, we may imagine that we have a magnet of bending angle $\theta/2$ with its axial image at zero distance from its end. Then Eq. (3-5) tells us that

$$L_o = -\frac{1}{\varepsilon}\tan(\varepsilon\theta/2). \qquad (4\text{-}105)$$

For the entire magnet, we see from symmetry that $L_{iz} = L_o$, and since $L_{ix} = L_o$ by hypothesis, then it follows that $L_{iz} = L_{ix}$, so there is double focusing at the image beyond the magnet. By setting Eq. (4-104) equal to Eq. (4-105), we find the necessary relation between θ and n:

$$\frac{1}{\delta}\cot(\delta\theta/2) = -\frac{1}{\varepsilon}\tan(\varepsilon\theta/2), \qquad (4\text{-}106)$$

where $\delta = (1-n)^{1/2}$ and $\varepsilon = n^{1/2}$. (Because of the minus sign, this condition can be satisfied only when the arguments of the trigonometric functions lie in adjacent quadrants.) The solutions can be found by trial and error, with results shown in Table 4-8 and Fig. 4-24. Note the very substantial values of F.

Magnets with $n = 0.831$ and $\theta = 270°$ are in use at the Leningrad 100 MeV synchrocyclotron,* their bending radii being 180 cm and 200 cm.

TABLE 4-8

$n > 0.5, u_1 = u_2 = 0$

n	0.95	0.90	0.8317	0.81
θ	195.4	216.55	270	310.8
$L_o = L_{ix} = L_{iz}$	11.14	4.65	1.68	0.937
F	39.95	19.99	11.88	10.625

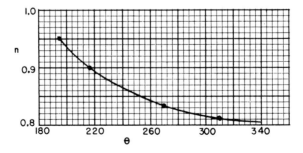

FIG. 4-24. Values of n and θ that give one radial and two axial images.

* 203, Barkovsky *et al.*

CASE 17. $n < 0.5$, $u_1 = u_2 = 0$

Double Focused, Nondispersed Final Image

It is also possible to so choose n that not only is there a double-focused image beyond the magnet but also a *radial* image at the magnet's center, as indicated in Fig. 4-25.

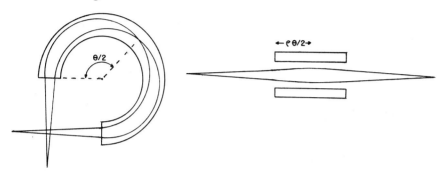

FIG. 4-25. A magnet with one axial and two radial images can be double focusing and nondispersive at the second image if $n < 0.5$.

Let $S_{ix} = S_0$, so that $M_x = +1$. We may imagine a magnet of angle $\theta/2$ with a dispersed radial image at zero distance from its exit face; then Eq. (2-18) gives

$$L_o = -\frac{1}{\delta}\tan(\delta\theta/2). \qquad (4\text{-}107)$$

Again with a magnet of angle $\theta/2$, we see that the axial image distance is infinite, so that Eq. (3-5) yields

$$L_o = \frac{1}{\varepsilon}\cot(\varepsilon\theta/2). \qquad (4\text{-}108)$$

Equating these expressions gives the necessary condition

$$\frac{1}{\varepsilon}\cot\left(\frac{\varepsilon\theta}{2}\right) = -\frac{1}{\delta}\tan\left(\frac{\delta\theta}{2}\right), \qquad (4\text{-}109)$$

and, as in the previous case, we argue that $L_{iz} = L_{ix}$.

When we compare Eqs. (4-109) and (4-106), we see that they are the same except for an interchange of ε with δ. That is, for a given θ, we replace $\delta_a = (1 - n_a)^{1/2}$ with $\varepsilon_b = (n_b)^{1/2}$, so that $1 - n_a = n_b$, whence $n_a + n_b = 1$, where subscript a refers to Case 16 and subscript b to the present example.

(Alternatively, solutions of Eq. (4-109) may be found by trial.) We obtain the results shown in Table 4-9.

TABLE 4-9

$n < 0.5$, $u_1 = u_2 = 0$

n	0.05	0.10	0.1683	0.19
θ	195.4	216.55	270	310.8
$L_o = L_{1x} = L_{1z}$	11.14	4.65	1.68	0.937
F	0	0	0	0

The values of F, found from Eq. (2-28), indicate that an infinite momentum change is needed to move the radial image out of the slit beyond the magnet; the image is said to be achromatic or nondispersed, since the images of all momenta are coincident. This is useful for those experiments where intensity is more important than homogeneity of energy. (Other situations where an achromatic image is formed will be described later.)

On the other hand, the central radial image is dispersed, so a slit at that point can select a narrow momentum band which is then imaged achromatically outside the magnet.

By the use of auxiliary windings, one of the Leningrad 270° magnets mentioned in the previous case can have its n value altered from 0.831 to 0.169, so that the final image is dispersed or achromatic, at will.

CASE 18. $n > 0.5$, $u_1 > 0$, $u_2 < 0$

Double Focusing

We repeat Eq. (2-28):

$$F = \frac{1}{\delta^2} \{L_o[\delta \sin \phi + \tan u_1(1 - \cos \phi)] + 1 - \cos \phi\},$$

where $\delta = (1 - n)^{1/2}$ and $\phi = \delta\theta$. It is clear that F will rise, thereby improving the resolution, if δ^2 is small; i.e., if n approaches unity. Note that a positive value of u_1 (desirable to create axial focusing at the entrance edge) also increases F. The unspecified exit edge angle, u_2, may be adjusted to produce double focusing.

There are an infinite number of possibilities for the various parameters, just as there were in Case 8. Karmohapatro* has worked out a range of

* 203, Karmohapatro.

choices in the form of charts. For $n = 0.8$, $\theta = 180°$, $L_o = 1.5$ or 2.0, and with u_1 ranging from 58° to 66°, he gives curves showing the requisite values of u_2 (all negative) and of $L_{ix} = L_{iz}$. For $n = 0.9$, and $\theta = 180°$, the choices of L_o are 2, 3, 4, and 5.

As an example, with $n = 0.9$, $\theta = 180°$, $L_o = 2$, and $u_1 = 60°$, then $u_2 = -27.4°$, $L_{ix} = L_{iz} = 2.7$, and $F = 26$.

BARBER'S RULE

Consider a uniform field magnet with normal entry and exit, so $n = u_1 = u_2 = 0$. Let C be the center of curvature of the bending radius ρ, as indicated in Fig. 4-26, wherein the angles A and B are identified. We wish to prove that

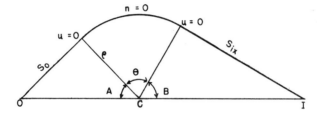

FIG. 4-26. Relations involved in Barber's rule.

$A + \theta + B = 180°$. From the figure, it is clear that

$$L_o = S_0/\rho = \tan A$$

and

$$L_{ix} = S_{ix}/\rho = \tan B.$$

Now Eq. (2-18), adjusted for this type magnet, reads

$$L_{ix} = \frac{L_o \cos \theta + \sin \theta}{L_o \sin \theta - \cos \theta},$$

and on substituting for L_o and L_{ix} as given above, we get

$$\tan B = -\frac{\tan A + \tan \theta}{1 - \tan A \tan \theta}. \tag{4-110}$$

Now suppose it were true that $A + B + \theta = 180°$. Then it follows that

$$B = 180° - (A + \theta)$$

and

$$\tan B = -\tan(A + \theta).$$

By a theorem of trigonometry, this may be written as

$$\tan B = -\frac{\tan A + \tan \theta}{1 - \tan A \tan \theta}.$$ (4-111)

Since this is the same as Eq. (4-110), we may conclude that the object, the center of curvature, and the image, all lie on one straight line. This is Barber's rule.[*]

The rule may also be applied, with modifications,[†] to the case where $u_1 = u_2 = 0$ but $1 > n > 0$. For radial motion, we draw a diagram (which does *not* represent real trajectories) indicating "deflection" through the angle $\phi = (1 - n)^{1/2}\theta \equiv \delta\theta$, with the object and image at "distances" $S_0\delta$ and $S_{ix}\delta$ (Fig. 4-27).

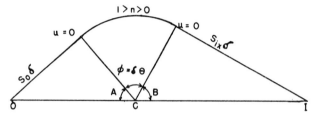

FIG. 4-27. Radial diagram for Barber's rule when $1 > n > 0$.

Then

$$S_0/\rho = (\tan A)/\delta \quad \text{and} \quad S_{ix}/\rho = (\tan B)/\delta,$$

and using these in Eq. (2-18) we get

$$\frac{\tan B}{\delta} = \frac{(\tan A \cos \phi)/\delta + (\sin \phi)/\delta}{(\delta \sin \phi \tan A)/\delta - \cos \phi},$$

whence it follows that

$$\tan B = -\frac{\tan A + \tan \phi}{1 - \tan A \tan \phi}.$$ (4-112)

As in the preceding paragraph, this same equation results if we assume that $A + \phi + B = 180°$. Hence the points O, C, and I in Fig. 4-27 lie on a straight line, although the actual object, image, and center of curvature are not colinear. This stratagem is sometimes useful.

* 49, Barber.
† 141, Judd.

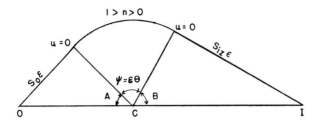

FIG. 4-28. Axial diagram for Barber's rule when $1 > n > 0$.

For axial motion, the diagram of Fig. 4-28 is used, where the "deflection" is through the angle $\psi = n^{1/2}\theta \equiv \varepsilon\theta$ and the "distances" are $S_0\varepsilon$ and $S_{iz}\varepsilon$. The same type arguments show that O and I are colinear with C, though this is not true of the real object and image.

5 Dispersive Multimagnet Systems

EFFECT OF REVERSED BENDING OF A MAGNET

Passage through a second magnet is described by matrices that are analogous to those of Eqs. (2-7)–(2-9), except that two adjustments must be made if the second magnet bends the beam in a direction opposite to that of the first.

It is implicit in the equations of radial motion that positive x lies in the direction of increasing ρ. Hence if we take the direction of positive x to be set by the first magnet (say to the left, when looking downstream, the bend being to the right), we must change the sign of x on entering and on leaving any subsequent magnet that bends the other way. Further, in order that a positive value of the slope x' shall lead to an increase of x, the sign of x' must also be altered on entering and on leaving any reversed-curvature magnet.

Hence if the transfer matrix through the first magnet is

$$\begin{pmatrix} A & B & C \\ D & E & F \\ 0 & 0 & 1 \end{pmatrix},$$

the matrix that applies to any reversed-curvature magnet is

$$\begin{pmatrix} -1 & 0 & 0 \\ 0 & -1 & 0 \\ 0 & 0 & 1 \end{pmatrix} \begin{pmatrix} A & B & C \\ D & E & F \\ 0 & 0 & 1 \end{pmatrix} \begin{pmatrix} -1 & 0 & 0 \\ 0 & -1 & 0 \\ 0 & 0 & 1 \end{pmatrix} = \begin{pmatrix} A & B & -C \\ D & E & -F \\ 0 & 0 & 1 \end{pmatrix}. \quad (5\text{-}1)$$

Thus the signs of the first two elements in the third column must be altered.

Let the second magnet have bending angle θ_2, radius ρ_2, field index n_2 (where $1 > n_2 > 0$), entrance edge angle u_3, and exit edge angle u_4. For convenience we write

$$\delta_2 = \sqrt{1 - n_2}, \qquad \phi_2 = \delta_2 \theta_2, \qquad t_3 = \tan u_3, \qquad t_4 = \tan u_4. \quad (5\text{-}2)$$

Let S_1 now represent the separation between magnets. (See Fig. 5-1.)

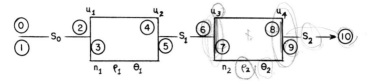

FIG. 5-1. Nomenclature with two magnets.

At any distance S_2 beyond the second magnet, the radial displacement x_{10} and slope x'_{10} may be found in terms of x_6 and x_6' by the expression:

$$
\begin{pmatrix} x_{10} \\ x'_{10} \\ \Delta p/p \end{pmatrix} = \begin{pmatrix} 1 & S_2 & 0 \\ 0 & 1 & 0 \\ 0 & 0 & 1 \end{pmatrix} \begin{pmatrix} 1 & 0 & 0 \\ \dfrac{t_4}{\rho_2} & 1 & 0 \\ 0 & 0 & 1 \end{pmatrix}
$$

$$
\times \begin{pmatrix} \cos\phi_2 & \dfrac{\rho_2 \sin\phi_2}{\delta_2} & \pm\dfrac{\rho_2}{\delta_2^{\,2}}(1-\cos\phi_2) \\ -\dfrac{\delta_2 \sin\phi_2}{\rho_2} & \cos\phi_2 & \pm\dfrac{\sin\phi_2}{\delta_2} \\ 0 & 0 & 1 \end{pmatrix}
$$

$$
\times \begin{pmatrix} 1 & 0 & 0 \\ \dfrac{t_3}{\rho_2} & 1 & 0 \\ 0 & 0 & 1 \end{pmatrix} \begin{pmatrix} x_6 \\ x_6' \\ \Delta p/p \end{pmatrix}. \tag{5-3}
$$

On substituting for x_6 and x_6' as given by Eq. (2-11), we find expressions of the form:

$$x_{10} = a_{10} x_1 + b_{10} x_1' + c_{10} \, \Delta p/p, \tag{5-4}$$

$$x'_{10} = d_{10} x_1 + e_{10} x_1' + f_{10} \, \Delta p/p. \tag{5-5}$$

Explicit expressions for $a_{10}, b_{10}, \ldots, f_{10}$ will be found in Chapter 6; the upper (lower) signs are used if the second magnet bends in the same (opposite) direction as does the first. For these alternatives, we identify c_{10} as c_{10}^{++} or c_{10}^{+-} respectively, and similarly with f_{10}.

By the same type arguments as were used with a single magnet, it is clear that

(1) the radial image distance of the second magnet may be found by setting $b_{10} = 0$ and in the resulting expression interpreting S_2 as the radial image distance S_{ix2},

(2) the radial magnification M_{x12} of the pair of magnets is given by a_{10} when the latter is evaluated at the image distances S_{ix2},

(3) the dispersion coefficient D_{12} of the pair of magnets is given by c_{10} when it is evaluated at the image distance S_{ix2}.

Similar remarks apply if there are three magnets, the third having parameters n_3, ρ_3, θ_3, u_5, and u_6, any distance beyond it being called S_3. The radial image distance is found from setting $b_{14} = 0$, the overall magnification is $M_{x123} = a_{14}$, and the total dispersion coefficient is $D_{123} = c_{14}$, and in all three of these expressions S_3 is interpreted as S_{ix3}.

The values and relationships between the radial coefficients a_j, b_j, ..., f_j with $j = 1, 2, ..., 14$ are given in Chapter 6. They may be converted to the axial coefficients $\bar{a}_j$, $\bar{b}_j$, ..., $\bar{f}_j$ by the procedures of Eqs. (3-1)–(3-3). Both sets of coefficients are used in finding the dimensions of the beam's envelope (see Chapters 7–9) and can also serve to determine the image distances, magnifications, and dispersions, whether or not there are images formed between the magnets.

But when each magnet forms an image that serves as the object for the next magnet, the magnification and dispersion may be found much more rapidly by the arguments to be presented next.

Two Magnets with an Intermagnet Image—General Relations

Consider an ion of momentum $p + \Delta p$ (where Δp is not yet specified) that leaves the tip of the object with displacement x_{01}. The displacement at the image plane of the first magnet is

$$x_{i1} = M_1 x_{01} + D_1 \Delta p/p. \tag{5-6}$$

(Since the magnifications to be discussed are all radial, we drop the subscript x.) This image serves as the object point for the second magnet, so that $x_{02} = x_{i1}$. At the second image plane, the displacement is

$$x_{i2} = M_2 x_{02} \pm D_2 \Delta p/p = M_1 M_2 x_{01} + (M_2 D_1 \pm D_2) \Delta p/p \tag{5-7}$$

as follows by substituting for x_{02}. The upper (lower) sign is used if the magnets bend in the same (opposite) directions. In terms of the properties M_{12} and D_{12} of the whole system, we may write

$$x_{i2} = M_{12} x_0 + D_{12} \Delta p/p, \tag{5-8}$$

where

$$M_{12} = M_1 M_2 \tag{5-9}$$

and

$$D_{12} = M_2 D_1 \pm D_2. \tag{5-10}$$

TWO OPPOSITELY BENDING MAGNETS WITH AN INTERMAGNET IMAGE

A slit of width s_i in the second image plane just intercepts the $p + \Delta p$ and the $p - \Delta p$ images. This defines Δp. (Note that these images are not completely separated in the first image plane.) The tip of the $p + \Delta p$ image has a negative displacement $-s_i/2$. (See Fig. 5-2.) Hence

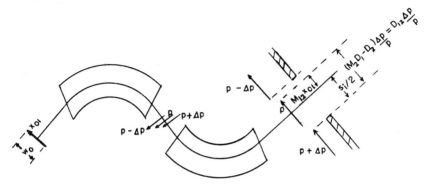

FIG. 5-2. Image and slit relations (not to scale).

$$-s_i/2 = M_{12}\, x_{01} + D_{12}\, \Delta p/p. \tag{5-11}$$

But $x_{01} = w_0/2$, so that

$$R_p^{+-} = \frac{\Delta p}{p} \; \frac{-s_i - M_{12}\, w_0}{2D_{12}}. \tag{5-12}$$

Now let $s_i = M_{12}\, w_0$ (where M_{12} is positive), so that s_i is just as wide as one image in the second image plane. Then the $p - \Delta p$, p, and $p + \Delta p$ images are just touching, with no overlap. Hence

$$R_p^{+-} = \frac{\Delta p}{p} = -\frac{M_{12}\, w_0}{D_{12}} \tag{5-13}$$

$$= -\frac{M_1 M_2\, w_0}{M_2 D_1(-D_2)}, \tag{5-14}$$

by Eqs. (5-9) and (5-10), using the lower sign (opposed magnets) in Eq. (5-10). By Eq. (2-29) $(D_1 = -M_1\rho_1 F_1)$ and its second magnet analog, this becomes

$$R_p^{+-} = \frac{\Delta p}{p} = -\frac{M_1 M_2\, w_0}{-M_1 M_2 \rho_1 F_1 + M_2 \rho_2 F_2} = -\frac{w_0}{-\rho_1 F_1 + \rho_2 F_2/M_1}. \tag{5-15}$$

Now M_1 is negative, so the two terms in the denominator add; the magnets aid each other in improving the resolution. Small values of w_0 and of $|M_1|$

and large values of ρ_1, ρ_2, F_1, and F_2 all act to reduce the momentum change Δp needed to move the $p - \Delta p$ and $p + \Delta p$ images out of the slit. Although M_2 does not appear explicitly in Eq. (5-15), its choice determines F_2, as seen earlier.

If identical magnets are used and if $M_1 = M_2 = -1$, then $F_1 = F_2 = F$, and

$$R_p^{+-} = \frac{\Delta p}{p} = \frac{w_o}{2\rho F}. \tag{5-16}$$

The resolution is improved by a factor two, over that obtained with just one of the magnets. (Compare Eqs. (5-16) and (2-34)).

Two Similarly Bending Magnets with an Intermagnet Image

The image slit s_i just intercepts the $p - \Delta p$ and $p + \Delta p$ images, thereby defining Δp. The tip of the $p + \Delta p$ image lies at $(s_i/2) + M_{12} w_o$ (assuming that M_{12} is the same for $p + \Delta p$ as for p, which is correct to a very good approximation, as will be shown in Chapter 17). (See Fig. 5-3.) Hence

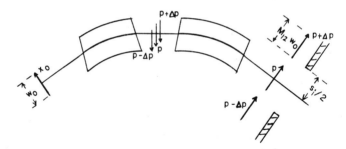

FIG. 5-3. Image and slit relations (not to scale).

$$(s_i/2) + M_{12} w_o = M_{12} x_0 + D_{12} \Delta p/p. \tag{5-17}$$

But $x_0 = w_o/2$, so that

$$R_p^{++} = \frac{\Delta p}{p} = \frac{s_i + M_{12} w_o}{2D_{12}}. \tag{5-18}$$

Now let $s_i = M_{12} w_o$, so the slit is just one image wide and the $p - \Delta p$ and $p + \Delta p$ images just touch the p image. Then, using Eqs. (5-9) and (5-10), we find

$$R_p^{++} = \frac{\Delta p}{p} = \frac{M_{12} w_o}{D_{12}} = \frac{M_1 M_2 w_o}{M_2 D_1 + D_2}, \tag{5-19}$$

where we use the upper sign in Eq. (5-10) since the magnets bend the same way. Then employing $D = -M\rho F$ (Eq. (2-29)), we get

$$R_p^{++} = \frac{\Delta p}{p} = \frac{M_1 M_2 w_o}{-M_1 M_2 \rho_1 F_1 - M_2 \rho_2 F_2} = \frac{w_o}{-\rho_1 F_1 - \rho_2 F_2/M_1}. \qquad (5\text{-}20)$$

Since M_1 is negative, the two terms in the denominator are of opposite sign. Therefore the $(++)$ array does not give as good resolution as does the $(+-)$ (Eq. (5-15)), other parameters being equal.

Indeed, under obvious circumstances (for example if $\rho_1 = \rho_2$, $F_1 = F_2$, and $M_1 = -1$), the denominator of Eq. (5-20) will vanish, so that an infinite change in momentum is needed to move the $p + \Delta p$ and $p - \Delta p$ images out of the slit; i.e., the image is achromatic. This sometimes useful property will be discussed at greater length in Chapter 12.

A Series of Magnets with Intermagnet Images

Suppose we have five magnets. Then

$$\frac{\Delta p}{p} = -\frac{w_o M_5 M_4 M_3 M_2 M_1}{M_5 M_4 M_3 M_2 D_1 \pm M_5 M_4 M_3 D_2 \pm M_5 M_4 D_3 \pm M_5 D_4 \pm D_5}. \qquad (5\text{-}21)$$

Until the direction of the bending angle of each magnet is specified, there is an ambiguity in the sign of the numerator. But this is irrelevant to the resolution, for it merely means that the locations of the final $p + \Delta p$ and $p - \Delta p$ images may possibly be interchanged. Using $D = -M\rho F$, we get

$$\frac{\Delta p}{p} = -\frac{w_o}{-\rho_1 F_1 \mp (\rho_2 F_2/M_1) \mp (\rho_3 F_3/M_2 M_1)}{\mp (\rho_4 F_4/M_3 M_2 M_1) \mp (\rho_5 F_5/M_4 M_3 M_2 M_1)}. \qquad (5\text{-}22)$$

For $\theta < 180°$, M is negative. Therefore

$$\frac{\Delta p}{p} = -\frac{w_o}{-\rho_1 F_1 \pm (\rho_2 F_2/|M_1|) \mp (\rho_3 F_3/|M_2||M_1|)}{\pm (\rho_4 F_4/|M_3||M_2||M_1|) \mp (\rho_5 F_5/|M_4||M_3||M_2||M_1|)}. \qquad (5\text{-}23)$$

Let the array be a switch magnet, two analyzers, and two more switches, oriented as indicated in Fig. 5-4. The upper (lower) sign in Eq. (5-23) is used

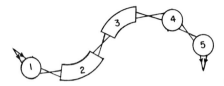

FIG. 5-4. An illustrative example of a
series of magnets with intermagnet images.

if the magnet under consideration bends in the same (opposite) direction as
does the first one. Hence

$$\frac{\Delta p}{p} = \frac{-w_o}{-\rho_1 F_1 + (\rho_2 F_2/|M_1|) + (\rho_3 F_3/|M_2||M_1|)}{\qquad - (\rho_4 F_4/|M_3||M_2||M_1|) + (\rho_5 F_5/|M_4||M_3||M_2||M_1|)}. \tag{5-24}$$

Magnet No. 5 aids Nos. 2 and 3, while Nos. 1 and 4 detract from the overall
resolution.

6 Radial Matrix Coefficients for Three Magnets

The following tabulation, which is the basis of many of the results given in this book, is supplied as a convenience to the reader, to help in understanding what is presented and to be of use in the analysis of magnet systems not here treated.

The coefficients are given in detailed form up to a point beyond the first magnet (station 6) and from there on in skeletal form to a point beyond the second magnet (station 10), where the detailed expressions are again given. Beyond that, only the skeletal form is presented. (See Fig. 6-1.)

It will be noted that the station 10 coefficients appear in two forms. The first is entirely in basic quantities and is useful for general analysis. The second involves the coefficients of station 7 and is of use in calculating beam envelopes, where numerical values of the coefficients at station 7 will already have been found. The second form is employed in the step-by-step procedures given in Chapter 9.

The reader is admonished to use these Chapter 6 radial coefficients, in the exact form here given, when axial coefficients are to be obtained by the procedures presented in Eqs. (3-1)–(3-3), because all of the symbols are present which must be converted. *Do not make a conversion from a simplified expression,* such as from a radial coefficient for an $n = 0$ magnet. Thus the expression $\sigma/\delta \equiv (\sin \phi)/(1 - n)^{1/2}$ converts properly to $(\sin \psi)/\varepsilon = (\sin \sqrt{n}\,\theta)/\sqrt{n}$, so for $n = 0$ we get θ as shown in Eq. (3-3); whereas if n has already been set equal to zero, σ/δ will have appeared as $\sigma = \sin \phi$, which incorrectly converts to $\sin \psi = \sin \sqrt{n}\,\theta = 0$.

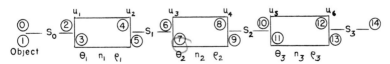

FIG. 6-1. Encircled station numbers for three magnets.

93

$$\delta = (1 - n)^{1/2}, \quad \phi = \delta\theta, \quad \sigma = \sin\phi, \quad \kappa = \cos\phi, \quad t = \tan u.$$

The radial (x) coefficients appear in the expressions

$$x_j = a_j x_1 + b_j x_1' + c_j \, \Delta p/p,$$
$$x_j' = d_j x_1 + e_j x_1' + f_j \, \Delta p/p.$$

To obtain axial (z) coefficients:

$$\delta \to \varepsilon = n^{1/2}, \quad \phi \to \psi = \varepsilon\theta, \quad t \to -t, \quad c = f = 0,$$

and if $n = 0$, then $\cos\psi = 1$, $\sin\psi = 0$ but $(\sin\psi)/\varepsilon = \theta$.

RADIAL (x) COEFFICIENTS

$a_2 = 1.$ (6-1)	$d_2 = 0.$ (6-4)
$b_2 = S_0.$ (6-2)	$e_2 = 1.$ (6-5)
$c_2 = 0.$ (6-3)	$f_2 = 0.$ (6-6)

$$a_3 = a_2 = 1. \tag{6-7}$$

$$d_3 = \frac{t_1}{\rho_1} a_2 + d_2 = \frac{t_1}{\rho_1}. \tag{6-10}$$

$$b_3 = b_2 = S_0. \tag{6-8}$$

$$e_3 = \frac{t_1}{\rho_1} b_2 + e_2 = \frac{t_1}{\rho_1} S_0 + 1. \tag{6-11}$$

$$c_3 = c_2 = 0. \tag{6-9}$$

$$f_3 = \frac{t_1}{\rho_1} c_2 + f_2 = 0. \tag{6-12}$$

$$a_4 = \kappa_1 a_3 + \frac{\rho_1\sigma_1}{\delta_1} d_3 \qquad = \kappa_1 + \frac{\sigma_1 t_1}{\delta_1}. \tag{6-13}$$

$$b_4 = \kappa_1 b_3 + \frac{\rho_1\sigma_1}{\delta_1} e_3 \qquad = S_0\left(\kappa_1 + \frac{\sigma_1 t_1}{\delta_1}\right) + \frac{\rho_1\sigma_1}{\delta_1}. \tag{6-14}$$

$$c_4 = \kappa_1 c_3 + \frac{\rho_1\sigma_1}{\delta_1} f_3 + \frac{\rho_1}{\delta_1^2}(1 - \kappa_1) = \frac{\rho_1}{\delta_1^2}(1 - \kappa_1). \tag{6-15}$$

$$d_4 = -\frac{\delta_1\sigma_1}{\rho_1} a_3 + \kappa_1 d_3 \qquad = \frac{t_1\kappa_1}{\rho_1} - \frac{\delta_1\sigma_1}{\rho_1}. \tag{6-16}$$

$$e_4 = -\frac{\delta_1\sigma_1}{\rho_1} b_3 + \kappa_1 e_3 \qquad = \frac{S_0}{\rho_1}(t_1\kappa_1 - \delta_1\sigma_1) + \kappa_1. \tag{6-17}$$

$$f_4 = -\frac{\delta_1\sigma_1}{\rho_1} c_3 + \kappa_1 f_3 + \frac{\sigma_1}{\delta_1} \qquad = \frac{\sigma_1}{\delta_1}. \tag{6-18}$$

$$a_5 = a_4 \qquad\qquad\qquad = \kappa_1 + \frac{\sigma_1 t_1}{\delta_1}. \qquad\qquad (6\text{-}19)$$

$$b_5 = b_4 \qquad\qquad\qquad = S_0\left(\kappa_1 + \frac{\sigma_1 t_1}{\delta_1}\right) + \frac{\rho_1 \sigma_1}{\delta_1}. \qquad (6\text{-}20)$$

$$c_5 = c_4 \qquad\qquad\qquad = \frac{\rho_1}{\delta_1{}^2}(1 - \kappa_1). \qquad\qquad (6\text{-}21)$$

$$d_5 = \frac{t_2}{\rho_1}a_4 + d_4 \qquad\quad = -\frac{1}{\rho_1}\left[\delta_1 \sigma_1 - (t_1 + t_2)\kappa_1 - \frac{t_1 t_2 \sigma_1}{\delta_1}\right].$$
$$\qquad\qquad\qquad\qquad\qquad\qquad\qquad\qquad\qquad\qquad (6\text{-}22)$$

$$e_5 = \frac{t_2}{\rho_1}b_4 + e_4 \qquad\quad = -\left\{\frac{S_0}{\rho_1}\left[\delta_1 \sigma_1 - (t_1 + t_2)\kappa_1 - \frac{t_1 t_2 \sigma_1}{\delta_1}\right]\right.$$
$$\left. - \frac{t_2 \sigma_1}{\delta_1} - \kappa_1\right\}. \qquad (6\text{-}23)$$

$$f_5 = \frac{t_2}{\rho_1}c_4 + f_4 \qquad\quad = \frac{t_2}{\delta_1{}^2}(1 - \kappa_1) + \frac{\sigma_1}{\delta_1}. \qquad (6\text{-}24)$$

$$a_6 = a_5 + S_1 d_5 = \kappa_1 + \frac{\sigma_1 t_1}{\delta_1} - \frac{S_1}{\rho_1}\left[\delta_1 \sigma_1 - (t_1 + t_2)\kappa_1 - \frac{t_1 t_2 \sigma_1}{\delta_1}\right]. \qquad (6\text{-}25)$$

$$b_6 = b_5 + S_1 e_5 = S_0\left(\kappa_1 + \frac{\sigma_1 t_1}{\delta_1}\right) + \frac{\rho_1 \sigma_1}{\delta_1}$$
$$- \frac{S_0 S_1}{\rho_1}\left[\delta_1 \sigma_1 - (t_1 + t_2)\kappa_1 - \frac{t_1 t_2 \sigma_1}{\delta_1}\right] + S_1\left(\kappa_1 + \frac{t_2 \sigma_1}{\delta_1}\right). \qquad (6\text{-}26)$$

$$c_6 = c_5 + S_1 f_5 = \frac{\rho_1}{\delta_1{}^2}(1 - \kappa_1) + \frac{S_1 t_2}{\delta_1{}^2}(1 - \kappa_1) + \frac{S_1 \sigma_1}{\delta_1}. \qquad (6\text{-}27)$$

$$d_6 = d_5 \qquad\qquad = -\frac{1}{\rho_1}\left[\delta_1 \sigma_1 - (t_1 + t_2)\kappa_1 - \frac{t_1 t_2 \sigma_1}{\delta_1}\right]. \qquad (6\text{-}28)$$

$$e_6 = e_5 \qquad\qquad = -\left\{\frac{S_0}{\rho_1}\left[\delta_1 \sigma_1 - (t_1 + t_2)\kappa_1 - \frac{t_1 t_2 \sigma_1}{\delta_1}\right] - \frac{t_2 \sigma_1}{\delta_1} - \kappa_1\right\}. \quad (6\text{-}29)$$

$$f_6 = f_5 \qquad\qquad = \frac{t_2}{\delta_1{}^2}(1 - \kappa_1) + \frac{\sigma_1}{\delta_1}. \qquad (6\text{-}30)$$

$$a_7 = a_6. \tag{6-31}$$

$$d_7 = \frac{t_3 \, a_6}{\rho_2} + d_6. \tag{6-34}$$

$$b_7 = b_6. \tag{6-32}$$

$$e_7 = \frac{t_3 \, b_6}{\rho_2} + e_6. \tag{6-35}$$

$$c_7 = c_6. \tag{6-33}$$

$$f_7 = \frac{t_3 \, c_6}{\rho_2} + f_6. \tag{6-36}$$

$$a_8 = \kappa_2 \, a_7 + \frac{\rho_2 \sigma_2}{\delta_2} \, d_7. \tag{6-37}$$

$$d_8 = \kappa_2 \, d_7 - \frac{\delta_2 \sigma_2}{\rho_2} \, a_7. \tag{6-40}$$

$$b_8 = \kappa_2 \, b_7 + \frac{\rho_2 \sigma_2}{\delta_2} \, e_7. \tag{6-38}$$

$$e_8 = \kappa_2 \, e_7 - \frac{\delta_2 \sigma_2}{\rho_2} \, b_7. \tag{6-41}$$

$$c_8 = \kappa_2 \, c_7 + \frac{\rho_2 \sigma_2}{\delta_2} f_7 \pm \frac{\rho_2}{\delta_2{}^2} (1 - \kappa_2).^* \tag{6-39}$$

$$f_8 = \kappa_2 f_7 - \frac{\delta_2 \sigma_2}{\rho_2} \, c_7 \pm \frac{\sigma_2}{\delta_2}.^* \tag{6-42}$$

$$a_9 = a_8. \tag{6-43}$$

$$d_9 = \frac{t_4}{\rho_2} \, a_8 + d_8. \tag{6-46}$$

$$b_9 = b_8. \tag{6-44}$$

$$e_9 = \frac{t_4}{\rho_2} \, b_8 + e_8. \tag{6-47}$$

$$c_9 = c_8. \tag{6-45}$$

$$f_9 = \frac{t_4}{\rho_2} \, c_8 + f_8. \tag{6-48}$$

$$a_{10} = a_9 + S_2 \, d_9.\dagger \tag{6-49}$$

$$d_{10} = d_9. \tag{6-52}$$

$$b_{10} = b_9 + S_2 \, e_9. \tag{6-50}$$

$$e_{10} = e_9. \tag{6-53}$$

$$c_{10} = c_9 + S_2 \, f_9. \tag{6-51}$$

$$f_{10} = f_9. \tag{6-54}$$

$$a_{11} = a_{10}. \tag{6-55}$$

$$d_{11} = \frac{t_5}{\rho_3} \, a_{10} + d_{10}. \tag{6-58}$$

$$b_{11} = b_{10}. \tag{6-56}$$

$$e_{11} = \frac{t_5}{\rho_3} \, b_{10} + e_{10}. \tag{6-59}$$

$$c_{11} = c_{10}. \tag{6-57}$$

$$f_{11} = \frac{t_5}{\rho_3} \, c_{10} + f_{10}. \tag{6-60}$$

* Use upper (lower) sign if second magnet bends in same (opposite) direction as does the first.

† See Eqs. (6-79)–(6-90) for more details on a_9–f_9.

$$a_{12} = \kappa_3 a_{11} + \frac{\rho_3 \sigma_3}{\delta_3} d_{11}. \quad (6\text{-}61)$$

$$d_{12} = \kappa_3 d_{11} - \frac{\delta_3 \sigma_3}{\rho_3} a_{11}. \quad (6\text{-}64)$$

$$b_{12} = \kappa_3 b_{11} + \frac{\rho_3 \sigma_3}{\delta_3} e_{11}. \quad (6\text{-}62)$$

$$e_{12} = \kappa_3 e_{11} - \frac{\delta_3 \sigma_3}{\rho_3} b_{11}. \quad (6\text{-}65)$$

$$c_{12} = \kappa_3 c_{11} + \frac{\rho_3 \sigma_3}{\delta_3} f_{11}$$

$$f_{12} = \kappa_3 f_{11} - \frac{\delta_3 \sigma_3}{\rho_3} c_{11} \pm \frac{\sigma_3}{\delta_3}. *$$

$$\pm \frac{\rho_3}{\delta_3^{\,2}} (1 - \kappa_3). * \quad (6\text{-}63)$$

$$(6\text{-}66)$$

$$a_{13} = a_{12}. \quad (6\text{-}67)$$

$$d_{13} = \frac{t_6}{\rho_3} a_{12} + d_{12}. \quad (6\text{-}70)$$

$$b_{13} = b_{12}. \quad (6\text{-}68)$$

$$e_{13} = \frac{t_6}{\rho_3} b_{12} + e_{12}. \quad (6\text{-}71)$$

$$c_{13} = c_{12}. \quad (6\text{-}69)$$

$$f_{13} = \frac{t_6}{\rho_3} c_{12} + f_{12}. \quad (6\text{-}72)$$

$$a_{14} = a_{13} + S_3 d_{13}. \quad (6\text{-}73)$$

$$d_{14} = d_{13}. \quad (6\text{-}76)$$

$$b_{14} = b_{13} + S_3 e_{13}. \quad (6\text{-}74)$$

$$e_{14} = e_{13}. \quad (6\text{-}77)$$

$$c_{14} = c_{13} + S_3 f_{13}. \quad (6\text{-}75)$$

$$f_{14} = f_{13}. \quad (6\text{-}78)$$

$$a_{10} = a_9 + S_2 d_9. \quad (6\text{-}79)$$

$$a_9 = -\frac{S_1 \delta_1 \sigma_1 \kappa_2}{\rho_1} + \frac{S_1 t_1 \kappa_1 \kappa_2}{\rho_1} + \frac{S_1 t_2 \kappa_1 \kappa_2}{\rho_1} + \frac{S_1 t_1 t_2 \sigma_1 \kappa_2}{\rho_1 \delta_1} + \frac{t_1 \sigma_1 \kappa_2}{\delta_1} + \kappa_1 \kappa_2$$

$$-\frac{S_1 \delta_1 t_3 \sigma_1 \sigma_2}{\rho_1 \delta_2} + \frac{S_1 t_1 t_3 \kappa_1 \sigma_2}{\rho_1 \delta_2} + \frac{S_1 t_2 t_3 \kappa_1 \sigma_2}{\rho_1 \delta_2} + \frac{S_1 t_1 t_2 t_3 \sigma_1 \sigma_2}{\rho_1 \delta_1 \delta_2} + \frac{t_1 t_3 \sigma_1 \sigma_2}{\delta_1 \delta_2}$$

$$+\frac{t_3 \kappa_1 \sigma_2}{\delta_2} - \frac{\rho_2 \delta_1 \sigma_1 \sigma_2}{\rho_1 \delta_2} + \frac{\rho_2 t_1 \kappa_1 \sigma_2}{\rho_1 \delta_2} + \frac{\rho_2 t_2 \kappa_1 \sigma_2}{\rho_1 \delta_2} + \frac{\rho_2 t_1 t_2 \sigma_1 \sigma_2}{\rho_1 \delta_1 \delta_2}. \quad (6\text{-}80)$$

* Use upper (lower) sign if third magnet bends in same (opposite) direction as does the first.

$$d_9 = -\frac{S_1 \delta_1 t_4 \sigma_1 \kappa_2}{\rho_1 \rho_2} + \frac{S_1 t_1 t_4 \kappa_1 \kappa_2}{\rho_1 \rho_2} + \frac{S_1 t_2 t_4 \kappa_1 \kappa_2}{\rho_1 \rho_2} + \frac{S_1 t_1 t_2 t_4 \sigma_1 \kappa_2}{\rho_1 \rho_2 \delta_1}$$

$$+ \frac{t_1 t_4 \sigma_1 \kappa_2}{\rho_2 \delta_1} + \frac{t_4 \kappa_1 \kappa_2}{\rho_2} - \frac{S_1 \delta_1 t_3 t_4 \sigma_1 \sigma_2}{\rho_1 \rho_2 \delta_2} + \frac{S_1 t_1 t_3 t_4 \kappa_1 \sigma_2}{\rho_1 \rho_2 \delta_2}$$

$$+ \frac{S_1 \delta_1 t_2 t_3 t_4 \kappa_1 \sigma_2}{\rho_1 \rho_2 \delta_2} + \frac{S_1 t_1 t_2 t_3 t_4 \sigma_1 \sigma_2}{\rho_1 \rho_2 \delta_1 \delta_2} + \frac{t_1 t_3 t_4 \sigma_1 \sigma_2}{\rho_1 \delta_1 \delta_2} + \frac{t_3 t_4 \kappa_1 \sigma_2}{\rho_2 \delta_2}$$

$$+ \frac{S_1 \delta_1 \delta_2 \sigma_1 \sigma_2}{\rho_1 \rho_2} - \frac{S_1 \delta_2 t_1 \kappa_1 \sigma_2}{\rho_1 \rho_2} - \frac{S_1 \delta_2 t_2 \kappa_1 \sigma_2}{\rho_1 \rho_2} - \frac{S_1 \delta_2 t_1 t_2 \sigma_1 \sigma_2}{\rho_1 \rho_2 \delta_1}$$

$$- \frac{t_1 \delta_2 \sigma_1 \sigma_2}{\rho_2 \delta_1} - \frac{\delta_2 \kappa_1 \sigma_2}{\rho_2} - \frac{S_1 \delta_1 t_3 \sigma_1 \kappa_2}{\rho_1 \rho_2} + \frac{S_1 t_1 t_3 \kappa_1 \kappa_2}{\rho_1 \rho_2} + \frac{S_1 t_2 t_3 \kappa_1 \kappa_2}{\rho_1 \rho_2}$$

$$+ \frac{S_1 t_1 t_2 t_3 \sigma_1 \kappa_2}{\rho_1 \rho_2 \delta_1} + \frac{t_1 t_3 \sigma_1 \kappa_2}{\rho_2 \delta_1} + \frac{t_3 \kappa_1 \kappa_2}{\rho_2} - \frac{\delta_1 t_4 \sigma_1 \sigma_2}{\rho_1 \delta_2} + \frac{t_1 t_4 \kappa_1 \sigma_2}{\rho_1 \delta_2}$$

$$+ \frac{t_2 t_4 \kappa_1 \sigma_2}{\rho_1 \delta_2} + \frac{t_1 t_2 t_4 \sigma_1 \sigma_2}{\rho_1 \delta_1 \delta_2} - \frac{\delta_1 \sigma_1 \kappa_2}{\rho_1} + \frac{t_1 \kappa_1 \kappa_2}{\rho_1} + \frac{t_2 \kappa_1 \kappa_2}{\rho_1} + \frac{t_1 t_2 \sigma_1 \kappa_2}{\rho_1 \delta_1}.$$

$$\tag{6-81}$$

$$b_{10} = b_9 + S_2 e_9. \tag{6-82}$$

$$b_9 = \kappa_2 b_7 + \frac{\rho_2 \sigma_2}{\delta_2} e_7. \tag{6-83}$$

$$e_9 = \frac{t_4}{\rho_2} \kappa_2 b_7 - \frac{\delta_2 \sigma_2}{\rho_2} b_7 + \frac{t_4 \sigma_2}{\rho_2} e_7 + \kappa_2 e_7, \tag{6-84}$$

where

$$b_7 = S_0 \left(\kappa_1 + \frac{t_1 \sigma_1}{\delta_1} \right) + S_1 \left(\kappa_1 + \frac{t_2 \sigma_1}{\delta_1} \right)$$

$$- \frac{S_0 S_1}{\rho_1} \left[\delta_1 \sigma_1 - (t_1 + t_2)\kappa_1 - \frac{t_1 t_2 \sigma_1}{\delta_1} \right] + \frac{\rho_1 \sigma_1}{\delta_1}, \tag{6-85}$$

$$e_7 = \frac{t_3}{\rho_2} b_7 - \left\{ \frac{S_0}{\rho_1} \left[\delta_1 \sigma_1 - (t_1 + t_2)\kappa_1 - \frac{t_1 t_2 \sigma_1}{\delta_1} \right] - \frac{t_2 \sigma_1}{\delta_1} - \kappa_1 \right\}. \tag{6-86}$$

For $b_{10} = 0$, whereby $S_2 = S_{ix2}$, these give

$$S_{ix2} = \frac{\kappa_2 b_7 + \rho_2 \sigma_2 e_7/\delta_2}{\dfrac{\delta_2 \sigma_2}{\rho_2} b_7 - \dfrac{t_4 \kappa_2}{\rho_2} b_7 - \kappa_2 e_7 - \dfrac{t_4 \sigma_2}{\delta_2} e_7}. \tag{6-87}$$

$$c_{10} = c_9 + S_2 f_9. \tag{6-88}$$

$$c_9 = S_1 \left[\frac{t_2 \kappa_2}{\delta_1{}^2}(1 - \kappa_1) + \frac{t_3 \sigma_1 \sigma_2}{\delta_1 \delta_2} + \frac{t_2 t_3 \sigma_2 (1 - \kappa_1)}{\delta_1^2 \delta_2} + \frac{\sigma_1 \kappa_2}{\delta_1} \right]$$

$$+ \frac{\rho_2 t_2 \sigma_2 (1 - \kappa_1)}{\delta_1{}^2 \delta_2} + \frac{\rho_1 t_3 \sigma_2 (1 - \kappa_1)}{\delta_1{}^2 \delta_2} + \frac{\rho_1 \kappa_2 (1 - \kappa_1)}{\delta_1{}^2}$$

$$+ \frac{\rho_2 \sigma_1 \sigma_2}{\delta_1 \delta_2} \pm \frac{\rho_2}{\delta_2{}^2}(1 - \kappa_2). \tag{6-89}$$

$$f_9 = \frac{S_1}{\rho_2} \left[\frac{t_2 t_3}{\delta_1{}^2}(1 - \kappa_1)\kappa_2 + \frac{t_2 t_4 (1 - \kappa_1)}{\delta_1{}^2} \kappa_2 - t_2 (1 - \kappa_1) \frac{\sigma_2 \delta_2}{\delta_1{}^2} \right.$$

$$\left. + \frac{t_2 t_3 t_4 (1 - \kappa_1) \sigma_2}{\delta_1{}^2 \delta_2} + \frac{t_3 \sigma_1 \kappa_2}{\delta_1} + \frac{t_4 \sigma_1 \kappa_2}{\delta_1} - \sigma_1 \sigma_2 \frac{\delta_2}{\delta_1} + \frac{t_3 t_4 \sigma_1 \sigma_2}{\delta_1 \delta_2} \right]$$

$$+ (1 - \kappa_1) \left[\frac{\rho_1}{\rho_2} \frac{t_3 \kappa_2}{\delta_1{}^2} + \frac{\rho_1}{\rho_2} \frac{t_4 \kappa_2}{\delta_1{}^2} - \frac{\rho_1}{\rho_2} \sigma_2 \frac{\delta_2}{\delta_1{}^2} + \frac{\rho_1}{\rho_2} \frac{t_3 t_4 \sigma_2}{\delta_1{}^2 \delta_2} \right.$$

$$\left. + \frac{t_2 t_4 \sigma_2}{\delta_1{}^2 \delta_2} + \frac{t_2 \kappa_2}{\delta_1{}^2} \right] + \frac{t_4 \sigma_1 \sigma_2}{\delta_1 \delta_2} + \frac{\sigma_1 \kappa_2}{\delta_1} \pm \frac{\sigma_2}{\delta_2} \pm \frac{t_4 (1 - \kappa_2)}{\delta_2{}^2}. \tag{6-90}$$

Notice that c_9 does not depend on S_0, t_1, or t_4, and that f_9 does not depend on S_0 or t_1.

SPECIAL FORMS; USEFUL FOR NUMERICAL CALCULATIONS OF BEAM ENVELOPES

$$a_7 = -\frac{S_1}{\rho_1} \left[\delta_1 \sigma_1 - (t_1 + t_2)\kappa_1 - \frac{t_1 t_2 \sigma_1}{\delta_1} \right] + \frac{t_1 \sigma_1}{\delta_1} + \kappa_1. \tag{6-91}$$

$$\frac{b_7}{\rho_1} = \frac{S_0}{\rho_1} \left(\kappa_1 + \frac{t_1 \sigma_1}{\delta_1} \right) + \frac{S_1}{\rho_1} \left(\kappa_1 + \frac{t_2 \sigma_1}{\delta_1} \right)$$

$$- \frac{S_0 S_1}{\rho_1{}^2} \left[\delta_1 \sigma_1 - (t_1 + t_2)\kappa_1 - \frac{t_1 t_2 \sigma_1}{\delta_1} \right] + \frac{\sigma_1}{\delta_1}. \tag{6-92}$$

$$\frac{c_7}{\rho_1} = \frac{(1 - \kappa_1)}{\delta_1{}^2} + \frac{S_1}{\rho_1} \left[\frac{t_2}{\delta_1{}^2}(1 - \kappa_1) + \frac{\sigma_1}{\delta_1} \right]. \tag{6-93}$$

$$d_7 \rho_2 = a_7 t_3 - \frac{\rho_2}{\rho_1} \left[\delta_1 \sigma_1 - (t_1 + t_2)\kappa_1 - \frac{t_1 t_2 \sigma_1}{\delta_1} \right]. \tag{6-94}$$

$$e_7 = \frac{b_7}{\rho_1}\frac{\rho_1}{\rho_2}t_3 - \frac{S_0}{\rho_1}\left[\delta_1\sigma_1 - (t_1 + t_2)\kappa_1 - \frac{t_1 t_2 \sigma_1}{\delta_1}\right] + \frac{t_2 \sigma_1}{\delta_1} + \kappa_1. \tag{6-95}$$

$$f_7 = \frac{c_7}{\rho_1}\frac{\rho_1}{\rho_2}t_3 + \frac{t_2}{\delta_1^2}(1 - \kappa_1) + \frac{\sigma_1}{\delta_1}. \tag{6-96}$$

$$a_{10} = a_7\left[\kappa_2 + \frac{S_2}{\rho_2}(\kappa_2 t_4 - \delta_2 \sigma_2)\right] + d_7\rho_2\left[\frac{\sigma_2}{\delta_2} + \frac{S_2}{\rho_2}\left(\frac{\sigma_2 t_4}{\delta_2} + \kappa_2\right)\right]. \tag{6-97}$$

$$\frac{b_{10}}{\rho_1} = \frac{b_7}{\rho_1}\left[\kappa_2 + \frac{S_2}{\rho_2}(\kappa_2 t_4 - \delta_2 \sigma_2)\right] + e_7\frac{\rho_2}{\rho_1}\left[\frac{\sigma_2}{\delta_2} + \frac{S_2}{\rho_2}\left(\frac{\sigma_2 t_4}{\delta_2} + \kappa_2\right)\right]. \tag{6-98}$$

$$\frac{c_{10}}{\rho_1} = \frac{c_7}{\rho_1}\left[\kappa_2 + \frac{S_2}{\rho_2}(\kappa_2 t_4 - \delta_2 \sigma_2)\right] + f_7\frac{\rho_2}{\rho_1}\left[\frac{\sigma_2}{\delta_2} + \frac{S_2}{\rho_2}\left(\frac{\sigma_2 t_4}{\delta_2} + \kappa_2\right)\right]$$
$$\pm \frac{\rho_2}{\rho_1}\frac{S_2}{\rho_2}\left[\frac{t_4}{\delta_2^2}(1 - \kappa_2) + \frac{\sigma_2}{\delta_2}\right] \pm \frac{\rho_2}{\rho_1\delta_2^2}(1 - \kappa_2). \tag{6-99}$$

$$d_{10}\rho_2 = a_7(\kappa_2 t_4 - \delta_2 \sigma_2) + d_7\rho_2\left(\frac{\sigma_2 t_4}{\delta_2} + \kappa_2\right). \tag{6-100}$$

$$e_{10} = \frac{b_7}{\rho_1}\frac{\rho_1}{\rho_2}(\kappa_2 t_4 - \delta_2 \sigma_2) + e_7\left(\frac{\sigma_2 t_4}{\delta_2} + \kappa_2\right). \tag{6-101}$$

$$f_{10} = \frac{c_7}{\rho_1}\frac{\rho_1}{\rho_2}(\kappa_2 t_4 - \delta_2 \sigma_2) + f_7\left(\frac{\sigma_2 t_4}{\delta_2} + \kappa_2\right) \pm \frac{t_4}{\delta_2^2}(1 - \kappa_2) \pm \frac{\sigma_2}{\delta_2}. \tag{6-102}$$

7 Radial Beam Envelopes

The subject matter of the next three chapters (phase-space ellipses and beam envelopes) is important for two reasons. In the first place, it yields a set of diagrams that helps one understand better how magnets effect ions going through them. Secondly, it is of great economic importance, for it permits the design of a magnet with a gap wide enough and high enough, but not unnecessarily so, for the particular accelerator with which it will be used. This latter aspect is worthy of emphasis and description.

The object distance and the maximum axial divergence of the beam as it leaves the object slit are both of significance in determining the beam height at the entrance to the magnet. This same divergence also enters into the beam height at the exit and at a height maximum (if there is one) inside the magnet. It is clear that we must know which of these three heights is the greatest. The gap height is a major contributor to the number of ampere turns required, and hence to the quantity of copper, the rating of the power supply, and the cost of operation. Thus a knowledge of the maximum axial divergence of the accelerator's beam is urgently needed.

If the magnet has a circular or semicircular pole, the field region has a much greater radial width than could be required, at a single angle, by the beam from any accelerator worthy of the name. In these two cases, and these only, one need not be concerned with the beam's radial divergence. This is far from the case, however, with sector magnets of fixed radius, for the field is built to exist only over the region where it will be required, plus an allowance for a buffer zone between the used region and the radial boundaries of the iron. (For example, in a uniform-field magnet with a "C"-shaped yoke, this buffer zone is usually 2 to 2.5 times the gap height, on *each* side of the region to be used.) Consequently this latter width must be kept at a minimum or else the magnet's weight, the amount of copper, and the power will rise inordinately.

The maximum width of a beam of monoenergetic ions inside the magnet is proportional to the maximum radial slope at the object slit; hence it is essential to know this slope. Furthermore, if the oncoming particles have a spread in momentum, Δp, the beam width includes a second term proportional to $\Delta p/p$. Thus it is of prime importance to know the largest value of $\Delta p/p$ that will be encountered.

Without all this information (or a reasonable guess at it), a sector magnet cannot be designed intelligently.

PHASE-SPACE ELLIPSE OF RADIAL MOTION

Inside an accelerator, the particles execute radial oscillations about the central path. These excursions may be described as

$$x = x_0 \sin \omega t = x_0 \sin \frac{2\pi v}{\lambda} t = x_0 \sin \frac{2\pi S}{\lambda}$$

where x_0 is the amplitude, ω is the radial angular velocity, S is the distance traveled at velocity v in time t, and λ is the wavelength of the oscillation. The slope of the path is given by

$$x' \equiv \frac{dx}{dS} = x_0 \frac{2\pi}{\lambda} \cos \frac{2\pi S}{\lambda} \equiv x_0' \cos \frac{2\pi S}{\lambda}.$$

Consequently we find that

$$\frac{x^2}{x_0{}^2} + \frac{x'^2}{x_0'^2} = 1. \tag{7-1}$$

This is the equation of the so-called radial phase-space ellipse. (See Fig. 7-1.)

FIG. 7-1. The radial phase-space ellipse.

Its major and minor axes coincide with the coordinates x and x'. The intercepts on these axes are x_0 and x_0', the maximum displacement and maximum slope. A single particle obeying Eq. (7-1) is represented as a single point on the ellipse, and as time and distance advance, the point moves clockwise round the ellipse. Particles executing oscillations of the same amplitude but different phase are also represented by points moving on the same ellipse. Particles with smaller amplitudes move on smaller ellipses inside the largest one.

Qualitative Behavior of Ellipse

In the ideal case, the focusing field inside the accelerator terminates abruptly, so that in the subsequent field-free region, the trajectories become straight lines. It is clear from Fig. 7-2 that the ray A, with maximum slope

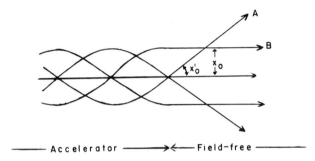

Fig. 7-2. Ideal radial motion inside and outside an accelerator.

x_0', left the accelerator at $x = 0$, while ray B departed with maximum displacement x_0 but with zero slope. As distinct from radioactive sources, where all slopes can exist at all displacements, *an accelerator's beam is such that maximum slope and maximum displacement are never both associated with a single particle.*

Because the beam is formed by ions of various phases and amplitudes, the slopes decrease from maximum to zero as the initial displacement goes from zero to the maximum. The beam's envelope widens trumpet-like, as shown in Fig. 7-3, as it traverses a drift space, but the maximum slope remains fixed. As will be shown in detail later, this results in a tipping forward of the ellipse, so that the projection on the x axis increases, while the projection on the x' axis stays constant. This tipping may be described as a shearing motion, the intersections with the x axis acting as fixed pivots, the area of the ellipse remaining constant. Note that point A maintains maximum slope and that it achieves maximum displacement only at infinity. Note also that the slope associated with x_{max} increases along the drift space.

It is well to emphasize, as will appear later, that except for a point source, the beam boundaries are always expanding or contracting; they are never parallel except at a transition from one condition to the other, no matter

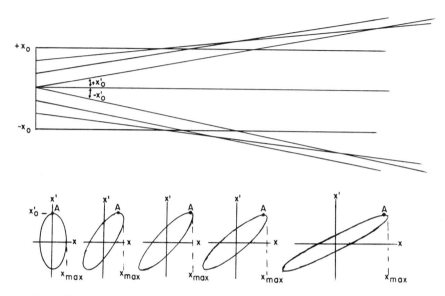

FIG. 7-3. The trajectories that form the envelope and the tipping of the ellipse as particles leave the source and traverse a field-free region.

what focusing or defocusing elements are supplied. In principle, *a "parallel beam" cannot exist with a source of finite width*, although it may be approximated very closely.

Let a beam of a single energy encounter a magnet with entrance edge slanted to defocus radially. All the slopes increase, so that x'_{max} rises to a greater value. If we consider the edge as a thin lens, it does not alter the displacements. Hence the edge shears the ellipse along the x' axis, the intersections with this axis acting as fixed pivots. The body of the magnet acts both as a drift space (that shears the ellipse to lengthen it along the x axis) and as a focusing lens (that shears the ellipse along the x' axis so as first to shorten and then to lengthen it). Consequently the ellipse "rotates" clockwise. When it is horizontal, the envelope's width is a maximum (a "bust"), and if a real image is ultimately to be formed, the rotation continues further until point A lies below the x axis (Fig. 7-4).

Assume that the exit edge also defocuses radially; then it lengthens the ellipse along x', since all slopes are increased. The following drift space shears the ellipse along the x axis. When the ellipse is upright, with a minimum width along x, a "waist" is said to exist. Somewhat further along, the shearing action brings point A to where its displacement is zero; the image plane has been reached. This is so because point A had zero displacement (and maximum, positive, slope) at the source; the image occurs when A again has zero displacement (although with a different and negative slope). Or we

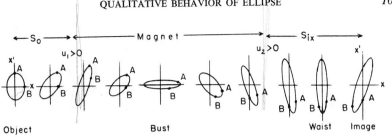

FIG. 7-4. Successive shapes of the radial ellipse as the ions move from object to image.

may consider point B (in Fig. 7-4) that started with maximum displacement (and zero slope); at the image it again has maximum displacement (though negative and perhaps of different magnitude) and a different slope.

Note that if the magnet does not drive point A below the x axis, the subsequent field-free region can never shift A back to the x' axis; an image cannot be formed, unless some additional lens is supplied.

If the beam contains ions of more than one momentum (e.g., three components p, $p + \Delta p$, and $p - \Delta p$), the corresponding three ellipses are coincident at the source, in the object space, and at the entrance edge. But as soon as the body of the magnet is penetrated, the ellipses begin to separate along x and x', since the $p + \Delta p$ ions move in a larger orbit than the p particles, and the $p - \Delta p$ projectiles in a smaller one, as is indicated in Fig. 7-5. (A more detailed explanation will be given later.) If Δp is defined

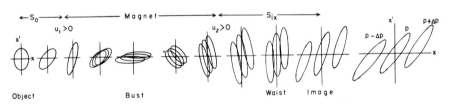

FIG. 7-5. Ellipse behavior when there are three momenta.

as that increment that is just resolved from p, then at the image plane the projections on the x axis of all three ellipses just fail to overlap.

It is obvious that the field in the magnet must be "as specified" (i.e., $n = 0$, $n = 0.5$, etc.) over a radial width as large as that covered by the radial ellipse at all points along the path. The required width of "good" field will be least if Δp is defined as just above, but economy of this sort can lead to trouble; the accelerator will produce particles of a wider spread in momentum than the desired band (otherwise there is no need for the analyzing magnet), and it is poor practice to allow these unwanted ions to be intercepted by the walls of the vacuum chamber inside the magnet. At the least, the walls may become radioactive and at the worst they may be punctured.

It is far better to make the chamber and "good" field wide enough to pass all the particles from the accelerator and to intercept the unwanted ones on the jaws of a water-cooled slit. For this reason $\Delta p/p$ should be considered as referring to the half-spread from the accelerator, when computing the radial envelope's width. Note that if p is variable and if Δp is constant, the envelope width *increases* as p is *lowered*, for it will be shown that the width includes a term proportional to $\Delta p/p$.

We now proceed to a quantitative study of beam envelope dimensions.

ELLIPSE COEFFICIENTS α, β, γ

We repeat the equation for an upright ellipse at the source:

$$\frac{x^2}{x_0^2} + \frac{x'^2}{x_0'^2} = 1. \tag{7-1}$$

For convenience we define

$$\alpha_1 \equiv 1/x_0^2, \tag{7-2}$$

$$\gamma_1 \equiv 1/x_0'^2. \tag{7-3}$$

So if x_1 and x_1' refer to any arbitrary point of the source, then we have

$$\alpha_1 x_1^2 + \gamma_1 x_1'^2 = 1. \tag{7-4}$$

The ions now travel a distance S_0 in a field-free region. The displacement and slope are then given by

$$\begin{pmatrix} x_2 \\ x_2' \end{pmatrix} = \begin{pmatrix} 1 & S_0 \\ 0 & 1 \end{pmatrix} \begin{pmatrix} x_1 \\ x_1' \end{pmatrix}. \tag{7-5}$$

Now if we have

$$\begin{pmatrix} U \\ V \end{pmatrix} = \begin{pmatrix} A & B \\ D & E \end{pmatrix} \begin{pmatrix} W \\ Y \end{pmatrix}$$

then it follows that

$$\begin{pmatrix} W \\ Y \end{pmatrix} = \begin{pmatrix} E & -B \\ -D & A \end{pmatrix} \begin{pmatrix} U \\ V \end{pmatrix}$$

provided $AE - BD = 1$, as will be the case. The second matrix is called the inverse of the first, and the theorem may be proved by multiplying the matrices together to obtain the unit matrix

$$\begin{pmatrix} 1 & 0 \\ 0 & 1 \end{pmatrix}.$$

Hence we write

$$\begin{pmatrix} x_1 \\ x_1' \end{pmatrix} = \begin{pmatrix} 1 & -S_0 \\ 0 & 1 \end{pmatrix} \begin{pmatrix} x_2 \\ x_2' \end{pmatrix}, \tag{7-6}$$

so that

$$x_1 = x_2 - S_0 x_2' \tag{7-7}$$

and

$$x_1' = x_2'. \tag{7-8}$$

Use these in Eq. (7-1) and obtain

$$\alpha_2 x_2{}^2 + 2\beta_2 x_2 x_2' + \gamma_2 x_2'^2 = 1, \tag{7-9}$$

where (Fig. 7-6)

$$\alpha_2 = \alpha_1, \tag{7-10}$$

$$\beta_2 = -\alpha_1 S_0, \tag{7-11}$$

$$\gamma_2 = \gamma_1 + \alpha_1 S_0{}^2. \tag{7-12}$$

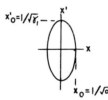

FIG. 7-6. Ellipse coefficients at the object.

The cross-product term $2\beta_2 x_2 x_2'$ indicates that the ellipse is tilted "forward," since we know that $x_{\max}$ has increased while $x'_{\max}$ is unchanged. By setting $x_2' = 0$ in Eq. (7-9), we see that α_2 measures the intercept on the x axis:

$$\alpha_2 = 1/x_{2\,\text{intercept}}^2 \tag{7-13}$$

while with $x_2 = 0$, Eq. (7-9) shows us that

$$\gamma_2 = 1/x_{2\,\text{intercept}}'^2. \tag{7-14}$$

Since β did not occur in Eq. (7-1), we infer that $\beta = 0$ is the criterion for an upright ellipse, such as occurs in the original object, in a bust, and in a waist. Note that for an ellipse tilted "forward" (as in Fig. 7-7), β is negative as shown by Eq. (7-11). Hence a positive β will imply an ellipse tilted "backward." Remembering this can afford a check on numerical results.

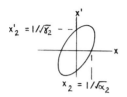

$x_2' = 1/\sqrt{x_2}$

$x_2 = 1/\sqrt{x_2}$

FIG. 7-7. Ellipse following a drift space.

The area of the tilted ellipse may be found by evaluating the quantity $\alpha_2\gamma_2 - \beta_2^2$. By Eqs. (7-10)–(7-12), we find

$$\alpha_2\gamma_2 - \beta_2^2 = \alpha_1(\gamma_1 + \alpha_1 S_0^2) - (-\alpha_1 S_0)^2$$
$$= \alpha_1\gamma_1 + \alpha_1^2 S_0^2 - \alpha_1^2 S_0^2 = \alpha_1\gamma_1, \qquad (7\text{-}15)$$

so by the use of Eqs. (7-2) and (7-3) we have

$$\alpha_2\gamma_2 - \beta_2^2 = 1/(x_0^2 x_0'^2). \qquad (7\text{-}16)$$

But the area of the upright ellipse is known to be

$$A = \pi x_0 x_0', \qquad (7\text{-}17)$$

so from Eq. (7-16) we find

$$A = \frac{\pi}{(\alpha_2\gamma_2 - \beta_2^2)^{1/2}}. \qquad (7\text{-}18)$$

For a given source, x_0 and x_0' are constant. Hence the area is constant, provided the energy does not change. (This constancy is known as Liouville's theorem.) Hence Eq. (7-16) is true at any station:

$$\alpha_j\gamma_j - \beta_j^2 = \frac{1}{x_0^2 x_0'^2}. \qquad (7\text{-}19)$$

(Some purists object to an "area" given by $\pi x_0 x_0'$, since this formally has the dimension of length. There is a way to avoid this pedantic discrepancy, but since it adds complications we will ignore it. After all, the ellipse does have an area in the figures.)

WIDTH OF THE ENVELOPE

We solve the general ellipse expression, Eq. (7-9) for x', getting

$$x' = -\frac{\beta x}{\gamma} \pm \frac{1}{\gamma}\left[\frac{\beta^2 x^2}{\gamma^2} - \frac{(\alpha x^2 - 1)}{\gamma}\right]^{1/2} = -\frac{\beta x}{\gamma} \pm \frac{1}{\gamma}[x^2(\beta^2 - \alpha\gamma) + \gamma]^{1/2}.$$

$$(7\text{-}20)$$

The $\pm$ sign shows that for any x there are two values of x', except for $x = x_{max}$, where, since x' then has but a single value, the second term must vanish. (See Fig. 7-8). This gives, making use of Eq. (7-19),

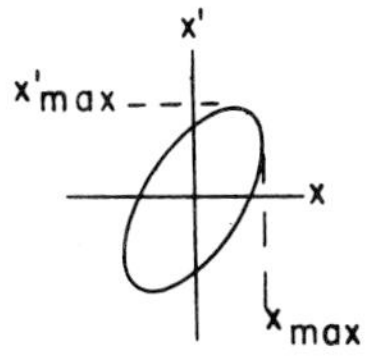

$$x_{max}^2 = \frac{\gamma}{\alpha\gamma - \beta^2} = \gamma x_0^2 x_0'^2. \qquad (7\text{-}21)$$

FIG. 7-8.

Inserting the subscript j, we obtain the important result

$$\boxed{x_{j\,max} = \gamma_j^{1/2} x_0 x_0',} \qquad (7\text{-}22)$$

which gives the half-width of the envelope for particles of momentum p.

The solution of Eq. (7-9) for x gives

$$x = -\frac{\beta x'}{\alpha} \pm \frac{1}{\alpha}[x'^2(\beta^2 - \alpha\gamma) + \alpha]^{1/2}. \qquad (7\text{-}23)$$

This is identical with Eq. (7-20) if we interchange x for x' and α for γ. Consequently we may write for the maximum slope of p particles,

$$\boxed{x'_{j\,max} = \alpha_j^{1/2} x_0 x_0'.} \qquad (7\text{-}24)$$

Methods for finding x_0 and x_0' will be described at the end of this chapter. We will now consider means for determining α and γ at any station.

ELLIPSE COEFFICIENTS EXPRESSED IN SEQUENCE

The way in which this may be done has been demonstrated in obtaining Eqs. (7-10)–(7-12). We now repeat the argument in words.

By using the inverse of the matrix that transforms from station $j - 1$ to station j, we express x_{j-1} and x'_{j-1} in terms of x_j, x_j', and the parameters of the optic element that has been traversed. These expressions for x_{j-1} and x'_{j-1} are used in the ellipse equation for station $j - 1$, which then becomes the ellipse equation of station j, the expressions for α_j, β_j, and γ_j being given in terms of α_{j-1}, β_{j-1}, and γ_{j-1}.

One may use this procedure to obtain the values of α, β, and γ at any station by starting at the source (station 1) and advancing step by step until the desired station is reached. The first eight steps are quoted below.

At object (upright ellipse),

$$\alpha_1 = \frac{1}{x_0{}^2},$$
(7-25)

$$\beta_1 = 0,$$
(7-26)

$$\gamma_1 = \frac{1}{x_0'^2}.$$
(7-27)

Through first drift space,

$$\alpha_2 = \alpha_1,$$
(7-28)

$$\beta_2 = -\alpha_1 S_0,$$
(7-29)

$$\gamma_2 = \gamma_1 + \alpha_1 S_0{}^2.$$
(7-30)

Through entrance edge of first magnet,

$$\alpha_3 = \alpha_2 - 2\beta_2 \frac{\tan u_1}{\rho_1} + \gamma_2 \left(\frac{\tan u_1}{\rho_1}\right)^2,$$
(7-31)

$$\beta_3 = \beta_2 - \gamma_2 \frac{\tan u_1}{\rho_1},$$
(7-32)

$$\gamma_3 = \gamma_2.$$
(7-33)

Through body of first magnet,

$$\alpha_4 = \alpha_3 \cos^2 \phi_1 + 2\beta_3 \frac{\delta_1}{\rho_1} \sin \phi_1 \cos \phi_1 + \gamma_3 \frac{\delta_1{}^2}{\rho_1{}^2} \sin^2 \phi_1,$$
(7-34)

$$\beta_4 = -\alpha_3 \frac{\rho_1}{\delta_1} \sin \phi_1 \cos \phi_1 + \beta_3(\cos^2 \phi_1 - \sin^2 \phi_1) + \gamma_3 \frac{\delta_1}{\rho_1} \sin \phi_1 \cos \phi_1,$$
(7-35)

$$\gamma_4 = \alpha_3 \frac{\rho_1{}^2}{\delta_1{}^2} \sin^2 \phi_1 - 2\beta_3 \frac{\rho_1}{\delta_1} \sin \phi_1 \cos \phi_1 + \gamma_3 \cos^2 \phi_1.$$
(7-36)

Through exit edge of first magnet,

$$\alpha_5 = \alpha_4 - 2\beta_4 \frac{\tan u_2}{\rho_1} + \gamma_4 \left(\frac{\tan u_2}{\rho_1}\right)^2,$$
(7-37)

$$\beta_5 = \beta_4 - \gamma_4 \frac{\tan u_2}{\rho_1}, \tag{7-38}$$

$$\gamma_5 = \gamma_4. \tag{7-39}$$

Through second drift space,

$$\alpha_6 = \alpha_5, \tag{7-40}$$

$$\beta_6 = \beta_5 - \alpha_5 S_1, \tag{7-41}$$

$$\gamma_6 = \gamma_5 - 2\beta_5 S_1 + \alpha_5 S_1^2. \tag{7-42}$$

Through entrance edge of second magnet,

$$\alpha_7 = \alpha_6 - 2\beta_6 \frac{\tan u_3}{\rho_2} + \gamma_6 \left(\frac{\tan u_3}{\rho_2}\right)^2, \tag{7-43}$$

$$\beta_7 = \beta_6 - \gamma_6 \frac{\tan u_3}{\rho_2}, \tag{7-44}$$

$$\gamma_7 = \gamma_6. \tag{7-45}$$

Through body of second magnet,

$$\alpha_8 = \alpha_7 \cos^2 \phi_2 + 2\beta_7 \frac{\delta_2}{\rho_2} \sin \phi_2 \cos \phi_2 + \gamma_7 \frac{\delta_2^2}{\rho_2^2} \sin^2 \phi_2, \tag{7-46}$$

$$\beta_8 = -\alpha_7 \frac{\rho_2}{\delta_2} \sin \phi_2 \cos \phi_2 + \beta_7(\cos^2 \phi_2 - \sin^2 \phi_2) + \gamma_7 \frac{\delta_2}{\rho_2} \sin \phi_2 \cos \phi_2, \tag{7-47}$$

$$\gamma_8 = \alpha_7 \frac{\rho_2^2}{\delta_2^2} \sin^2 \phi_2 - 2\beta_7 \frac{\rho_2}{\delta_2} \sin \phi_2 \cos \phi_2 + \gamma_7 \cos^2 \phi_2. \tag{7-48}$$

The pattern should now be clear. The trio of expressions for all edges is similar, as is the trio for magnet bodies, and the trio for drift spaces (if we recall that in the first we have $\beta_1 = 0$ for the upright object ellipse).

It is evident that if this technique is employed, it will be a practical necessity to compute numerical values of α, β, and γ at successive stations, since algebraic expressions in terms of basic parameters become inordinately cumbersome for j exceeding 3. Thus, writing $S_0/\rho = L_o$, we find

$$\alpha_2 = \frac{1}{x_0^2}, \tag{7-49}$$

$$\beta_2 = -\frac{\rho_1}{x_0^2} L_o, \tag{7-50}$$

$$\gamma_2 = \frac{\rho_1^2}{x_0^2}\left[L_o^2 + \left(\frac{x_0}{\rho_1 x_0'}\right)^2\right],$$ (7-51)

$$\alpha_3 = \frac{1}{x_0^2}\left\{1 + 2L_o \tan u_1 + \left[L_o^2 + \left(\frac{x_0}{\rho_1 x_0'}\right)^2\right]\tan^2 u_1\right\},$$ (7-52)

$$\beta_3 = -\frac{\rho_1}{x_0^2}\left\{L_o + \left[L_o^2 + \left(\frac{x_0}{\rho_1 x_0'}\right)^2\right]\tan u_1\right\},$$ (7-53)

$$\gamma_3 = \frac{\rho_1^2}{x_0^2}\left\{L_o^2 + \left(\frac{x_0}{\rho_1 x_0'}\right)^2\right\}.$$ (7-54)

A sequence of numerical evaluations of α_j, β_j, and γ_j, through successive values of j, involves the accumulation of round-off approximations that can lead to seriously erroneous results at stations far downstream.

Fortunately, a much simpler procedure is available by which α_j, β_j, and γ_j are expressed in terms of a_j, b_j, ..., f_j. These latter coefficients have already been calculated as functions of the basic parameters and have been tabulated in Chapter 6. This procedure will be described next.

ELLIPSE COEFFICIENTS EXPRESSED IN TERMS OF RADIAL MATRIX COEFFICIENTS

Assume an initial ellipse for a particle, of momentum p, with coordinates x_i and x_i':

$$\alpha_i x_i^2 + 2\beta_i x_i x_i' + \gamma_i x_i'^2 = 1.$$ (7-55)

Some set of optic elements transforms the coordinates to x_j and x_j' at station j:

$$\begin{pmatrix} x_j \\ x_j' \end{pmatrix} = \begin{pmatrix} a_j & b_j \\ d_j & e_j \end{pmatrix}\begin{pmatrix} x_i \\ x_i' \end{pmatrix}.$$ (7-56)

Hence the inverse matrix expression

$$\begin{pmatrix} x_i \\ x_i' \end{pmatrix} = \begin{pmatrix} e_j & -b_j \\ -d_j & a_j \end{pmatrix}\begin{pmatrix} x_j \\ x_j' \end{pmatrix}$$ (7-57)

gives us

$$x_i = e_j x_j - b_j x_j',$$ (7-58)

$$x_i' = -d_j x_j + a_j x_j'.$$ (7-59)

Substitution of these into the initial ellipse expression, Eq. (7-55), leads to the ellipse for station j:

$$\alpha_j x_j^2 + 2\beta_j x_j x_j' + \gamma_j x_j'^2 = 1, \tag{7-60}$$

where

$$\alpha_j = e_j^2 \alpha_i - 2d_j e_j \beta_i + d_j^2 \gamma_i, \tag{7-61}$$

$$\beta_j = -b_j e_j \alpha_i + (b_j d_j + a_j e_j)\beta_i - a_j d_j \gamma_i, \tag{7-62}$$

$$\gamma_j = b_j^2 \alpha_i - 2a_j b_j \beta_i + a_j^2 \gamma_i. \tag{7-63}$$

The initial ellipse in most cases is upright. This will be so if the object is the beam just as it emerges from the accelerator, whose focusing fields ideally terminate abruptly. With greater likelihood, the object is a slit or aperture that is illuminated by a pair of quadrupoles between it and the accelerator. The quadrupoles are adjusted to give the smallest beam spot at the plane of the aperture, which is then adjusted to fit. This means that the phase-space ellipses (both radial and axial) at the aperture are not those of images but rather are characteristic of waists, and these indeed are upright, as seen earlier.

Hence we may take the initial ellipse to be upright, so that $\alpha_i = \alpha_1 = 1/x_0^2$, $\beta_i = 0$, and $\gamma_i = \gamma_1 = 1/x_0'^2$. The last three equations then become

$$\alpha_j = \frac{e_j^2}{x_0^2} + \frac{d_j^2}{x_0'^2}, \tag{7-64}$$

$$\beta_j = -\frac{b_j e_j}{x_0^2} - \frac{a_j d_j}{x_0'^2}, \tag{7-65}$$

$$\gamma_j = \frac{b_j^2}{x_0^2} + \frac{a_j^2}{x_0'^2}. \tag{7-66}$$

Henceforth we will assume that these are the expressions that are appropriate.

For convenience in calculating numerical values it will be profitable to rearrange these expressions as follows:

$$\alpha_j = \frac{1}{x_0^2} N_{\alpha j}, \tag{7-67}$$

$$\beta_j = -\frac{\rho_1}{x_0^2} N_{\beta j}, \tag{7-68}$$

$$\gamma_j = \frac{\rho_1^2}{x_0^2} N_{\gamma j}, \tag{7-69}$$

where

$$N_{\alpha j} = e_j{}^2 + \left(\frac{x_0}{\rho_1 x_0{}'}\right)^2 (\rho_1 d_j)^2, \tag{7-70}$$

$$N_{\beta j} = \frac{b_j}{\rho_1} e_j + \left(\frac{x_0}{\rho_1 x_0{}'}\right)^2 a_j(\rho_1 d_j), \tag{7-71}$$

$$N_{\gamma j} = \left(\frac{b_j}{\rho_1}\right)^2 + \left(\frac{x_0}{\rho_1 x_0{}'}\right)^2 a_j{}^2. \tag{7-72}$$

When calculating α_j, β_j, or γ_j, the factors $1/x_0{}^2$, $\rho_1/x_0{}^2$, and $\rho_1{}^2/x_0{}^2$ should be left in symbolic form, while the N's are determined as numerics. Note that $(x_0/\rho_1 x_0{}')^2$ has a constant numerical value. The reason for this admonition will become apparent further on.

Since the algebraic expressions for $a_j, b_j, \ldots$ have been tabulated in terms of the basic properties of the magnets and drift spaces, we have here a rapid means of *directly* finding the radial ellipse coefficients at any desired station.

LIOUVILLES'S THEOREM AGAIN

It has been seen in Eq. (7-19) that

$$\alpha_j \gamma_j - \beta_j{}^2 = \frac{1}{x_0{}^2 x_0'^2}.$$

This is a constant, so that the area of the ellipse, given in Eq. (7-18) as

$$A = \frac{\pi}{(\alpha_j \gamma_j - \beta_j{}^2)^{1/2}}$$

also is constant (provided the energy of the ions does not change). Let us now see how this invariance is expressed in terms of the coefficients a_j, b_j, d_j, and e_j. We find the value of $\alpha_j \gamma_j - \beta_j{}^2$ using the general Eqs. (7-61)–(7-63). After multiplying out and canceling, we discover that

$$\alpha_j \gamma_j - \beta_j{}^2 = (\alpha_j \gamma_j - \beta_j{}^2)(a_j e_j - b_j d_j)^2,$$

so that

$$a_j e_j - b_j d_j = 1. \tag{7-73}$$

This is an alternative expression of the fact that the area of the phase-space ellipse remains constant—a characteristic known as Liouville's theorem. All the matrices used in transport equations must obey this restriction, and it is easy to show that those which have been employed do indeed do so.

Effect of Dispersion on the Radial Ellipse

Between the object and the magnet and during passage through the entrance edge, particles of all momenta follow the same paths (assuming that there is no separation of momenta in the object). But inside the magnet, dispersion plays a role, the more energetic ions taking paths with larger radii of curvature. Just before the exit edge is reached, we have

$$x_4 = a_4 x_1 + b_4 x_1' + c_4 \, \Delta p/p, \tag{7-74}$$

$$x_4' = d_4 x_1 + e_4 x_1' + f_4 \, \Delta p/p. \tag{7-75}$$

The first two terms in each expression apply to particles with momentum p, while the last term depends on ions with momentum $p + \Delta p$. We now imagine that x_1 and x_1' are so chosen that x_4 and x_4' represent the maximum displacement and slope of the p-ions. Hence we may write the above expressions as

$$x_4 = x_{4p \, \text{max}} + c_4 \, \Delta p/p, \tag{7-76}$$

$$x_4' = x_{4p \, \text{max}}' + f_4 \, \Delta p/p. \tag{7-77}$$

Therefore when we find the value of $x_{4p \, \text{max}}$ (the half-width of the envelope of p-ions), the addition of $c_4 \, \Delta p/p$ will give the half-width of the envelope that contains both the p-ions and the $p + \Delta p$-ions. A similar remark applies to the slopes.

Thus in the general case, by use of Eqs. (7-22) and (7-69), we see that Eq. (7-76) becomes

$$x_{j \, \text{max}} = \gamma_j^{1/2} x_0 x_0' + c_j \, \Delta p/p$$
$$= (N_{\gamma j} \rho_1^{2}/x_0^{2})^{1/2} x_0 x_0' + c_j \, \Delta p/p, \tag{7-78}$$

$$\boxed{x_{j \, \text{max}} = N_{\gamma j}^{1/2} \rho_1 x_0' + c_j \, \Delta p/p.} \tag{7-79}$$

In a similar manner, the use of Eqs. (7-24) and (7-67) makes (7-77) become

$$x_{j \, \text{max}}' = \alpha_j^{1/2} x_0 x_0' + f_j \, \Delta p/p$$
$$= (N_{\alpha j}/x_0^{2})^{1/2} x_0 x_0' + f_j \, \Delta p/p. \tag{7-80}$$

so

$$\boxed{x_{j \, \text{max}}' = N_{\alpha j}^{1/2} x_0' + f_j \, \Delta p/p.} \tag{7-81}$$

These expressions, Eqs. (7-79) and (7-81), *give the half-width and maximum slope at station j*. Note that x_0' and $\rho_1 x_0'$ are numerical constants throughout the whole system and that Δp is the half-spread in momentum from the accelerator. To ensure that $x_{j\,max}$ and $x'_{j\,max}$ indeed measure the greatest values to be attained, p should be the *least* nominal momentum from the accelerator, if it is of variable energy or handles a variety of particles.

The interpretation of these equations in terms of the phase-space ellipse is indicated in Fig. 7-9.

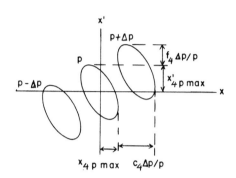

FIG. 7-9. Relative positions of the phase-space ellipses.

We are now in a position to understand more fully the behavior of the $p - \Delta p$, p, and $p + \Delta p$ ellipses displayed in Fig. 7-5.

Between the object and the magnet, Eqs. (6-3) and (6-6) show that

$$c_2 = 0 \qquad \text{and} \qquad f_2 = 0,$$

so that x_{max} and x'_{max} are independent of $\Delta p/p$, as shown by Eqs. (7-79) and (7-81). All the ellipses are coincident, as at the source.

During passage through the body of the magnet, we see from Eqs. (6-15) and (6-18) that

$$c_4 = (\rho/\delta^2)(1 - \cos \phi) \qquad \text{and} \qquad f_4 = (\sin \phi)/\delta,$$

where now ϕ is a variable, so that both c_4 and f_4 increase (the latter up to $\phi = 90°$). Eqs. (7-79) and (7-81) and Fig. 7-9 thus show that the overall spread in x and x' of the three ellipses is increasing; i.e., the ellipses are separating.

After the particles leave the magnet, ϕ is now a constant, and conditions are specified by c_6 and f_6, given in Eqs. (6-27) and (6-30) as

$$c_6 = (\rho/\delta^2)(1 - \cos \phi) + S_1 \tan u_2(1 - \cos \phi)/\delta^2 + S_1(\sin \phi)/\delta,$$

$$f_6 = \tan u_2(1 - \cos \phi)/\delta^2 + (\sin \phi)/\delta.$$

The variable is now S_1, the distance past the magnet, so a further separation of the ellipses takes place, but only along x. If the images are just resolved when S_1 becomes the image distance S_{ix1}, it is evident that at this point the ellipses for the first and only time do not overlap along x. Any momentum-separating slit therefore must be located at the image plane.

WIDTH OF RADIAL BUST IN FIRST MAGNET

Equations (7-34)–(7-36) give the values of α_4, β_4, and γ_4 that specify the radial ellipse after the ions have passed through the body of the magnet of bending angle $\theta_1 = \phi_1/\delta_1 = \phi_1/(1 - n_1)^{1/2}$. (See Fig. 7-10). In these expressions, if we replace ϕ_1 by ϕ_1', where $\phi_1' < \phi_1$, we then have the coefficients

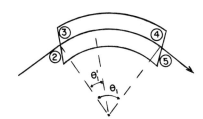

FIG. 7-10.

describing the ellipse at some point *inside* the magnet. The point of interest is that at which there is a bust, and there the ellipse is upright; this is characterized by $\beta_4 = 0$. Hence in (7-35) we set

$$\beta_4 = 0 \qquad (7\text{-}82)$$

and write ϕ_1' for ϕ_1. Eq. (7-35) then becomes

$$-\alpha_3 \frac{\rho_1}{\delta_1} \sin \phi_1' \cos \phi_1' + \beta_3(\cos^2 \phi_1' - \sin^2 \phi_1')$$

$$+ \gamma_3 \frac{\delta_1}{\rho_1} \sin \phi_1' \cos \phi_1' = 0. \quad (7\text{-}83)$$

From this it follows that

$$\cot \phi_1' - \tan \phi_1' = \frac{(\alpha_3 \rho_1/\delta_1) - \gamma_3 \delta_1/\rho_1}{\beta_3}. \qquad (7\text{-}84)$$

Now by Eqs. (7-67)–(7-69), we have

$$\alpha_3 = \frac{1}{x_0^2} N_{\alpha 3}, \qquad (7\text{-}85)$$

$$\beta_3 = -\frac{\rho_1}{x_0^2} N_{\beta 3}, \qquad (7\text{-}86)$$

$$\gamma_3 = \frac{\rho_1{}^2}{x_0{}^2} N_{\gamma 3}, \qquad (7\text{-}87)$$

and by Eqs. (7-52)–(7-54), we see that

$$N_{\alpha 3} = 1 + 2L_0 \tan u_1 + \left[L_0{}^2 + \left(\frac{x_0}{\rho_1 x_0{}'} \right)^2 \right] \tan^2 u_1, \qquad (7\text{-}88)$$

$$N_{\beta 3} = L_0 + \left[L_0{}^2 + \left(\frac{x_0}{\rho_1 x_0{}'} \right)^2 \right] \tan u_1, \qquad (7\text{-}89)$$

$$N_{\gamma 3} = L_0{}^2 + \left(\frac{x_0}{\rho_1 x_0{}'} \right)^2. \qquad (7\text{-}90)$$

Therefore Eq. (7-84) may be written

$$\cot \phi_1{}' - \tan \phi_1{}' = \frac{(N_{\alpha 3}/\delta_1) - N_{\gamma 3} \delta_1}{-N_{\beta 3}}. \qquad (7\text{-}91)$$

When the right-hand side of this is evaluated numerically, the value of $\phi_1{}'$ may be read from Fig. 7-11.

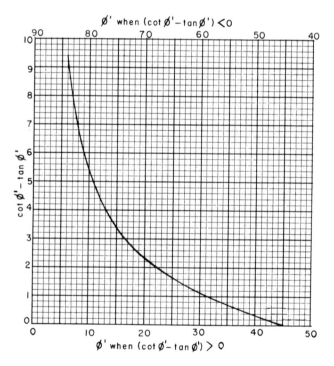

FIG. 7-11. Curve to locate the position of the bust.

We then determine γ_4' by replacing ϕ_1 with ϕ_1' in Eq. (7-36), obtaining

$$\gamma_4' = \alpha_3 \frac{\rho_1^2}{\delta_1^2} \sin^2 \phi_1' - 2\beta_3 \frac{\rho_1}{\delta_1} \sin \phi_1' \cos \phi_1' + \gamma_3 \cos^2 \phi_1'. \quad (7\text{-}92)$$

This may be written in the form

$$\gamma_4' = \frac{\rho_1^2}{x_0^2} N_{\gamma 4}', \quad (7\text{-}93)$$

where

$$N_{\gamma 4}' = \frac{N_{\alpha 3}}{\delta_1^2} \sin^2 \phi_1' + \frac{2N_{\beta 3}}{\delta_1} \sin \phi_1' \cos \phi_1' + N_{\gamma 3} \cos^2 \phi_1'. \quad (7\text{-}94)$$

The half-width of the bust is given by

$$x_{\text{bust}} = \gamma_4'^{1/2} x_0 x_0' + c_4' \, \Delta p/p, \quad (7\text{-}95)$$

or

$$x_{\text{bust}} = N_{\gamma 4}'^{1/2} \rho_1 x_0' + \frac{\rho_1}{\delta_1^2} (1 - \cos \phi_1') \, \Delta p/p, \quad (7\text{-}96)$$

where c_4' is c_4 (as in Eq. (6-15)) evaluated at ϕ_1'.

Contrary to what might be expected naively, the bust does not necessarily occur at the middle of the magnet. As shown earlier, if a real image is to be formed, the body of the magnet must rotate the ellipse slightly beyond the condition for a bust, and this can happen very close to the exit edge. We list below the conditions at which the bust is at the midpoint for three typical magnets.

For $n = 0$ and $u_1 = u_2 = 0$:

$$\cot \phi_1' - \tan \phi_1' = {}_0L - 1/L_0. \quad (7\text{-}97)$$

The bust is at the midpoint if $M_x = -1$.

For $n = 0$ and $\tan u_1 = \tan u_2 = 1/L_0$:

$$\cot \phi_1' - \tan \phi_1' = \frac{4 - L_0^2 + (1/L_0 - 1)(x_0/\rho_1 x_0')^2}{-[2L_0 + (x_0/\rho_1 x_0')^2/L_0]}. \quad (7\text{-}98)$$

The bust is at the midpoint if $M_x = -1$ and $(x_0/\rho_1 x_0')^2 \approx 0$.

For $n = 0.5$ and $u_1 = u_2 = 0$:

$$\cot \phi_1' - \tan \phi_1' = \frac{\sqrt{2} - [L_0^2 + (x_0/\rho_1 x_0')^2]/\sqrt{2}}{-L_0}. \quad (7\text{-}99)$$

The bust is at the midpoint if $M_x = -1$ and $(x_0/\rho_1 x_0')^2 \approx 0$.

WIDTH OF RADIAL BUST IN SECOND MAGNET

If a radial image is formed between the two magnets, one must not assume that the bust in the second is to be calculated exactly as was the bust in the first, because the object for the second magnet is dispersed, which was not the case for the earlier computation. The correct procedure is the same as if no intermagnet image existed, and is outlined in what follows.

The coefficients α_8, β_8, and γ_8 describe the ellipse just before passage through the exit face of the second magnet, which is of angular length $\theta_2 = \phi_2/\delta_2 = \phi_2/(1 - n_2)^{1/2}$. The bust occurs at some interior angle $\phi_2' < \phi_2$ and is characterized by an upright ellipse. Hence we set

$$\beta_8 = 0. \tag{7-100}$$

By a procedure analogous to that used with the first bust, this determines ϕ_2' through the expression

$$\cot \phi_2' - \tan \phi_2' = \frac{(\alpha_7 \rho_2/\delta_2) - \gamma_7 \delta_2/\rho_2}{\beta_7} \tag{7-101}$$

$$= \frac{(N_{\alpha7}/\delta_2) - N_{\gamma7}\delta_2}{-N_{\beta7}}. \tag{7-102}$$

Here the N's are numerics calculated by use of Eqs. (7-70)–(7-72). (Detailed expressions for the more common magnet types will be given in Chapter 9.) The value of ϕ_2' is then read from Fig. 7-11. The analog of Eq. (7-94) is then

$$N'_{\gamma8} = \frac{N_{\alpha7}}{\delta_2^2} \sin^2 \phi_2' + \frac{2N_{\beta7}}{\delta_2} \sin \phi_2' \cos \phi_2' + N_{\gamma7} \cos^2 \phi_2'. \tag{7-103}$$

The half-width of the second bust is given by

$$x_{\text{bust}} = N'^{1/2}_{\gamma8} \rho_1 x_0' + c_8' \Delta p/p, \tag{7-104}$$

where c_8' is c_8 (Eq. (6-39)) evaluated at $\phi_2 = \phi_2'$:

$$c_8' = c_7 \cos \phi_2' + f_7 \frac{\rho_2}{\delta_2} \sin \phi_2' \pm \frac{\rho_2}{\delta_2^2} (1 - \cos \phi_2'). \tag{7-105}$$

Here the upper (lower) sign is used if the magnets bend in the same (opposite) directions. Explicit expressions for c_7 and f_7 are given in Eqs. (6-33) and (6-36).

Ideally, $\Delta p/p$ refers to the output from the accelerator and it will be found that the second bust can be several times as wide as the first. It may be that two magnets of the same large width, or one each of different widths, are beyond available funds. In that case, and if an intermagnet image is formed, a slit can be used at that image to intercept all particles except those that fall within the pass band $(\Delta p/p)_1$ of the first magnet. This $(\Delta p/p)_1$ may then be used when computing the second bust, with the possible result that two narrow magnets will suffice.

Such a procedure distributes the heat burden over the two sets of slits. Disadvantages are that two sets must be provided and that it is not possible to send the entire beam to the second image plane by opening up the slits, nor to use the magnets so as to form an achromatic image of full intensity, as will be described in Chapter 16.

EMITTANCE

The emittance ϵ of a beam of ions is here defined as

$$\epsilon = \text{Area}/\pi = x_0 x_0', \qquad (7\text{-}106)$$

where the area is that of the xx' phase-space ellipse. A corresponding definition applies to the zz' ellipse. Since the area is constant (as long as the velocity does not change), the emittance remains fixed in spite of passage of the particles through magnets or other lens systems. This means that if the diameter of the beam is reduced by some means, its divergence will increase, and vice-versa. The only way to improve the emittance (i.e. make it smaller) is to intercept some of the particles.

Emittance is reduced, of course, by an increase in velocity, of which the longitudinal component gets a much larger share than the transverse component, so that the slope x' decreases. To avoid this artificial improvement in emittance, or to be able to compare the emittance of various ion sources when the emittance is measured at different energies, a normalized emittance is used, wherein it is multiplied by the momentum:

$$\epsilon_{\text{normalized}} = x_0 x_0' \beta/(1 - \beta^2)^{1/2}, \qquad (7\text{-}107)$$

where $\beta = v/c$. For our purposes, where the velocity is constant, this elaboration is unnecessary.

(Occasionally it will be found that emittance is defined as $\epsilon = \text{Area} = \pi x_0 x_0'$.)

Since the quantities x_0/x_0' and z_0/z_0' play a role in most of the expressions dealing with magnets, their values must be ascertained. Both x_0 and z_0 are easily found from the dimensions of the object, so the slopes will become known when we find the emittance in each plane.

It might seem that the slope x_0' could be found by noting the diameter D of the beam at some distance S from the object, for from Fig. 7-12 it would

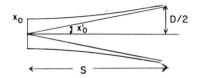

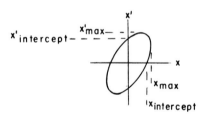

Fig. 7-12. An incorrect evaluation of x_0'.

seem that $x_0' = D/2S$. This is not correct in principle, however, since the x_0' ray does not reach the bounds of the envelope until $S = \infty$.

An appropriate procedure that averages a large number of observations consists in plotting the ellipse in a drift space and then measuring its area with a planimeter or by "counting squares." Then

$$x_0' = \text{Area}/\pi x_0. \tag{7-108}$$

Alternatively, and less accurately, since $\epsilon = x_0 x_0'$, by Eq. (7-22), we have

$$\epsilon = x_{\text{max}}/\gamma^{1/2}. \tag{7-109}$$

Then, using Eq. (7-14), we find

$$\epsilon = x_{\text{max}} x'_{\text{intercept}} \tag{7-110}$$

and similarly

$$\epsilon = x'_{\text{max}} x_{\text{intercept}}. \tag{7-111}$$

Fig. 7-13.

Emittance may be measured experimentally by inserting in the beam a slotted diaphragm that intercepts some ions and passes others that form illuminated bands on some detecting screen at a distance S downstream (Fig. 7-14). (A photographic film may be used, or a copper or aluminum plate that becomes radioactive and is later placed on a photo film to produce an autoradiograph. Alternatively, the pattern may be detected electrically by a narrow probe wire that is moved across it.) At the edge of each illuminated band, we have (Fig. 7-15):

$$x'_j = (h_j - x_j)/S, \tag{7-112}$$

$$x'_{j-1} = (h_{j-1} - x_{j-1})/S. \tag{7-113}$$

The x_j are known from the dimensions of the slotted diaphragm and the h_j

are measured. A best-fit ellipse is drawn through the plotted points, the area is measured, and on dividing by π, we have the emittance (Fig. 7-16).

A single observation of $x_0' = x'_{max}$ gives less trustworthy results, since there is no guarantee that the true x_0' beam just grazed a slot edge; it may have been intercepted. Obviously, many and narrow slots are desirable; since

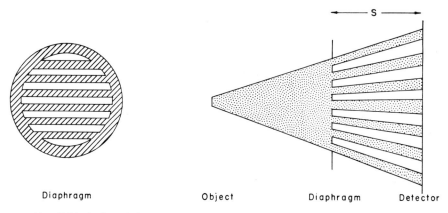

Diaphragm   Object   Diaphragm   Detector

FIG. 7-14. A slotted plate and a detector plate, used to measure emittance.

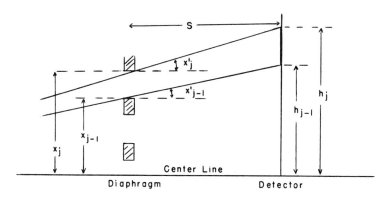

Diaphragm   Detector

FIG. 7-15. Geometrical relations.

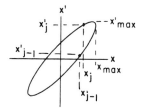

FIG. 7-16. The location of experimental points whereby the ellipse is plotted.

the point at x'_{max} never corresponds with x_{max}, the sketched-in ellipse must involve some extrapolation which is reduced as the number of points is increased. The extent of the slots should more than cover the beam width, so at least one slot is not used on each side of the pattern. Its midpoint can be located by omitting the central slot, or by some such artifice.

In order that at least preliminary calculations on a magnet system may be carried out in the absence of emittance data, it may be said that x_0' and z_0' from most accelerators are measured in a few milliradians.

8 Axial Beam Envelopes

The axial ellipse coefficients $\bar{\alpha}_j$, $\bar{\beta}_j$, and $\bar{\gamma}_j$ are similar to the radial coefficients α_j, β_j, and γ_j except that the sign of $\tan u$ must be changed. When the axial ellipse coefficients are derived from the axial matrix coefficients $\bar{a}_j$, $\bar{b}_j$, ..., the latter are obtained from the radial coefficients a_j, b_j, ... by the conversion process of Eqs. (3-1)–(3-3). Since axial motion is not effected by a change in momentum, to first order, we set $\Delta p = 0$.

Thus the upright ellipse of the object is specified by

$$\bar{\alpha}_1 = 1/z_0^2, \tag{8-1}$$

$$\bar{\beta}_1 = 0, \tag{8-2}$$

$$\bar{\gamma}_1 = 1/z_0'^2. \tag{8-3}$$

At any station j the half-height and half-divergence are

$$z_{j\,max} = \bar{\gamma}_j^{1/2} z_0 z_0' \equiv \bar{N}_{\gamma j}^{1/2} \rho_1 z_0', \tag{8-4}$$

$$z'_{j\,max} = \bar{\alpha}_j^{1/2} z_0 z_0' \equiv \bar{N}_{\alpha j}^{1/2} z_0', \tag{8-5}$$

where the $\bar{N}$'s are numerics with values as shown in the examples that follow.

At the end of the object distance $S_0 = \rho L_o$, in analogy with Eqs. (7-28)–(7-30), we have

$$\bar{\alpha}_2 = \bar{\alpha}_1 \qquad = \frac{1}{z_0^2} \qquad \equiv \frac{1}{z_0^2} \bar{N}_{\alpha 2}, \tag{8-6}$$

$$\bar{\beta}_2 = -\bar{\alpha}_1 S_0 \qquad = -\frac{\rho}{z_0^2} L_o \qquad \equiv -\frac{\rho}{z_0^2} \bar{N}_{\beta 2}, \tag{8-7}$$

$$\bar{\gamma}_2 = \bar{\gamma}_1 + \bar{\alpha}_1 S_0^2 = \frac{\rho^2}{z_0^2} \left[L_o^2 + \left(\frac{z_0}{\rho z_0'} \right)^2 \right] \equiv \frac{\rho^2}{z_0^2} \bar{N}_{\gamma 2}. \tag{8-8}$$

Traversal of the first entrance edge is described by the analogs of Eqs. (7-31)–(7-33):

$$\bar{\alpha}_3 = \bar{\alpha}_2 + 2\bar{\beta}_2 \frac{\tan u_1}{\rho} + \bar{\gamma}_2 \left(\frac{\tan u_1}{\rho}\right)^2, \tag{8-9}$$

$$\bar{\beta}_3 = \bar{\beta}_2 + \bar{\gamma}_2 \frac{\tan u_1}{\rho}, \tag{8-10}$$

$$\bar{\gamma}_3 = \bar{\gamma}_2. \tag{8-11}$$

Substitution from the above yields the analogs of Eqs. (7-52)–(7-54):

$$\bar{\alpha}_3 = \frac{1}{z_0^2} \left\{ 1 - 2L_0 \tan u_1 + \left[L_0^2 + \left(\frac{z_0}{\rho z_0'}\right)^2 \right] \tan^2 u_1 \right\} \equiv \frac{1}{z_0^2} \bar{N}_{\alpha 3}, \tag{8-12}$$

$$\bar{\beta}_3 = -\frac{\rho}{z_0^2} \left\{ L_0 - \left[L_0^2 + \left(\frac{z_0}{\rho z_0'}\right)^2 \right] \tan u_1 \right\} \equiv -\frac{\rho}{z_0^2} \bar{N}_{\beta 3}, \tag{8-13}$$

$$\bar{\gamma}_3 = \frac{\rho^2}{z_0^2} \left\{ L_0^2 + \left(\frac{z_0}{\rho z_0'}\right)^2 \right\} \equiv \frac{\rho^2}{z_0^2} \bar{N}_{\gamma 3}. \tag{8-14}$$

Passage through the body of the first magnet is expressed by equations similar to Eqs. (7-34)–(7-36) after conversion to the axial mode:

$$\bar{\alpha}_4 = \bar{\alpha}_3 \cos^2 \psi + 2\bar{\beta}_3 \frac{\varepsilon}{\rho} \sin \psi \cos \psi + \bar{\gamma}_3 \frac{\varepsilon^2}{\rho^2} \sin^2 \psi, \tag{8-15}$$

$$\bar{\beta}_4 = -\bar{\alpha}_3 \frac{\rho}{\varepsilon} \sin \psi \cos \psi + \bar{\beta}_3 (\cos^2 \psi - \sin^2 \psi) + \bar{\gamma}_3 \frac{\varepsilon}{\rho} \sin \psi \cos \psi, \tag{8-16}$$

$$\bar{\gamma}_4 = \bar{\alpha}_3 \frac{\rho^2}{\varepsilon^2} \sin^2 \psi - 2\bar{\beta}_3 \frac{\rho}{\varepsilon} \sin \psi \cos \psi + \bar{\gamma}_3 \cos^2 \psi. \tag{8-17}$$

At stations further downstream we use the analogs of Eqs. (7-67)–(7-69) (assuming the object to be an upright ellipse):

$$\bar{\alpha}_j = \frac{1}{z_0^2} \bar{N}_{\alpha j}, \tag{8-18}$$

$$\bar{\beta}_j = -\frac{\rho}{z_0^2} \bar{N}_{\beta j}, \tag{8-19}$$

$$\bar{\gamma}_j = \frac{\rho^2}{z_0^2} \bar{N}_{\gamma j}, \tag{8-20}$$

where

$$\bar{N}_{\alpha j} = \bar{e}_j{}^2 + \left(\frac{z_0}{\rho z_0{}'}\right)^2 (\rho \bar{d}_j)^2, \tag{8-21}$$

$$\bar{N}_{\beta j} = \frac{\bar{b}_j}{\rho}\,\bar{e}_j + \left(\frac{z_0}{\rho z_0{}'}\right)^2 \bar{a}_j(\rho \bar{d}_j), \tag{8-22}$$

$$\bar{N}_{\beta j} = \left(\frac{\bar{b}_j}{\rho}\right)^2 + \left(\frac{z_0}{\rho z_0{}'}\right)^2 \bar{a}_j{}^2. \tag{8-23}$$

Here the axial coefficients $\bar{a}_j$, $\bar{b}_j$, ... are derived from the radial coefficients a_j, b_j, ... by the conversion process of Eqs. (3-1)–(3-3).

AXIAL MOTION WHEN $n = 0$

We now have $\cos \psi = 1$, $\sin \psi = 0$, but $(\sin \psi)/\varepsilon = \theta$, so that Eqs. (8-15)–(8-17) (which describe the ellipse just before the exit edge) become

$$\bar{\alpha}_4 = \bar{\alpha}_3, \tag{8-24}$$

$$\bar{\beta}_4 = -\bar{\alpha}_3\,\rho\theta + \bar{\beta}_3 \qquad = -\bar{\alpha}_3\,S + \bar{\beta}_3, \tag{8-25}$$

$$\bar{\gamma}_4 = \bar{\alpha}_3\,\rho^2\theta^2 - 2\bar{\beta}_3\,\rho\theta + \bar{\gamma}_3 = \bar{\alpha}_3\,S^2 - 2\bar{\beta}_3\,S + \bar{\gamma}_3, \tag{8-26}$$

where $S = \rho\theta$. By comparing these expressions with Eqs. (8-6)–(8-8) for the object distance (and recalling that $\beta_1 = 0$), we see that the body of an $n = 0$ magnet acts like a field-free region of length $S = \rho\theta$ as far as axial motion is concerned. Any axial force must be supplied by the edges; a particular example will now be discussed.

AXIAL MOTION WHEN $n = 0$ AND $\tan u_1 = 1/L_0$

Just inside the entrance edge, the general expression for the axial slope is

$$z_3{}' = \bar{d}_3 z_1 + \bar{e}_3 z_1{}'. \tag{8-27}$$

From Eq. (6-11) we have the radial expression $e_3 = L_0 \tan u_1 + 1$, so the axial equation is $\bar{e}_3 = -L_0 \tan u_1 + 1$. When we set $\tan u_1 = 1/L_0$, then we get $\bar{e}_3 = 0$. Choose also $z_1 = 0$. Hence $z_3{}' = 0$.

Thus this particular choice of entrance edge angle will reduce to zero the axial slope of any particle that started from the axis, no matter what its original slope. Put the other way around, if $S_0 = \rho/\tan u_1$, then S_0 is the focal length of the axial lens formed by the entrance edge (see Fig. 8-1). With

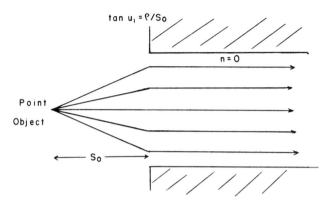

FIG. 8-1. When $\tan u_1 = \rho/S_0$ and $n = 0$, S_0 is the axial focal length.

$n = 0$, no axial image will be formed unless by some additional lens, such as the exit edge.

The pattern of ellipses for a source with finite half-height $z_1 = z_0$ is as shown in Fig. 8-2. The dotted point with $z_1 = 0$ and $z_1' = z_0'$ is brought

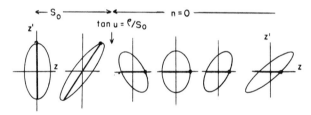

FIG. 8-2. Ellipse patterns for $n = 0$ and $\tan u_1 = \rho/S_0$. The heavy line indicates the degenerate ellipse of a point source.

by the entrance edge to $z_3' = 0$, and no subsequent length of magnet with $n = 0$ can drive it back to $z = 0$.

It is clear from Fig. 8-2 that the axial envelope first decreases in height to a minimum (a waist) and expands thereafter. We will now find where the waist occurs, what its value is, and at what distance the height again returns to its entrance edge value. With $n = 0$, Eq. (8-17) becomes

$$\bar{\gamma}_4 = \bar{\alpha}_3 \rho^2\theta^2 - 2\bar{\beta}_3 \rho\theta + \bar{\gamma}_3 \tag{8-28}$$

$$= \bar{\alpha}_3 S^2 - 2\bar{\beta}_3 S + \bar{\gamma}_3, \tag{8-29}$$

where $S = \rho\theta$ is a distance beyond the entrance edge. (We have not yet specified ρ and θ.) On substituting for $\bar{\alpha}_3$, $\bar{\beta}_3$, and $\bar{\gamma}_3$ from Eqs. (8-12), (8-13), and (8-14), and using $\tan u_1 = 1/L_0$, we find

$$\bar{\gamma}_4 = \frac{1}{z_0'^2} \left(\frac{S^2}{S_0^2} - \frac{2S}{S_0} + \frac{z_0'^2}{z_0^2} S_0^2 + 1 \right). \tag{8-30}$$

At S, the square of the half-height of the envelope is given by

$$z_{4\,max}^2 = \bar{\gamma}_4 z_0{}^2 z_0'^2 \tag{8-31}$$

$$= z_0{}^2 + z_0'^2 S_0{}^2 + z_0{}^2\left(\frac{S^2}{S_0{}^2} - \frac{2S}{S_0}\right) \tag{8-32}$$

$$= z_{2\,max}^2 + z_0{}^2\left(\frac{S^2}{S_0{}^2} - \frac{2S}{S_0}\right), \tag{8-33}$$

where $z_{2\,max}$ is the half-height at the entrance, as may be proved readily. As S increases from zero, we see that the axial envelope starts to shrink, reaching a minimum of value $z_{min} = z_0'S$ when $S = S_0$. (At this point, the ions that started with $z_1 = 0$ and $z_1' = z_0'$ momentarily appear at the boundary of the envelope.) The envelope then expands, attaining its entrance edge value when $S = 2S_0$, as indicated in Fig. 8-3.

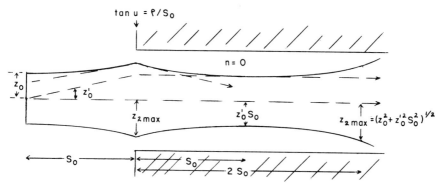

FIG. 8-3. The axial envelope when $n = 0$ and $\tan u_1 = \rho/S_0$. Its curvature is here greatly exaggerated.

We may make the useful observation that a magnet's gap no higher than that required at the entrance will be adequate at the exit (for $n = 0$ and $\tan u_1 = 1/L_o$) provided that the length $\rho\theta$ is less than $2S_0$; i.e., if

$$\theta < 2L_o. \tag{8-34}$$

Since $L_o = 2\cot(\theta/2)$ (Eq. (4-63)), the critical angle is $\theta = 123.4°$.

AXIAL MOTION WHEN $1 > n > 0$ AND $u_1 = u_2 = 0$

Since the body of a magnet with an inhomogeneous field supplies axial forces, an axial bust will occur in its interior. (We consider only the usual case where the edge angles are zero.) Thus the gap height must be greater than that required at its entrance and exit. The bust is downstream from the input face by the angular distance $\theta' = \psi'/\varepsilon = \psi'/n^{1/2}$, where ψ' is given by

$$\cot \psi' - \tan \psi' = \frac{(\bar{\alpha}_3 \, \rho/\varepsilon) - \bar{\gamma}_3 \, \varepsilon/\rho}{\bar{\beta}_3} \tag{8-35}$$

$$= \frac{(\bar{N}_{\alpha 3}/\varepsilon) - \bar{N}_{\gamma 3} \, \varepsilon}{-\bar{N}_{\beta 3}}. \tag{8-36}$$

The half-height is

$$z_{\text{bust}} = \bar{\gamma}_4'^{1/2} z_0 \, z_0' = \bar{N}_{\gamma 4}'^{1/2} \rho z_0', \tag{8-37}$$

where

$$\bar{N}_{\gamma 4}' = \bar{N}_{\alpha 3} \frac{\sin^2 \psi'}{\varepsilon^2} + 2\bar{N}_{\beta 3} \frac{\sin \psi'}{\varepsilon} \cos \psi' + \bar{N}_{\gamma 3} \cos^2 \psi'. \tag{8-38}$$

The expressions for $\bar{N}_{\alpha 3}$, $\bar{N}_{\beta 3}$, and $\bar{N}_{\gamma 3}$ are given by Eqs. (8-12)–(8-14), wherein we set $u_1 = 0$.

For $n = 0.5$, we have

$$\cot \psi' - \tan \psi' = \frac{\sqrt{2} - [L_o{}^2 + (z_0/\rho z_0')^2]/\sqrt{2}}{-L_o} \tag{8-39}$$

and

$$\bar{N}_{\gamma 4}' = 2 \sin^2 \psi' + 2\sqrt{2} \, L_o \sin \psi' \cos \psi' + [L_o{}^2 + (z_0/\rho z_0')^2]\cos^2 \psi'. \tag{8-40}$$

A Pitfall to Avoid

Consider axial motion in connection with two magnets, each with $M_z = -1$ so that $S_{0z1} = S_{iz1} = S_{0z2}$. The first axial image has the same height as the object and acts as the object for the second magnet. Since $S_{0z1} = S_{0z2}$, one might expect the envelope to have the same height at the entrance to the second magnet as it does at the entrance to the first. But this need not be the case. Thus for $t_1 = t_2 = 1/L_o$, the maximum slope at the object (assumed to have an upright ellipse) is not as great as that at the first image, as may be seen by solving for the value of $z_6'{}_{\max} = \bar{\alpha}_6^{1/2} z_0 z_0'$. Therefore the envelope expands more in approaching the second magnet than it does in approaching the first. The difference can be small (below detection with a 10-inch slide rule, though observable with a desk calculator), but the effect is there and can cause the unwary to make a fruitless search for an arithmetical error.

9 Routine for Envelopes in One or Two Magnets

INTRODUCTION

In this chapter, we present a step-by-step procedure designed to minimize the effort in finding the axial and radial extent of the field required in one or two magnets. A ten-inch slide rule is adequate.

Two general cases are treated:

(1) Both magnets have uniform fields. The bending angles, radii, and edge angles are arbitrary.

(2) Both magnets have nonuniform fields; the field indices are not necessarily equal but lie between 0 and $+1$. All edge angles are zero. The bending angles and radii are arbitrary.

Since an edge changes only the slope of a trajectory, the width or height of an envelope is the same on either side of an edge. Calculations are made for station numbers that are encircled in Fig. 9-1. To reduce the number of

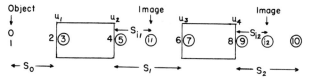

FIG. 9-1. Encircled numbers indicate stations for which algebraic expressions are given for envelope dimensions.

equations, certain ones have been chosen that can readily reduce to those applicable further upstream. Thus expressions for $j = 5$ are obtained from those at $j = 7$ by setting $S_1 = 0$, etc. If there is only one magnet, S_1 may be interpreted as the distance to some auxiliary equipment (such as a quadrupole) where knowledge of the beam's envelope is required.

131

Recall that $\varepsilon = n^{1/2}$, $\delta = (1 - n)^{1/2}$, $\phi = \delta\theta$, and $\psi = \varepsilon\theta$, where n is the field index and θ is the bending angle; $u_1, \ldots, u_4$ are the edge angles in order of passage. *All distances are measured from the effective edges.*

PRELIMINARY STEPS

Determine the values of x_0, x_0', z_0, and z_0'. Compute these numerics:

$$N_1 = \rho_1 x_0', \tag{9-1}$$

$$N_2 = (x_0/\rho_1 x_0')^2, \tag{9-2}$$

$$\bar{N}_1 = \rho_1 z_0', \tag{9-3}$$

$$\bar{N}_2 = (z_0/\rho_1 z_0')^2, \tag{9-4}$$

$$N_3 = \rho_1 \, \Delta p/p. \tag{9-5}$$

In this, p is the nominal momentum from the accelerator (the *least* momentum if the machine is of variable energy), while Δp is the associated half-spread. If Δp is not known from the accelerator's specifications, it must be estimated, or measured by energy-sensitive detectors. The general relation between momentum p, kinetic energy E, half-spread ΔE, and the rest-mass energy $E_0 = m_0 c^2$ is

$$\frac{\Delta p}{p} = \left(\frac{E + E_0}{E + 2E_0}\right) \frac{\Delta E}{E}. \tag{9-6}$$

For $E \ll E_0$,

$$\frac{\Delta p}{p} = \frac{\Delta E}{2E}. \tag{9-7}$$

For $E \gg E_0$,

$$\frac{\Delta p}{p} = \frac{\Delta E}{E}. \tag{9-8}$$

The axial half-height of the envelope at station j is

$$z_{j\,\text{max}} = \left[\left(\frac{\bar{b}_j}{\rho_1}\right)^2 + \bar{N}_2 \bar{a}_j^{\,2}\right]^{1/2} \bar{N}_1 \tag{9-9}$$

and the radial half-width is

$$x_{j\,\text{max}} = \left[\left(\frac{b_j}{\rho_1}\right)^2 + N_2 a_j^{\,2}\right]^{1/2} N_1 + \frac{c_j}{\rho_1} N_3. \tag{9-10}$$

Special equations for busts, as well as for $\bar{a}_j$, $\bar{b}_j$, a_j, b_j, and c_j will be listed.

UNIFORM FIELDS—AXIAL ENVELOPES

$n_1 = n_2 = 0$, u_1, u_2, u_3, u_4 are arbitrary.

First Entry

$$\bar{a}_2 = 1, \tag{9-11}$$

$$\frac{\bar{b}_2}{\rho_1} = \frac{S_0}{\rho_1}. \tag{9-12}$$

Use Eqs. (9-11) and (9-12) in Eq. (9-9).
Leaving S_1/ρ_1 in symbolic form, find numerical values for:

$$\bar{a}_7 = 1 - \theta_1 \tan u_1 - \frac{S_1}{\rho_1} [\tan u_1 + \tan u_2 - \theta_1 \tan u_1 \tan u_2], \tag{9-13}$$

$$\frac{\bar{b}_7}{\rho_1} = \theta_1 + \frac{S_0}{\rho_1} (1 - \theta_1 \tan u_1) + \frac{S_1}{\rho_1} (1 - \theta_1 \tan u_2)$$

$$- \frac{S_0}{\rho_1} \frac{S_1}{\rho_1} [\tan u_1 + \tan u_2 - \theta_1 \tan u_1 \tan u_2]. \tag{9-14}$$

First Exit

In Eqs. (9-13) and (9-14), set $S_1 = 0$, thereby obtaining $\bar{a}_5$ and $\bar{b}_5/\rho_1$. Use these in Eq. (9-9).

First Axial Image

In Eqs. (9-13) and (9-14), set $S_1 = S_{iz1}$, the first magnet's axial image distance, thus finding $\bar{a}_{i1}$ and $\bar{b}_{i1}/\rho_1$. Use these in Eq. (9-9).

Second Entry

In Eqs. (9-13) and (9-14), set S_1 equal to the separation between magnets, to obtain $\bar{a}_7$ and $\bar{b}_7/\rho_1$. Use these in Eq. (9-9).

Using the numerical values of $\bar{a}_7$ and $\bar{b}_7/\rho_1$ just determined (where S_1 is the separation), find numerical values for the following:

$$\bar{d}_7 \rho_2 = -\bar{a}_7 \tan u_3 - \frac{\rho_2}{\rho_1} [\tan u_1 + \tan u_2 - \theta_1 \tan u_1 \tan u_2], \tag{9-15}$$

$$\bar{e}_7 = - \left(\frac{b_7}{\rho_1}\right) \frac{\rho_1}{\rho_2} \tan u_3 - \frac{S_0}{\rho_1} [\tan u_1 + \tan u_2 - \theta_1 \tan u_1 \tan u_2]$$

$$+ 1 - \theta_1 \tan u_2. \tag{9-16}$$

Using these values and leaving S_2/ρ_2 in symbolic form, evaluate:

$$\bar{a}_{10} = \bar{a}_7 \left[1 - \frac{S_2}{\rho_2} \tan u_4 \right] + \bar{d}_7 \rho_2 \left[\theta_2 + \frac{S_2}{\rho_2} (1 - \theta_2 \tan u_4) \right], \qquad (9\text{-}17)$$

$$\frac{\bar{b}_{10}}{\rho_1} = \frac{\bar{b}_7}{\rho_1} \left[1 - \frac{S_2}{\rho_2} \tan u_4 \right] + \bar{e}_7 \frac{\rho_2}{\rho_1} \left[\theta_2 + \frac{S_2}{\rho_2} (1 - \theta_2 \tan u_4) \right]. \qquad (9\text{-}18)$$

Second Exit

Set $S_2 = 0$ in Eqs. (9-17) and (9-18), obtaining $\bar{a}_9$ and $\bar{b}_9/\rho_1$. Use these in Eq. (9-9).

Second Axial Image

Set $S_2 = S_{iz2}$ (the second magnet's axial image distance) in Eqs. (9-17) and (9-18), thus finding $\bar{a}_{12}$ and $\bar{b}_{12}/\rho_1$. Use in Eq. (9-9).

Axial Height at Any Distance S_2 beyond the Second Magnet

Set S_2 equal to this distance in Eqs. (9-17) and (9-18) and apply the results in Eq. (9-9).

UNIFORM FIELDS—RADIAL ENVELOPES

$n_1 = n_2 = 0$, u_1, u_2, u_3, u_4 are arbitrary.

First Entry

$$a_2 = 1, \qquad (9\text{-}19)$$

$$\frac{b_2}{\rho_1} = \frac{S_0}{\rho_1}, \qquad (9\text{-}20)$$

$$c_2 = 0, \qquad (9\text{-}21)$$

Use Eqs. (9-19)–(9-21) in Eq. (9-10).

First Radial Bust

Find numerical values of the following:

$$N_{\alpha 3} = 1 + 2 \frac{S_0}{\rho_1} \tan u_1 + \left[\left(\frac{S_0}{\rho_1} \right)^2 + N_2 \right] \tan^2 u_1, \qquad (9\text{-}22)$$

$$N_{\beta 3} = \frac{S_0}{\rho_1} + \left[\left(\frac{S_0}{\rho_1} \right)^2 + N_2 \right] \tan u_1, \qquad (9\text{-}23)$$

$$N_{\gamma 3} = \left(\frac{S_0}{\rho_1} \right)^2 + N_2. \qquad (9\text{-}24)$$

Now $\phi_1' = \theta_1/2$ provided $M_{x1} = -1$ and $u_1 = u_2 = 0$. If these conditions are not met, determine the value of

$$\cot \phi_1' - \tan \phi_1' = (N_{\alpha3} - N_{\gamma3})/(-N_{\beta3}) \tag{9-25}$$

and then find ϕ_1' from the curve of Fig. 7-11. Then determine

$$N_{\gamma4}' = N_{\alpha3} \sin^2 \phi_1' + 2N_{\beta3} \sin \phi_1' \cos \phi_1' + N_{\gamma3} \cos^2 \phi_1', \tag{9-26}$$

$$\frac{c_4'}{\rho_1} = 1 - \cos \phi_1'. \tag{9-27}$$

The half-width of the bust is given by

$$x_{\text{bust}} = N_{\gamma4}'^{1/2} N_1 + \frac{c_4'}{\rho_1} N_3. \tag{9-28}$$

Now leaving S_1/ρ_1 in symbolic form, find numerical values for

$$a_7 = (\cos \theta_1 + \sin \theta_1 \tan u_1)$$

$$- \frac{S_1}{\rho_1} [\sin \theta_1 - (\tan u_1 + \tan u_2)\cos \theta_1 - \tan u_1 \tan u_2 \sin \theta_1], \tag{9-29}$$

$$\frac{b_7}{\rho_1} = \frac{S_0}{\rho_1} (\cos \theta_1 + \sin \theta_1 \tan u_1) + \frac{S_1}{\rho_1} (\cos \theta_1 + \sin \theta_1 \tan u_2) + \sin \theta_1$$

$$- \frac{S_0 S_1}{\rho_1 \rho_1} [\sin \theta_1 - (\tan u_1 + \tan u_2)\cos \theta_1 - \tan u_1 \tan u_2 \sin \theta_1],$$

$$\tag{9-30}$$

$$\frac{c_7}{\rho_1} = 1 - \cos \theta_1 + \frac{S_1}{\rho_1} [\tan u_2(1 - \cos \theta_1) + \sin \theta_1]. \tag{9-31}$$

First Exit

In Eqs. (9-29)–(9-31) set $S_1 = 0$, thus finding a_5, b_5/ρ_1, and c_5/ρ_1. Use these in Eq. (9-10).

First Radial Image

In Eqs. (9-29)–(9-31), set $S_1 = S_{ix1}$, the first magnet's radial image distance, to obtain a_{i1}, b_{i1}/ρ_1, and c_{i1}/ρ_1. Use in Eq. (9-10).

Second Entry

In Eqs. (9-29)–(9-31), set S_1 equal to the separation between the magnets, thus finding a_7, b_7/ρ_1, and c_7/ρ_1. Use these in Eq. (9-10).

Now using these values of a_7, b_7/ρ_1, and c_7/ρ_1 just determined, find numerical values for the following:

$$d_7 \rho_2 = a_7 \tan u_3 - \frac{\rho_2}{\rho_1}[\sin \theta_1 - (\tan u_1 + \tan u_2)\cos \theta_1$$

$$- \tan u_1 \tan u_2 \sin \theta_1], \qquad (9\text{-}32)$$

$$e_7 = \frac{b_7}{\rho_1}\frac{\rho_1}{\rho_2} \tan u_3 - \frac{S_0}{\rho_1}[\sin \theta_1 - (\tan u_1 + \tan u_2)\cos \theta_1$$

$$- \tan u_1 \tan u_2 \sin \theta_1] + \tan u_2 \sin \theta_1 + \cos \theta_1, \qquad (9\text{-}33)$$

$$f_7 = \frac{c_7}{\rho_1}\frac{\rho_1}{\rho_2} \tan u_3 + \tan u_2(1 - \cos \theta_1) + \sin \theta_1. \qquad (9\text{-}34)$$

Using these and keeping S_2/ρ_2 in symbols, evaluate:

$$a_{10} = a_7\left[\cos \theta_2 + \frac{S_2}{\rho_2}(\tan u_4 \cos \theta_2 - \sin \theta_2)\right]$$

$$+ d_7 \rho_2\left[\sin \theta_2 + \frac{S_2}{\rho_2}(\tan u_4 \sin \theta_2 + \cos \theta_2)\right], \qquad (9\text{-}35)$$

$$\frac{b_{10}}{\rho_1} = \frac{b_7}{\rho_1}\left[\cos \theta_2 + \frac{S_2}{\rho_2}(\tan u_4 \cos \theta_2 - \sin \theta_2)\right]$$

$$+ e_7\frac{\rho_2}{\rho_1}\left[\sin \theta_2 + \frac{S_2}{\rho_2}(\tan u_4 \sin \theta_2 + \cos \theta_2)\right], \qquad (9\text{-}36)$$

$$\frac{c_{10}}{\rho_1} = \frac{c_7}{\rho_1}\left[\cos \theta_2 + \frac{S_2}{\rho_2}(\tan u_4 \cos \theta_2 - \sin \theta_2)\right]$$

$$+ \frac{\rho_2}{\rho_1}f_7\left[\sin \theta_2 + \frac{S_2}{\rho_2}(\tan u_4 \sin \theta_2 + \cos \theta_2)\right]$$

$$\pm \frac{\rho_2}{\rho_1}\frac{S_2}{\rho_2}[\tan u_4(1 - \cos \theta_2) + \sin \theta_2] \pm \frac{\rho_2}{\rho_1}(1 - \cos \theta_2). \quad (9\text{-}37)$$

Use the upper (lower) signs if the magnets bend in the same (opposite) direction. If $c_{10}/\rho_1 < 0$, use $|c_{10}/\rho_1|$. (See the end of this chapter for the justification.)

Second Radial Bust

Using the values of a_7, b_7/ρ_1, $d_7\rho_2$, and e_7 found when S_1 equals the separation of the magnets, determine the values of:

$$N_{\alpha 7} = e_7{}^2 + \left[(d_7 \rho_2) \frac{\rho_1}{\rho_2} \right]^2 N_2, \qquad (9\text{-}38)$$

$$N_{\beta 7} = \frac{b_7}{\rho_1} e_7 + a_7 (d_7 \rho_2) \frac{\rho_1}{\rho_2} N_2, \qquad (9\text{-}39)$$

$$N_{\gamma 7} = \left(\frac{b_7}{\rho_1} \right)^2 + a_7{}^2 N_2. \qquad (9\text{-}40)$$

Now $\phi_2' = \theta_2/2$ if $M_{x2} = -1$ and if $u_3 = u_4 = 0$. If not, find

$$\cot \phi_2' - \tan \phi_2' = (N_{\alpha 7} - N_{\gamma 7})/(-N_{\beta 7}) \qquad (9\text{-}41)$$

and determine ϕ_2' from the chart of Fig. 7-11, reading ϕ_2' for ϕ'. Then compute

$$N_{\gamma 8}' = N_{\alpha 7} \sin^2 \phi_2' + 2 N_{\beta 7} \sin \phi_2' \cos \phi_2' + N_{\gamma 7} \cos^2 \phi_2', \qquad (9\text{-}42)$$

$$\frac{c_8'}{\rho_1} = \frac{c_7}{\rho_1} \cos \phi_2' + \frac{\rho_2}{\rho_1} f_7 \sin \phi_2' \pm \frac{\rho_2}{\rho_1} (1 - \cos \phi_2'). \qquad (9\text{-}43)$$

Use the upper (lower) sign if the magnets bend in the same (opposite) direction. Use $|c_8'/\rho_1|$ if $c_8'/\rho_1 < 0$.

The half-width of the bust is

$$x_{\text{bust}} = N_{\gamma 8}'^{1/2} N_1 + \frac{c_8'}{\rho_1} N_3. \qquad (9\text{-}44)$$

Second Exit

In Eqs. (9-35)–(9-37), set $S_2 = 0$ to obtain a_9, b_9/ρ_1, and c_9/ρ_1. Use these in Eq. (9-10).

Second Radial Image

In Eqs. (9-35)–(9-37), set $S_2 = S_{ix2}$, the second magnet's radial image distance, thus finding a_{i2}, b_{i2}/ρ_1, and c_{i2}/ρ_1. Use in Eq. (9-10).

Radial Width at Any Distance past Second Magnet

In Eqs. (9-35)–(9-37), set S_2 equal to this distance. Use the results in Eq. (9-10).

NONUNIFORM FIELDS—AXIAL ENVELOPES

$1 > n_1 > 0$, $1 > n_2 > 0$, $u_1 = u_2 = u_3 = u_4 = 0$.

First Entry

$$\bar{a}_2 = 1, \tag{9-45}$$

$$\frac{\bar{b}_2}{\rho_1} = \frac{S_0}{\rho_1}. \tag{9-46}$$

Use these in Eq. (9-9).

First Bust

$$\bar{N}_{\alpha 3} = 1, \tag{9-47}$$

$$\bar{N}_{\beta 3} = \frac{S_0}{\rho_1}, \tag{9-48}$$

$$\bar{N}_{\gamma 3} = \left(\frac{S_0}{\rho_1}\right)^2 + \bar{N}_2. \tag{9-49}$$

$\psi_1' = \psi_1/2$ if $M_z = -1$ and if $\bar{N}_2 \approx 0$. If not, find

$$\cot \psi_1' - \tan \psi_1' = \frac{(\bar{N}_{\alpha 3}/\varepsilon_1) - \bar{N}_{\gamma 3}\,\varepsilon_1}{-\bar{N}_{\beta 3}} \tag{9-50}$$

and determine ψ_1' from Fig. 7-11. Then find

$$\bar{N}'_{\gamma 4} = \bar{N}_{\alpha 3}\frac{\sin^2 \psi_1'}{\varepsilon_1^2} + 2\bar{N}_{\beta 3}\frac{\sin \psi_1'}{\varepsilon_1}\cos \psi_1' + \bar{N}_{\gamma 3}\cos^2 \psi_1'. \tag{9-51}$$

The half-height of the bust is

$$z_{\text{bust}} = \bar{N}'^{1/2}_{\gamma 4}\bar{N}_1. \tag{9-52}$$

Leaving S_1/ρ_1 in symbolic form, find numerical values for

$$\bar{a}_7 = \cos \psi_1 - \frac{S_1\varepsilon_1}{\rho_1}\sin \psi_1, \tag{9-53}$$

$$\frac{\bar{b}_7}{\rho_1} = \frac{\sin \psi_1}{\varepsilon_1} + \frac{S_0}{\rho_1}\cos \psi_1 + \frac{S_1}{\rho_1}\cos \psi_1 - \frac{S_0 S_1}{\rho_1\rho_1}\varepsilon_1 \sin \psi_1. \tag{9-54}$$

First Exit. In Eqs. (9-53) and (9-54), set $S_1 = 0$, thus finding $\bar{a}_5$ and $\bar{b}_5/\rho_1$. Use these in Eq. (9-9).

First Axial Image. In Eqs. (9-53) and (9-54), set $S_1 = S_{iz1}$, the first magnet's axial image distance, to obtain $\bar{a}_{11}$ and $\bar{b}_{11}/\rho_1$. Use in Eq. (9-9).

Second Entry

In Eqs. (9-53) and (9-54), set S_1 equal to the separation between magnets. This gives $\bar{a}_7$ and $\bar{b}_7/\rho_1$. Use Eq. (9-9).
Now determine

$$\bar{d}_7 \rho_2 = -\frac{\rho_2}{\rho_1} \varepsilon_1 \sin \psi_1, \tag{9-55}$$

$$\bar{e}_7 = -\frac{S_0}{\rho_1} \varepsilon_1 \sin \psi_1 + \cos \psi_1. \tag{9-56}$$

Using these and $\bar{a}_7$ and $\bar{b}_7/\rho_1$ (found above, with S_1 as the separation), and keeping S_2/ρ_2 as symbols, evaluate the following:

$$\bar{a}_{10} = \bar{a}_7\left(\cos \psi_2 - \frac{S_2}{\rho_2} \varepsilon_2 \sin \psi_2\right) + \bar{d}_7 \rho_2\left(\frac{\sin \psi_2}{\varepsilon_2} + \frac{S_2}{\rho_2} \cos \psi_2\right), \tag{9-57}$$

$$\frac{\bar{b}_{10}}{\rho_1} = \frac{\bar{b}_7}{\rho_1}\left(\cos \psi_2 - \frac{S_2}{\rho_2} \varepsilon_2 \sin \psi_2\right) + \bar{e}_7 \frac{\rho_2}{\rho_1}\left(\frac{\sin \psi_2}{\varepsilon_2} + \frac{S_2}{\rho_2} \cos \psi_2\right). \tag{9-58}$$

Second Axial Bust

Using the values of $\bar{a}_7$ and $\bar{b}_7/\rho_1$ as found when S_1 is the separation, and $\bar{d}_7 \rho_2$ and $\bar{e}_7$ as given by Eqs. (9-55) and (9-56) evaluate:

$$\bar{N}_{\alpha 7} = \bar{e}_7{}^2 + \left[(\bar{d}_7 \rho_2)\frac{\rho_1}{\rho_2}\right]^2 \bar{N}_2, \tag{9-59}$$

$$\bar{N}_{\beta 7} = \frac{\bar{b}_7}{\rho_1} \bar{e}_7 + (\bar{d}_7 \rho_2)\frac{\rho_1}{\rho_2} \bar{N}_2, \tag{9-60}$$

$$\bar{N}_{\gamma 7} = \left(\frac{\bar{b}_7}{\rho_1}\right)^2 + \bar{a}_7{}^2 \bar{N}_2. \tag{9-61}$$

Now $\psi_2' = \psi_2/2$ if $M_{z2} = -1$ and if $\bar{N}_2 \approx 0$. If not, find

$$\cot \psi_2' - \tan \psi_2' = \frac{(\bar{N}_{\alpha 7}/\varepsilon_2) - \bar{N}_{\gamma 7} \varepsilon_2}{-\bar{N}_{\beta 7}} \tag{9-62}$$

and determine ψ_2' from Fig. 7-11, reading ψ_2' for ϕ'. Then find

$$\bar{N}'_{\gamma 8} = \bar{N}_{\alpha 7} \frac{\sin^2 \psi_2'}{\varepsilon_2{}^2} + 2\bar{N}_{\beta 7} \frac{\sin \psi_2'}{\varepsilon_2} \cos \psi_2' + \bar{N}_{\gamma 7} \cos^2 \psi_2'. \tag{9-63}$$

The half-height of the bust is

$$z_{\text{bust}} = \bar{N}'^{1/2}_{\gamma 8} \bar{N}_1. \tag{9-64}$$

Second Exit

In Eqs. (9-57) and (9-58) set $S_2 = 0$ to obtain $\bar{a}_9$ and $\bar{b}_9/\rho_1$. Use Eq. (9-9).

Second Axial Image

In Eqs. (9-57) and (9-58) set $S_2 = S_{iz2}$ the second magnet's axial image distance, finding $\bar{a}_{i2}$ and $\bar{b}_{i2}/\rho_1$. Use in Eq. (9-9).

Axial Height at Any Distance past Second Magnet

In Eqs. (9-57) and (9-58), set S_2 equal to this distance, then use Eq. (9-9).

NONUNIFORM FIELDS—RADIAL ENVELOPES

$1 > n_1 > 0, 1 > n_2 > 0, u_1 = u_2 = u_3 = u_4 = 0.$

First Entry

$$a_2 = 1, \tag{9-65}$$

$$\frac{b_2}{\rho_1} = \frac{S_0}{\rho_1}. \tag{9-66}$$

Use these in Eq. (9-10).

First Bust

$$N_{\alpha 3} = 1, \tag{9-67}$$

$$N_{\beta 3} = S_0/\rho_1, \tag{9-68}$$

$$N_{\gamma 3} = (S_0/\rho_1)^2 + N_2. \tag{9-69}$$

Now $\phi_1' = \phi_1/2$ if $M_{x1} = -1$ and if $N_2 \approx 0$. If not, determine

$$\cot \phi_1' - \tan \phi_1' = \frac{(N_{\alpha 3}/\delta_1) - N_{\gamma 3}\delta_1}{-N_{\beta 3}} \tag{9-70}$$

and find ϕ_1' from Fig. 7-11. Then evaluate:

$$N_{\gamma 4}' = N_{\alpha 3}\frac{\sin^2 \phi_1'}{\delta_1^2} + 2N_{\beta 3}\frac{\sin \phi_1'}{\delta_1}\cos \phi_1' + N_{\gamma 3}\cos^2 \phi_1', \tag{9-71}$$

$$\frac{c_4'}{\rho_1} = (1 - \cos \phi_1')/\delta_1^2. \tag{9-72}$$

The half-width of the bust is

$$x_{\text{bust}} = N_{y4}'^{1/2} N_1 + \frac{c_4'}{\rho_1} N_3.$$ (9-73)

Leaving S_1/ρ_1 in symbolic form, find the values of:

$$a_7 = -\frac{S_1}{\rho_1}\delta_1 \sin \phi_1 + \cos \phi_1,$$ (9-74)

$$\frac{b_7}{\rho_1} = \frac{S_0}{\rho_1}\cos \phi_1 + \frac{S_1}{\rho_1}\cos \phi_1 - \frac{S_0}{\rho_1}\frac{S_1}{\rho_1}\delta_1 \sin \phi_1 + \frac{\sin \phi_1}{\delta_1},$$ (9-75)

$$\frac{c_7}{\rho_1} = \frac{1 - \cos \phi_1}{\delta_1{}^2} + \frac{S_1}{\rho_1}\frac{\sin \phi_1}{\delta_1}.$$ (9-76)

First Exit

In Eqs. (9-74)–(9-76), set $S_1 = 0$, finding a_5, b_5/ρ_1, and c_5/ρ_1. Use Eq. (9-10).

First Radial Image

In Eqs. (9-74)–(9-76), set $S_1 = S_{ix1}$, the first magnet's radial image distance, obtaining a_{i1}, b_{i1}/ρ_1, and c_{i1}/ρ_1. Use Eq. (9-10).

Second Entry

In Eqs. (9-74)–(9-76), set S_1 equal to the separation between the magnets. This gives a_7, b_7/ρ_1, and c_7/ρ_1. Use in Eq. (9-10).

Now evaluate:

$$d_7\rho_2 = -\frac{\rho_2}{\rho_1}\delta_1 \sin \phi_1,$$ (9-77)

$$e_7 = -\frac{S_0}{\rho_1}\delta_1 \sin \phi_1 + \cos \phi_1,$$ (9-78)

$$f_7 = \frac{\sin \phi_1}{\delta_1}.$$ (9-79)

Using these values and keeping S_2/ρ_2 as symbols, evaluate the following:

$$a_{10} = a_7\left[\cos \phi_2 - \frac{S_2}{\rho_2}\delta_2 \sin \phi_2\right] + d_7\rho_2\left[\frac{\sin \phi_2}{\delta_2} + \frac{S_2}{\rho_2}\cos \phi_2\right],$$ (9-80)

$$\frac{b_{10}}{\rho_1} = \frac{b_7}{\rho_1}\left[\cos \phi_2 - \frac{S_2}{\rho_2}\delta_2 \sin \phi_2\right] + e_7\frac{\rho_2}{\rho_1}\left[\frac{\sin \phi_2}{\delta_2} + \frac{S_2}{\rho_2}\cos \phi_2\right],$$ (9-81)

$$\frac{c_{10}}{\rho_1} = \frac{c_7}{\rho_1}\left[\cos\phi_2 - \frac{S_2}{\rho_2}\delta_2\sin\phi_2\right] + f_7\frac{\rho_2}{\rho_1}\left[\frac{\sin\phi_2}{\delta_2} + \frac{S_2}{\rho_2}\cos\phi_2\right]$$

$$\pm\frac{S_2\rho_2}{\rho_2\rho_1}\frac{\sin\phi_2}{\delta_2} \pm \frac{\rho_2}{\rho_1}\frac{(1-\cos\phi_2)}{\delta_2^{\ 2}}. \tag{9-82}$$

Use the upper (lower) sign if the magnets bend in the same (opposite) directions. Use $|c_{10}/\rho_1|$ if $c_{10}/\rho_1 < 0$.

Second Bust

$$N_{\alpha7} = e_7^{\ 2} + \left[(d_7\rho_2)\frac{\rho_1}{\rho_2}\right]^2 N_2, \tag{9-83}$$

$$N_{\beta7} = \frac{b_7}{\rho_1}e_7 + a_7(d_7\rho_2)\frac{\rho_1}{\rho_2}N_2, \tag{9-84}$$

$$N_{\gamma7} = \left(\frac{b_7}{\rho_1}\right)^2 + a_7^{\ 2}N_2. \tag{9-85}$$

Now $\phi_2' = \phi_2/2$ if $M_{x2} = -1$ and if $N_2 \approx 0$. If not, determine

$$\cot\phi_2' - \tan\phi_2' = \frac{(N_{\alpha7}/\delta_1) - N_{\gamma7}\delta_1}{-N_{\beta7}} \tag{9-86}$$

and find ϕ_2' from Fig. 7-11, reading ϕ_2' for ϕ_1. Then evaluate:

$$N'_{\gamma8} = N_{\alpha7}\frac{\sin^2\phi_2'}{\delta_2^{\ 2}} + 2N_{\beta7}\frac{\sin\phi_2'}{\delta_2}\cos\phi_2' + N_{\gamma7}\cos^2\phi_2', \tag{9-87}$$

$$\frac{c_8'}{\rho_1} = \frac{c_7}{\rho_1}\cos\phi_2' + \frac{\rho_2}{\rho_1}f_7\frac{\sin\phi_2'}{\delta_2} \pm \frac{\rho_2}{\rho_1}\frac{(1-\cos\phi_2')}{\delta_2^{\ 2}}. \tag{9-88}$$

The half-width of the bust is

$$x_{\text{bust}} = N'^{1/2}_{\gamma8}N_1 + \frac{c_8'}{\rho_1}N_3. \tag{9-89}$$

Second Exit

In Eqs. (9-80)–(9-82), set $S_2 = 0$ to get a_9, b_9/ρ_1, and c_9/ρ_1.

Second Radial Image

In Eqs. (9-80)–(9-82), set $S_2 = S_{ix2}$, the second magnet's radial image distance, thus finding a_{i2}, b_{i2}/ρ_1, and c_{i2}/ρ_1. Use in Eq. (9-10).

Radial Width at Any Distance past the Second Magnet

Let S_2 equal this distance, in Eqs. (9-80)–(9-82). Use Eq. (9-10).

The argument, promised earlier, for using the absolute value of c_{10} in Eqs. (9-37) and (9-82) (to be employed in finding the total width of the $p - \Delta p$, p, and $p + \Delta p$ images) when c_{10} is negative, is best given with the aid of Fig. 9-2. The overall radial magnification M of the two magnets, the half-

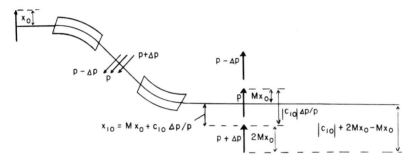

FIG. 9-2.

width x_0 of the object, and $\Delta p/p$ are all positive, but c_{10} is sufficiently negative so that the tip of the $p + \Delta p$ image has a negative displacement given by $x_{10} = Mx_0 + c_{10} \Delta p/p$. The distance from the p image's tip to the $p + \Delta p$ image's tail is $(|c_{10}| \Delta p/p) + 2Mx_0$. The half-width of the entire pattern (from the axis to the tail of the $p + \Delta p$ image) is obtained by subtracting Mx_0, as indicated. Hence

$$\text{Half-width} = Mx_0 + |c_{10}| \Delta p/p. \qquad (9\text{-}90)$$

10 Achromatic Systems— General Considerations

INTRODUCTION

There are occasions when a beam of ions with a spread in energy must be sent through one or more bending magnets because of some necessary change in direction, yet it is desirable to do this without dispersion. This need can arise when the image should be of maximum intensity, rather than of homogeneity of energy. In some cases it may be required that the particles be sent further downstream beyond the image, and this is best done if they spread the least in width.'

An examination of the fundamental first order matrix for transport through a magnet, Eq.(2-11), makes it evident that a radius of curvature has been assigned only to the particles of standard momentum p; ions of greater and less momentum are assumed to follow sinusoidal paths about the central p orbit. On this basis, the expression for the lateral deviation from the central path was found to contain the dispersive term $c\,\Delta p/p$, where c is a matrix element at the distance in question, most significantly the image distance. Similarly, the expression for the path slope with respect to the central ray contained the dispersive term $f\,\Delta p/p$, where f is another matrix element.

To the extent that this procedure gives an acceptable approximation to the truth, we may then say that the lateral displacement and the slope will be achromatic (i.e., independent of momentum) if the coefficients c and f can be made to vanish. This is the basis of first order achromatism.

A more detailed study of the true state of affairs reveals some limitations, at least qualitatively. When, for example, we set $c = 0$, we obtain an expression for the required object distance, and this turns out to be a function of the radius of curvature ρ; by the implication of the theory, this is associated with the ion of standard momentum p. Now if the band of momenta is so wide that the $p + \Delta p$ ion has a radius $\rho + \Delta\rho$ so greatly different from ρ that the assumption of a sinusoidal path about the trajectory of the p orbit is no longer valid, then we should recalculate the orbit, with $p + \Delta p$ replaced by a new "central" value p' and with $\rho + \Delta\rho$ replaced by a new value ρ'. Consequently if the object distance has been chosen to bring achromatism to the ρ orbit, it will not be correct for the ρ' orbit.

We thus recognize that achromatism cannot be attained for an arbitrarily wide band of momenta. It can exist only for a band as wide as that for which the matrix equations adequately express the dispersion in a nonachromatic system. Since there is no abrupt threshold, there is no criterion as to how wide is too wide, except in very gross terms; a slow enough ion may not even traverse the magnet.

A similar difficulty arises in the mirror-symmetric systems to be discussed later, wherein an array of magnets and drift spaces embodies a plane of symmetry half way through. The arguments on achromatism will be seen to hinge on the postulated existence of intermediate, dispersed, radial images lying entirely in this plane. Such a concept, of course, is an approximation, valid only over the range of momenta for which the image distances may be assumed to be approximately constant. (An expression for the change of image distance with $\Delta p/p$ will be found in Chapter 17.)

Some apparent exceptions to these remarks will be presented in Chapter 14, but they involve the approximations that the input beam is infinitely narrow, or if of finite width, that the paths are rigorously parallel.

Keeping in mind these limitations (which all too seldom are adequately stressed in the literature), we may now proceed with the argument.

Consider a system wherein we designate the station number at some distance S beyond the final magnet as $j = s$. By Eqs. (7-78) and (7-80), the radial envelope's half-width at S is

$$x_{s\,\text{max}} = \gamma_s^{1/2}x_0\,x_0' + c_s\,\Delta p/p \tag{10-1}$$

and its radial maximum slope is

$$x'_{s\,\text{max}} = \alpha_s^{1/2}x_0\,x_0' + f_s\,\Delta p/p. \tag{10-2}$$

These expressions may also be written as

$$x_{s\,\text{max}} = (\gamma_{s-1} - 2\beta_{s-1}S + \alpha_{s-1}S^2)^{1/2}x_0\,x_0' + c_s\,\Delta p/p, \tag{10-3}$$

$$x'_{s\,\text{max}} = (\alpha_{s-1})^{1/2}x_0\,x_0' + f_s\,\Delta p/p. \tag{10-4}$$

(With one magnet, $j = s = 6$ as shown by Eqs. (7-42) and (7-40); for two, $j = s = 10$; for three, $j = s = 14$.)

We note first that there is an *inevitable* widening of the beam as S increases beyond the waist, even if $\Delta p = 0$, for it will be recalled that β changes sign from plus to minus as the waist in the image space is approached and passed. Furthermore, there is an *additional* widening if Δp and c_s and f_s are all finite.

Doubly Achromatic Systems

If $c_s = 0$ and $f_s = 0$, then both $x_{s\,max}$ and $x'_{s\,max}$ are independent of Δp, for all values of S. If also $S = S_{ix}$, then $c_s = c_i = 0$ and $f_s = f_i = 0$, so that the image and the slope in the image space do not depend on the momentum. This condition we call "doubly achromatic."

The radial phase-space ellipse patterns at the image and beyond are then somewhat as sketched in Fig. 10-1. The ellipses of all momenta are coincident.

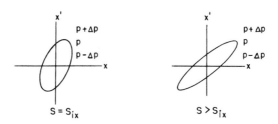

FIG. 10-1. Doubly achromatic ellipse patterns.

Such a doubly achromatic system is the ideal one, since there is no lateral separation of particles of different energy and the radial envelope is as narrow as it can be, at the image and beyond it. We will see later that this situation can be attained with three magnets or with two magnets and one quadrupole.

Singly Achromatic Systems

Somewhat more restricted systems are those in which only the image is nondispersed (i.e., achromatic), but further along the ions of different momenta become separated because the slope is dependent on the momentum and hence the envelope width is also. We see from Chapter 6 that for one, two, or three magnets, we have

$$c_6 = c_5 + S_1 f_5 \qquad \text{and} \qquad f_6 = f_5,$$

$$c_{10} = c_9 + S_2 f_9 \qquad \text{and} \qquad f_{10} = f_9,$$

$$c_{14} = c_{13} + S_3 f_{13} \qquad \text{and} \qquad f_{14} = f_{13}.$$

Hence in general

$$c_s = c_{s-1} + S f_{s-1} \qquad \text{and} \qquad f_s = f_{s-1}, \tag{10-5}$$

where the station $s - 1$ is just outside the final magnet, while station s is at distance S beyond it.

In some systems, it is not possible to make both $c_s = 0$ and $f_s = 0$, as would be required for double achromatism, since both c_{s-1} and f_{s-1} are finite. Nevertheless there is a distance S given by

$$S = -\frac{c_{s-1}}{f_{s-1}} \qquad (10\text{-}6)$$

at which there is no dispersion, since then we have

$$c_s = c_{s-1} - \left(\frac{c_{s-1}}{f_{s-1}}\right) f_{s-1} = 0. \qquad (10\text{-}7)$$

If this particular value of S corresponds to the image distance S_{ix}, then the image is achromatic. But since $f_{s-1} = f_s = f_i$ is finite, the radial slope in the image space does depend on the momentum. The phase-space ellipses at the image and beyond behave as indicated in Fig. 10-2. At the image, the beam

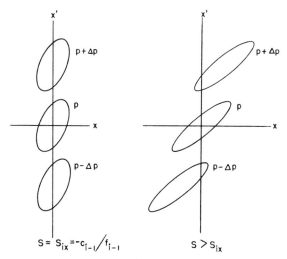

FIG. 10-2. Singly achromatic ellipse patterns.

width is the least and is achromatic, but further downstream the width increases with momentum and with distance. This is of no concern if the ions are used at the image; it is undesirable but not necessarily intolerable if they must be transported further, since beam pipes and quadrupoles must then have larger apertures.

It will be shown that this condition can be obtained with two magnets (bending either in the same or in opposite directions), or with one magnet that bends in excess of 180°, or with one magnet plus two quadrupoles.

Many of the "achromatic" systems described in the literature are of this achromatic-image-only type.

11 Doubly Achromatic Systems

Mirror Symmetry

It has been seen that double achromatism (beam width and slope independent of momentum in the final image space) will exist if $c_s = 0$ and $f_s = 0$ at a distance S beyond the last magnet. To determine the conditions under which this may be true involves a fair amount of algebraic manipulation in a two-magnet system, and a discouragingly large amount with three magnets.

A much quicker approach will now be described,* although it is applicable *only* if the system has mirror symmetry about its midpoint. This means that the ions travel through "optic elements" $e_1, e_2, \ldots, e_n$ in the first half of their journey and then through $e_n, \ldots, e_2, e_1$ in the second half, the net bends in each half being equal and in the same direction. The plane of symmetry is perpendicular to the central orbit of momentum p.

Consider the radial displacement and slope in the first half (Fig. 11-1). The path starts at x_1 and x_1' and ends at x_n and x_n'. If M is the transport matrix through this half, we have

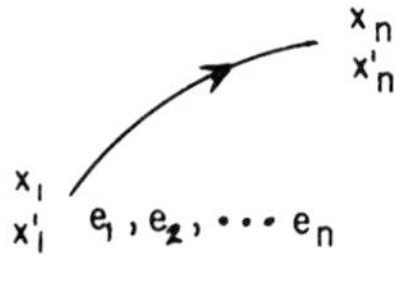

$$\binom{x_n}{x_n'} = M \binom{x_1}{x_1'}. \tag{11-1}$$

Fig. 11-1. Path in first half

Now imagine that the ions travel backwards from point n to point 1, with the magnetic fields reversed. The optic elements are traversed in the order $e_n, \ldots, e_2, e_1$ and the path is exactly the same, except that the slopes are

---

* 33, Penner; 223, Turner; 219, Turner.

reversed, since they are measured with respect to the direction of motion. (See Fig. 11-2.) Let the matrix be M_B, so that we have

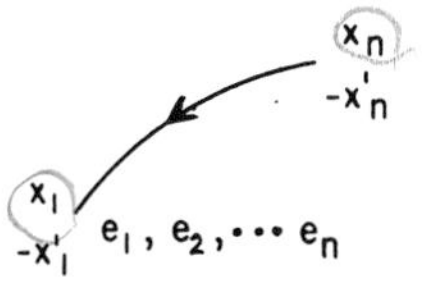

$$\begin{pmatrix} x_1 \\ -x_1' \end{pmatrix} = M_B \begin{pmatrix} x_n \\ -x_n' \end{pmatrix}. \qquad (11\text{-}2)$$

FIG. 11-2. Path in first half, but reversed.

We now reflect this backward path about the plane of symmetry, returning the fields to their original direction. The optic elements are now traveled in the order $e_n, \ldots, e_2, e_1$ (Fig. 11-3). Let the matrix be M_R.

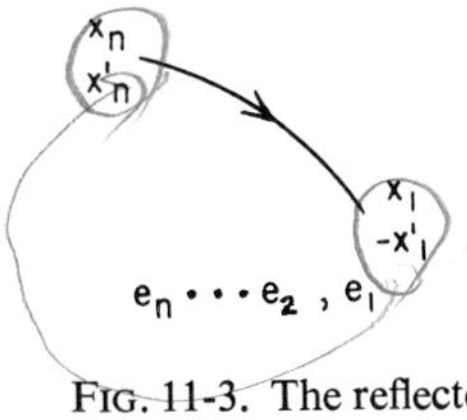

$$\begin{pmatrix} x_1 \\ -x_1' \end{pmatrix} = M_R \begin{pmatrix} x_n \\ -x_n' \end{pmatrix}. \qquad (11\text{-}3)$$

FIG. 11-3. The reflected reversed path.

In both of these last two cases, the initial and final parameters are the same and the ions traverse the same order of optic elements $e_n, \ldots, e_2, e_1$. Therefore

$$M_B = M_R. \qquad (11\text{-}4)$$

Now it is true that

$$\begin{pmatrix} 1 & 0 \\ 0 & -1 \end{pmatrix} \begin{pmatrix} x_1 \\ x_1' \end{pmatrix} = \begin{pmatrix} x_1 \\ -x_1' \end{pmatrix} \quad \text{and} \quad \begin{pmatrix} 1 & 0 \\ 0 & -1 \end{pmatrix} \begin{pmatrix} x_n \\ x_n' \end{pmatrix} = \begin{pmatrix} x_n \\ -x_n' \end{pmatrix},$$

so if for convenience we write

$$A = \begin{pmatrix} 1 & 0 \\ 0 & -1 \end{pmatrix}, \qquad (11\text{-}5)$$

then Eq. (11-3) becomes

$$A \begin{pmatrix} x_1 \\ x_1' \end{pmatrix} = M_R A \begin{pmatrix} x_n \\ x_n' \end{pmatrix}. \qquad (11\text{-}6)$$

In this, substitute Eq. (11-1), obtaining

$$A\begin{pmatrix} x_1 \\ x_1' \end{pmatrix} = M_R \, AM\begin{pmatrix} x_1 \\ x_1' \end{pmatrix}. \tag{11-7}$$

Hence

$$A = M_R \, AM$$

and

$$AM^{-1} = M_R AMM^{-1} = M_R \, A.$$

Then

$$AM^{-1}A = M_R AA = M_R,$$

so finally

$$M_R = \begin{pmatrix} 1 & 0 \\ 0 & -1 \end{pmatrix} M^{-1} \begin{pmatrix} 1 & 0 \\ 0 & -1 \end{pmatrix}. \tag{11-8}$$

This is the "reflected" matrix that transports through the elements $e_n, \ldots,$ $e_2, e_1,$ when M is the matrix that transports through $e_1, e_2, \ldots, e_n$.

The same conclusions hold if M is the 3×3 matrix

$$M = \begin{pmatrix} a & b & c \\ d & e & f \\ 0 & 0 & 1 \end{pmatrix}, \tag{11-9}$$

where $ae - bd = 1$. The inverse matrix is

$$M^{-1} = \begin{pmatrix} e & -b & bf - ce \\ -d & a & cd - af \\ 0 & 0 & 1 \end{pmatrix}. \tag{11-10}$$

This may be verified by multiplying out MM^{-1}, which is found to yield the unit matrix

$$\begin{pmatrix} 1 & 0 & 0 \\ 0 & 1 & 0 \\ 0 & 0 & 1 \end{pmatrix}.$$

We now put Eq. (11-10) into the 3 by 3 analog of Eq. (11-8) and multiply. The result is

$$M_R = \begin{pmatrix} e & b & bf - ce \\ d & a & af - cd \\ 0 & 0 & 1 \end{pmatrix}. \tag{11-11}$$

Therefore the matrix that transports through the entire system $e_1, e_2, \ldots,$ $e_n, e_n, \ldots, e_2, e_1$ is (by use of Eqs. (11-9) and (11-11))

$$M_R M = \begin{pmatrix} A & B & C \\ D & E & F \\ 0 & 0 & 1 \end{pmatrix}, \qquad (11\text{-}12)$$

where

$$
\boxed{
\begin{array}{lll}
A = a^*e^* + b^*d^*, & B = 2e^*b^*, & C = 2b^*f^*, \\
D = 2d^*a^*, & E = a^*e^* + b^*d^*, & F = 2a^*f^*.
\end{array}
}
$$

$$(11\text{-}13)$$

This is the desired result. $A, B, C, \ldots$ are the coefficients of radial displacement at some point distance S beyond the final magnet, and $a^*, b^*, c^*, \ldots$ are the coefficients at the plane of symmetry. (The asterisk has been added as a distinguishing symbol.)

We note, first, that if we make $f^* = 0$, then F vanishes and the slopes of the orbits at the plane of symmetry will be independent of $\Delta p/p$. Hence if we arrange that the central path of standard momentum p crosses this plane perpendicularly, then so also will the central paths of ions of other momenta. Now suppose we cause radial (and dispersed) images to be formed at the symmetry plane (within the limits of those momenta for which the image distances are approximately equal, as noted earlier); then the subsequent pattern of paths through the second half of the system will duplicate that in the first half, just as though each path underwent reflection at a mirror, thus causing a nondispersed final image at the downstream side of the array.

Secondly, we note that if $f^* = 0$, then *both* C and F vanish, so the beam in the final image space will be achromatic both in width and slope, for the reasons given earlier; it will be "doubly achromatic."

It may be remarked that although setting $a^* = 0$ and $b^* = 0$ in Eq. (11-13) would also make both C and F vanish, such a procedure is not allowed, since it would violate the restriction that $a^*e^* - b^*d^* = 1$.

If setting $f^* = 0$ leads to an absurdity (e.g., $\theta = 0$), we conclude that double achromatism is impossible.

We will now give several examples of doubly achromatic systems.

THREE MAGNETS—DOUBLY ACHROMATIC

Case 1 $(+ - +)$

Assume an array of three uniform-field magnets that bend to right, left, and right, the first and third through angle θ_1 and the second through $2\theta_2$

(Fig. 11-4). The net bending angle is

$$\Theta = 2\theta_1 - 2\theta_2. \tag{11-14}$$

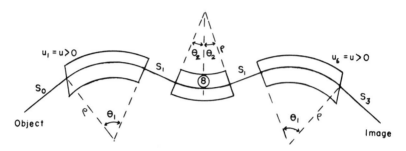

FIG. 11-4. Doubly achromatic array of three magnets.

We do not, as yet, specify the relations between θ_1 and $2\theta_2$. The magnets are separated by S_1 and have bending radii ρ. Axial focusing, when used, is supplied by the first and sixth edges; $u_1 = u_6 = u$, all other edge angles being zero, for simplicity. The optical system is symmetric about the midpoint of the second magnet.

At a distance S_3 beyond the third magnet (at station 14) we have

$$x_{14\,max} = \gamma_{14}^{1/2} x_0 x_0' + c_{14} \Delta p/p, \tag{11-15}$$

$$x'_{14\,max} = \alpha_{14}^{1/2} x_0 x_0' + f_{14} \Delta p/p. \tag{11-16}$$

These can be given as

$$x_{14\,max} = (\gamma_{13} - 2\beta_{13} S_3 + \alpha_{13} S_3^2)^{1/2} x_0 x_0' + (c_{13} + f_{13} S_3) \Delta p/p, \tag{11-17}$$

$$x'_{14\,max} = \alpha_{13}^{1/2} x_0 x_0' + f_{13} \Delta p/p. \tag{11-18}$$

With rising S_3 there is bound to be a widening of the beam, but the width and slope will be independent of momentum if c_{14} and f_{14} both vanish. Since the system is symmetric, these coefficients may be identified with C and F of Eq. (11-13), and both will vanish if f^* at the plane of symmetry is made zero. This plane may be treated as though it lay just inside the exit face of the second magnet of bending angle θ_2 in a two-magnet system in which the first bends through angle θ_1. The symmetry plane is thus at station 8 of two opposed magnets. We set

$$f^* = f_8^{+-} = 0. \tag{11-19}$$

By reference to Eq. (6-42) and applicable earlier expressions (wherein $t_2 = t_3 = 0$), we thence obtain the necessary condition on the separation distance $S_1 = \rho L_1$:

$$L_1 = (\sin \theta_1 \cos \theta_2 + \cos \theta_1 \sin \theta_2 - 2 \sin \theta_2)/(\sin \theta_1 \sin \theta_2), \tag{11-20}$$

which may be rearranged as

$$L_1 = \frac{\sin(\theta_1 + \theta_2) - 2\sin\theta_2}{\sin\theta_1 \sin\theta_2}. \tag{11-21}$$

This is the only requirement needed to guarantee a doubly achromatic beam beyond the third magnet.

In principle, we may now set $b_{14} = 0$, which is the condition for a radial image at distance S_3 beyond the last magnet. In the resulting expression we use the separation distance as determined above and obtain an equation for the object distance as a function of L_1, θ_1, θ_2, and u. In practice this is too tedious, as may be discovered by attempting to write out the expression for b_{14}, even when all u's are zero except u_1 and u_6.

As a simplification, we demand a radial image at the symmetry plane. This requires that

$$b^* = b_8 = 0 \tag{11-22}$$

(which is much simpler to evaluate than would be $b_{14} = 0$). This leads to

$$L_1[L_0 t\kappa_1\kappa_2 - L_0\sigma_1\kappa_2 + \kappa_1\kappa_2] + L_0[\kappa_1\kappa_2 - \sigma_1\sigma_2 + t(\sigma_1\kappa_2 + \kappa_1\sigma_2)]$$
$$+ \sigma_1\kappa_2 + \kappa_1\sigma_2 = 0 \tag{11-23}$$

where $\sigma = \sin\theta$ and $\kappa = \cos\theta$ for short.

The overall symmetry requires the final radial image distance to equal the object distance, so

$$L_{ix3} = L_0. \tag{11-24}$$

Now substitute L_1 given by Eq. (11-20) (from $f_8^{+-} = 0$) into Eq. (11-23) (from $b_8 = 0$) to find that

$$L_0 = L_{ix3} = \frac{1}{(H_2/H_1) - t}, \tag{11-25}$$

where

$$H_1 = \cos\theta_1 \sin 2\theta_2 - \tfrac{1}{2}(\sin 2\theta_1 + \sin 2\theta_2), \tag{11-26}$$

$$H_2 = \sin\theta_1 \sin 2\theta_2 - \sin^2\theta_1. \tag{11-27}$$

To obtain double focusing at the final image, symmetry indicates that we need an axial image at the midpoint of the second magnet. (See Fig. 11-5.) We require

$$L_{iz1} = L_1 + \theta_2. \tag{11-28}$$

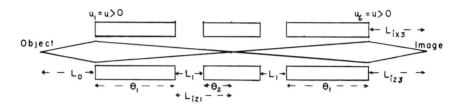

FIG. 11-5. Relations in the doubly achromatic, double focusing system.

But by Eq. (3-6) we have the relation (with $n = t_2 = 0$):

$$L_{iz1} = \frac{L_o(1 - t\theta_1) + \theta_1}{L_o t - 1}.$$ (11-29)

Equating these last two expressions leads to

$$L_o = \frac{1}{t - 1/H_3},$$ (11-30)

where

$$H_3 = L_1 + \theta_1 + \theta_2.$$ (11-31)

Now use Eq. (11-30) (double focus condition) in Eq. (11-25) ($f_8^{+-} = 0$ and $b_8 = 0$ condition) to find that

$$t = \frac{1}{2}\left(\frac{H_2}{H_1} + \frac{1}{H_3}\right).$$ (11-32)

This is the tangent of the edge angles $u = u_1 = u_6$ needed for double focusing of the doubly achromatic image at $L_{ix3} = L_o$ given by Eq. (11-25), provided L_1 is in accord with Eq. (11-21).

We will now apply these expressions to several examples.

Case 1a. $L_o = L_{ix3} = \infty$, all $u = 0$ (no axial focusing).*
With $L_o = \infty$ and $t = 0$, Eq. (11-25) shows that $H_2 = 0$, whence we see from Eq. (11-27) that

$$2\theta_2 = \theta_1;$$

i.e., all magnets bend the same amount, so the net bend is $\Theta = \theta_1$. In Eq. (11-20) for L_1, we divide all terms by σ_2, set $\theta_2 = \theta_1/2$, and use the general relation that $\cot(\theta_1/2) = (1 + \cos \theta_1)/\sin \theta_1$ to find that

$$L_1 = (2 \cos \theta_1 - 1)/\sin \theta_1.$$ (11-33)

* 207, Bruck *et al.*; 33, Penner; 211, Teng; 216, Milman.

This shows that L_1 ranges from infinity to zero as θ_1 rises from zero to 60°. Hence the net bend must be somewhat less than 60°, in order to allow room for the magnets' coils.

Case 1b. $L_o = L_{ix3} > 0$ but finite, all $u = 0$ (no axial focusing). For $t = 0$, Eq. (11-25) shows that

$$L_o = H_1/H_2. \tag{11-34}$$

The magnets' separation is given by Eq. (11-21), here repeated:

$$L_1 = \frac{\sin(\theta_1 + \theta_2) - 2\sin\theta_2}{\sin\theta_1 \sin\theta_2}.$$

Any choice of θ_1 and θ_2, such as will give the desired net bend $\Theta = 2(\theta_1 - \theta_2)$, thus determines $L_o = L_{ix3}$ and L_1. Figures 11-6 and 11-7, showing L_1 and H_1/H_2 as functions of θ_1 and θ_2, will be helpful for orientation. For example, to obtain $\Theta = 60°$, we may try $\theta_1 = 40°$ and $\theta_2 = 10°$ (two 40° magnets and one of 20°). The figures show that $L_1 = 3.75$ and $L_o = L_{ix3} = 2.07$. Alternatively, we could use $\theta_1 = 50°$ and $\theta_2 = 20°$, obtaining $L_1 = 1$ and $L_o = L_{ix3} = 4.2$, etc.

Case 1c. $L_o = L_i > 0$ but finite, $u_1 = u_6 = u > 0$ (double focusing).
Any suitable choice of θ_1 and θ_2 determines L_1, H_1, H_2, and H_3, so that t is fixed and hence L_o is. For example, for $\Theta = 60°$, we take $\theta_1 = 40°$ and $\theta_2 = 10°$. Then by Fig. 11-6 or Eq. (11-21), we find $L_1 = 3.75$; by Fig. 11-7 or Eqs. (11-26) and (11-27), we get $H_1/H_2 = 2.07$; by Fig. 11-8 or Eq. (11-31), we have $H_3 = 4.62$; then by Eq. (11-32), $t = 0.3497$, so $u = 19.27°$, and finally by Eq. (11-30), we have $L_o = L_{ix3} = L_{iz3} = 7.50$.

Case 1d. $L_o = L_i = \infty$, $u_1 = u_6 = u > 0$ (double focusing).*
From Eq. (11-25), $L_o = 1/[(H_2/H_1) - t]$, we now obtain

$$t = H_2/H_1. \tag{11-35}$$

Use this in Eq. (11-32), $t = \frac{1}{2}[(H_2/H_1) + 1/H_3]$, to find that

$$H_3 = H_1/H_2. \tag{11-36}$$

Now H_1 and H_2, given by Eqs. (11-26) and (11-27), involve trigonometric functions of θ_1 and θ_2, while by Eq. (11-31) we have $H_3 = L_1 + \theta_1 + \theta_2$. Hence Eq. (11-36) must be solved by graphical methods, such as by superposing Fig. 11-6 on Fig. 11-7. Since this would result in a cluttered diagram,

* 211, Teng.

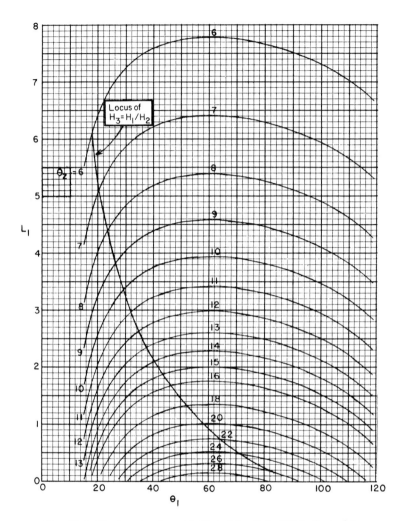

FIG. 11-6. The function $L_1 = [\sin(\theta_1 + \theta_2) - 2\sin\theta]/(\sin\theta_1\sin\theta_2)$.

we have instead drawn a line on each of these figures that indicates the locus where H_3 and H_1/H_2 have the same values.

Thus for $\Theta = 60°$, by Figs. 11-7 and 11-8, we find that $\theta_1 = 45.6°$ and $\theta_2 = 15.6°$ will give $H_3 = H_1/H_2 = 2.83$. Then by Eq. (11-32), we get $t = \frac{1}{2}(1/2.83 + 1/2.83) = 0.3533$ so that $u = 19.45°$. Eq. (11-25) then shows that $L_0 = \infty$, as expected. The separation $L_1 = 1.75$ is found from Eq. (11-21) or Fig. 11-6, where as a convenience a line has been drawn passing through

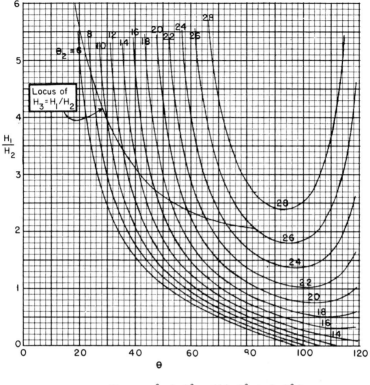

FIG. 11-7. $\dfrac{H_1}{H_2} = \dfrac{\cos \theta_1 \sin 2\theta_2 - \frac{1}{2}(\sin 2\theta_1 + \sin 2\theta_2)}{\sin \theta_1 \sin 2\theta_2 - \sin^2 \theta_1}$.

the values of θ_1 and θ_2 for which $H_3 = H_1/H_2$. Note that $L_1 \approx 0$ when $\theta_1 \approx 90°$ and $\theta_2 \approx 27°$, so that $\Theta_{max} \approx 126°$.

Case 2 $(+ + +)$

Three uniform-field magnets (Fig. 11-9) all bend in the same direction, the first and third through angle θ_1 and the second through $2\theta_2$. The net bend is

$$\Theta = 2\theta_1 + 2\theta_2. \tag{11-37}$$

Axial focusing is given by the first and last edge angles; $u_1 = u_6 = u > 0$. All other edge angles are zero. The magnets' separation is S_1 and all bending radii are ρ. Since the magnets are symmetrical about the midpoint, there will be double achromatism in the final image space if $f^* = 0$ at the plane of

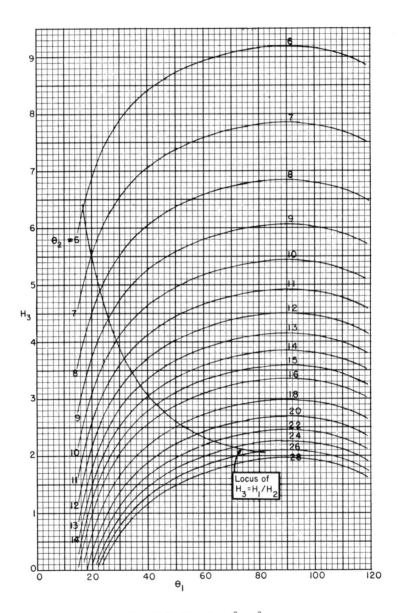

Fɪɢ. 11-8. $H_3 = L_1 + \theta_1 + \theta_2$.

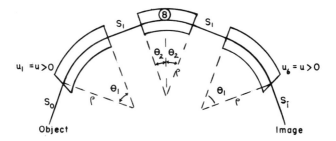

FIG. 11-9. Doubly achromatic array of three magnets.

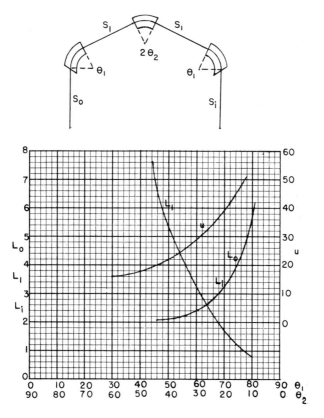

FIG. 11-10. Three magnets, doubly achromatic, doubly focusing.

$$\theta_1 + 2\theta_2 + \theta_1 = 180°.$$

symmetry; this is station 8 of a two magnet array (θ_1 and θ_2) with both magnets bending the same way. We set

$$f^* = f_8^{++} = 0, \tag{11-38}$$

so by Eq. (6-42) we obtain

$$S_1/\rho = L_1 = \cot \theta_1 + \cot \theta_2. \tag{11-39}$$

For simplicity we assume a radial image at the midpoint, so we must have

$$b_8 = 0. \tag{11-40}$$

This gives, as in the previous case (with $\sigma = \sin \theta$ and $\kappa = \cos \theta$),

$$L_1[L_0 t\kappa_1\kappa_2 - L_0\sigma_1\kappa_2 + \kappa_1\kappa_2] + L_0[\kappa_1\kappa_2 - \sigma_1\sigma_2 + t(\sigma_1\kappa_2 + \kappa_1\sigma_2)]$$
$$+ \sigma_1\kappa_2 + \kappa_1\sigma_2 = 0. \tag{11-41}$$

In this we put the value of L_1 found above and obtain

$$L_0 = 1/(H_4 - t), \tag{11-42}$$

where

$$H_4 = \frac{\sin^2 \theta_1}{\sin \theta_1 \cos \theta_1 + \sin \theta_2 \cos \theta_2}. \tag{11-43}$$

To obtain double focusing we proceed as in the previous case by equating $L_{iz} = L_1 + \theta_2$ to $L_{iz} = [L_0(1 - t\theta_1) + \theta_1]/(L_0 t - 1)$, which gives

$$L_0 = L_i = 1/(t - 1/H_3), \tag{11-44}$$

where, as in Eq. (11-31),

$$H_3 = L_1 + \theta_1 + \theta_2. \tag{11-45}$$

Equating Eqs. (11-42) and (11-44) yields

$$t = \tfrac{1}{2}[H_4 + 1/H_3]. \tag{11-46}$$

Because of the cotangent terms in Eq. (11-39), the separation L_1 is very large unless θ_1 and θ_2 are large. Figure 11-10 shows L_1, L_0 ($=L_i$), and u as functions of θ_1 and θ_2 for $\Theta = 180°$, such as might be used between a synchrotron and its injector.

Figure 11-11 exhibits the parameters for $\Theta = 270°$.

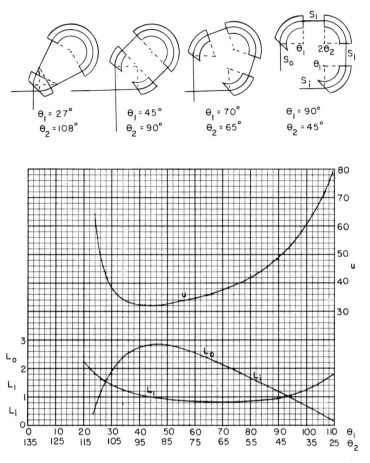

FIG. 11-11. Three magnets, doubly achromatic, doubly focusing.

$$\theta_1 + 2\theta_2 + \theta_1 = 270°.$$

TWO MAGNETS AND ONE QUADRUPOLE—DOUBLY ACHROMATIC

We have seen that an achromatic image and an achromatic slope in the space beyond the last magnet can be produced by three magnets, in either the $(+ - +)$ or the $(+ + +)$ array. This encourages the supposition that such a doubly achromatic system can be attained with a $(+ 0 +)$ arrangement; i.e., a quadrupole (that causes no bending but focuses radially) placed between two magnets bending the same way (see Fig. 11-12).*

* 209, Vladimirsky and Koshkarev; 33, Penner; 220, Randall.

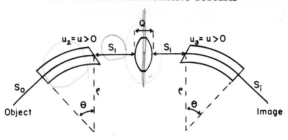

FIG. 11-12. Another doubly achromatic arrangement.

For symmetry, let $\theta_1 = \theta_2$, $n_1 = n_2 = 0$, $u_1 = u_4 = 0$, $u_2 = u_3 = u > 0$, Q = length of quadrupole, and S_1 = distance of quadrupole from either magnet. The plane of symmetry is at the center of the quadrupole, and at this point we have

$$
\begin{pmatrix} x^* \\ x'^* \\ \dfrac{\Delta p}{\rho} \end{pmatrix} = \begin{pmatrix} \cos\tau & \dfrac{\sin\tau}{K} & 0 \\ -K\sin\tau & \cos\tau & 0 \\ 0 & 0 & 1 \end{pmatrix} \begin{pmatrix} a_6 & b_6 & c_6 \\ d_6 & e_6 & f_6 \\ 0 & 0 & 1 \end{pmatrix} \begin{pmatrix} x_1 \\ x_1' \\ \dfrac{\Delta p}{p} \end{pmatrix}. \tag{11-47}
$$

The first matrix on the right can be shown* to be descriptive of a radially focusing quadrupole of length $Q/2$, and in which

$$
\tau = KQ/2 \tag{11-48}
$$

and

$$
K^2 = G/B_0\,\rho_0. \tag{11-49}
$$

Here G is the quadrupole's gradient; $G = dB_x/dz = dB_z/dx$, the path being along y, while $B_0\,\rho_0$ measures the momentum of the ion. Note that K has the dimension 1/length. On carrying out the indicated multiplication, we obtain

$$
\begin{pmatrix} x^* \\ x'^* \\ \dfrac{\Delta p}{p} \end{pmatrix} = \begin{pmatrix} a^* & b^* & c^* \\ d^* & e^* & f^* \\ 0 & 0 & 1 \end{pmatrix} \begin{pmatrix} x_1 \\ x_1' \\ \dfrac{\Delta p}{p} \end{pmatrix}, \tag{11-50}
$$

---

* 13, Livingood; 33, Penner.

where the coefficients at the symmetry plane are

$$a^* = a_6 \cos \tau + d_6 \frac{\sin \tau}{K}, \tag{11-51}$$

$$b^* = b_6 \cos \tau + e_6 \frac{\sin \tau}{K}, \tag{11-52}$$

$$c^* = c_6 \cos \tau + f_6 \frac{\sin \tau}{K}, \tag{11-53}$$

$$d^* = -a_6 K \sin \tau + d_6 \cos \tau, \tag{11-54}$$

$$e^* = -b_6 K \sin \tau + e_6 \cos \tau, \tag{11-55}$$

$$f^* = -c_6 K \sin \tau + f_6 \cos \tau. \tag{11-56}$$

As in the earlier case of three magnets, we demand a double-focused (and dispersed) image at the plane of symmetry. This lies at the center of the quadrupole, so the particles cannot be greatly displaced in traversing its half-length. Consequently we neglect its presence for the moment, and for simplification we suppose that $S_0 = \infty$. The value of u_2 needed for double focusing is given by Eq. (4-38); we divide each term by $S_0{}^2$ before setting $S_0 = \infty$ and thus find

$$\tan u_2 = \tfrac{1}{2} \tan \theta. \tag{11-57}$$

Suppose $\theta = 45°$ (so the total bend is 90°). Then $\tan u_2 = 0.5$ and $u_2 = 26.57°$.

Still neglecting the quadrupole, we find the distance S_1 (now approximately the same as S_{ix1}) from Eq. (2-21) (wherein $S_0 = \infty$ and $u_1 = 0$):

$$S_1/\rho = 1/(\tan \theta - \tan u_2) = 2 \cot \theta = 2. \tag{11-58}$$

By symmetry it is obvious that the second half of the system will form a doubly focused image at $S_{ix2} = \infty$ beyond the second magnet, but we have still to arrange for the particles to be doubly achromatic in that region. To do so, we reinvoke the presence of the quadrupole which does have an influence on the slope of the rays at the symmetry plane, no matter how thin the quadrupole may be. In Eq. (11-56), set

$$f^* = 0. \tag{11-59}$$

By Eq. (11-13) this will make $C = F = 0$ in the final image space, thus producing double achromatism. This yields

$$K \tan \tau = f_6/c_6. \tag{11-60}$$

On substituting from Eqs. (6-27) and (6-30), we obtain

$$K \tan \tau = \frac{(1 - \cos \theta) \tan u_2 + \sin \theta}{\rho \left\{ 1 - \cos \theta + \dfrac{S_1}{\rho} [(1 - \cos \theta) \tan u_2 + \sin \theta] \right\}}$$

$$= \frac{0.427}{\rho}. \tag{11-61}$$

Now $K \tan \tau = K \tan(KQ/2) \approx K^2 Q/2$ if $KQ/2$ is small, say $<25°$. Hence $K^2 Q = 0.854/\rho$. The focal length of a converging quadrupole, measured from its effective edge is (see Eq. (19-59)):

$$f_e = 1/(K \tan \tau) \approx 1/(K^2 Q) \qquad \text{for small } \tau. \tag{11-62}$$

Hence, finally, the focal length of the quadrupole needed for double achromatism is $f_e = \rho/0.854 = 1.17 \, \rho$.

12 Beam Bending by Two Magnets with Achromatic Image

INTRODUCTION

As here used, beam bending means that both magnets bend the path in the same direction.
The radial envelope's half-width and maximum slope at a distance S_2 beyond the second magnet are given by

$$x_{10\,max} = [\gamma_9 - 2\beta_9 S_2 + \alpha_9 S_2{}^2]^{1/2} x_0 x_0' + c_{11}^{++} \Delta p/p, \qquad (12\text{-}1)$$

$$x'_{10\,max} = \alpha_9^{1/2} x_0 x_0' + f_{10}^{++} \Delta p/p. \qquad (12\text{-}2)$$

We will now indicate that double achromatism is impossible, or at least impractical. To attain it, both c_{10}^{++} and f_{10}^{++} must vanish.

If the magnets are symmetric, we use the short cut of Eq. (11-13), whereby $C (=c_{10}^{++})$ and $F (=f_{10}^{++})$ will both be zero if f^* is zero at the plane of symmetry. This point may be identified as station 6, provided S_1 is replaced by $S_1/2$. By Eq. (6-30), we have

$$f^* = f_6 = [\tan u_2(1 - \cos \theta_1)/\delta_1{}^2] + \sin \theta_1/\delta_1. \qquad (12\text{-}3)$$

To have symmetry we must have $u_3 = u_2$, and to avoid disastrous axial defocusing, these edge angles must not be negative. Hence to make $f_6 = 0$, either with $u_2 = u_3 > 0$ or with $u_2 = u_3 = 0$, θ must lie between $180°$ and $360°$. Such a pretzel-like array of two magnets is not appealing, so we neglect it.

If the system is asymmetric, the short cut is not available. For double achromatism we need $f_{10}^{++} = 0$ and $c_{10}^{++} = 0$. But $f_{10}^{++} = f_9^{++}$ and $c_{10}^{++} = c_9^{++} + S_2 f_9^{++}$, so we must have $c_9^{++} = f_9^{++} = 0$. In the cases that have been investigated in the present study ($n_1 = n_2 = 0$ with only $u_1 > 0$ or only $u_4 > 0$), the result of setting $c_9^{++} = 0$ leads to a different value of S_1 than if we set $f_9^{++} = 0$. Hence we conclude that double achromatism is impossible

165

and we must be content with only an achromatic image, the radial slope in the image space being momentum dependent. This situation can be attained, as will now be demonstrated. We will consider three methods of attack. Though identical in principle, they differ in detail.

First Method

The coefficient of $\Delta p/p$ in the expression for $x_{10\,\text{max}}$ is $c_{10}^{++} = c_9^{++} + f_9^{++}S_2$. We write the general expression for c_{10}^{++} using Eqs. (6-88)–(6-90) (adjusted to apply to the magnets under consideration), equate it to zero, and solve for S_2, the distance of no dispersion. This turns out to be a function of S_1, the separation between the two magnets.

We then set $b_{10} = 0$, using Eqs. (6-85)–(6-87), and solve for S_2, which now by definition is the second magnet's radial image distance S_{ix2}; it is found to depend on S_0 and S_1.

To make this image distance coincide with the distance of no dispersion, we equate them. This gives the necessary relation between S_0 and S_1. But S_0 is related to the first magnet's radial image distance S_{ix1} by Eq. 2-18, and it is found that the intermagnet image lies midway between them; i.e.,

$$S_1 = 2S_{ix1}. \tag{12-4}$$

Thus there is a critical separation which will produce an achromatic image at one particular distance S_{ix2}. We may then express S_{ix2} in terms of its object distance $S_{0x2}(=S_1/2)$ so that S_{ix2} finally can be given as a function of S_1 or of S_0.

Second Method

For two magnets bending the same way, a radial image lying between them, and the final slit being one image wide, Eq. (5-20) shows that

$$R_p^{++} = \frac{\Delta p}{p} = \frac{w_0}{-\rho_1 F_1 - \rho_2 F_2/M_{x1}}. \tag{12-5}$$

The second image will be achromatic (i.e., an infinite change in momentum is needed to separate the $p + \Delta p$ and p images) if we have

$$-\rho_1 F_1 M_{x1} = \rho_2 F_2. \tag{12-6}$$

For simplicity, in the cases to be considered, we assume $\rho_1 = \rho_2$ and $\theta_1 = \theta_2$, although these restrictions are not necessary.

We first find the algebraic expression for $-F_1 M_{x1}$ (which is a function of S_0) by the use of Eqs. (2-24) and (2-28).

Now F_2 (also found from Eq. (2-28), adapted to the second magnet) depends on S_{0x2}, which may be written $S_1 - S_{ix1}$, where S_{ix1} is a function of S_0 by Eq. (2-18). Hence we obtain F_2 in terms of S_0 and S_1.

Equating F_2 to $-F_1 M_{x1}$ gives the necessary relation between S_0 and S_1 for an achromatic final image. Since S_0 is connected with S_{ix1} by Eq. (2-18), we are able to recognize that

$$S_1 = 2S_{ix1}.$$

This is the same result as was obtained by the first method. In some cases, the second method is quicker. The image distance S_{ix2} is obtained by setting $b_{10} = 0$, as before.

Third Method

This is applicable only for a system with mirror symmetry. From this we deduce at once that $L_{ix2} = L_o$. From Eq. (11-13) we see that setting $b^* = 0$ at the symmetry plane does three things: First, it causes a radial, dispersed image at the symmetry plane; second, it makes $B (= b_{10})$ vanish, so an image is formed at S_2 beyond the second magnet; and third, it makes $C (= c_{10}^{++})$ vanish, so that this image is achromatic. Now b^* is b_6 (as given by Eq. (6-26)) wherein S_1 is replaced by $S_1/2$, since the symmetry plane is midway between the magnets. From $b_6 = 0$ we obtain L_1 as a function of L_o and also note that $L_1 = 2L_{ix1}$, as expected.

Having used one or another of these three methods, further information is obtained as follows.

The radial magnification is found from $M_x = M_{x1} M_{x2}$, where the magnifications of the individual magnets are given by Eq. (2-24) as a function of L_o for the first and of L_{ox2} for the second. These distances are then each expressed in terms of L_1, using relations found earlier. Hence M_x is finally displayed in terms of L_1.

The condition for double focusing cannot be prescribed in specific terms, since it depends on which of the four edge angles are finite. We set $L_{ix2} = L_{iz2}$, expressing each in parameters that depend on L_1, to finally obtain a relation between the edge angle and L_1.

The axial magnification of the system is often found from those of the separate magnets, while in some cases it is simpler to employ the expression $M_z = \bar{a}_{10}$. With either method, the value of L_o or of L_{ix2} appropriate for an achromatic final image must be used.

The intermagnet image is dispersed; in some applications a slit is used at this point, so that a narrow band of momenta is transmitted to form the second (and achromatic) image.

In the following examples, we quote only the results, omitting the tedious detailed procedures outlined above.

CASE A. $u_1 = u_2 = u_3 = u_4 = 0$, $n_1 = n_2 = 0$, $\theta_1 = \theta_2$, $\rho_1 = \rho_2$ (Fig. 12-1)

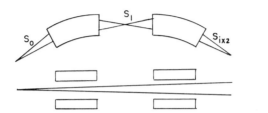

FIG. 12-1.

$$L_o = L_{ix2} = \frac{L_1 + 2\tan\theta}{L_1 \tan\theta - 2},\qquad (12\text{-}7)$$

whence

$$L_1 = 2L_{ix1} = \frac{2(L_o + \tan\theta)}{L_o \tan\theta - 1},\qquad (12\text{-}8)$$

$$M_x = -1.\qquad (12\text{-}9)$$

There is no axial focusing. All distances are large unless $\theta > 90°$. For $L_o = L_{ix2} = \infty$, we find $L_1 = 2\cot\theta$.

A special instance ($L_o = \infty$) of a more general type of this case ($\theta_1 \neq \theta_2$) and $\rho_1 \neq \rho_2$) has been studied by Atterling.*

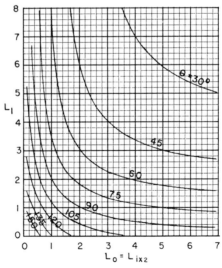

FIG. 12-2. Case A. Achromatic image. $n_1 = n_2 = 0$, all $u = 0$, $\theta_1 = \theta_2$, $\rho_1 = \rho_2$.

* 213, Atterling.

CASE B. $u_1 > 0$, $u_2 = u_3 = u_4 = 0$, $n_1 = n_2 = 0$, $\theta_1 = \theta_2$, $\rho_1 = \rho_2$ (Fig. 12-3)

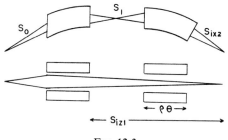

FIG. 12-3.

For an achromatic image, we must have

$$L_o = \frac{L_1 + 2\tan\theta}{L_1 \tan\theta - 2 - \tan u_1(L_1 + 2\tan\theta)},\qquad(12\text{-}10)$$

whence

$$L_1 = 2L_{ix1} = 2L_{ox2} = \frac{2[L_o(1 + \tan u_1 \tan\theta) + \tan\theta]}{L_o(\tan\theta - \tan u_1) - 1}.\qquad(12\text{-}11)$$

And also

$$L_{ix2} = \frac{L_1 + 2\tan\theta}{L_1 \tan\theta - 2},\qquad(12\text{-}12)$$

from which

$$L_1 = \frac{2(L_{ix2} + \tan\theta)}{L_{ix2}\tan\theta - 1}.\qquad(12\text{-}13)$$

Now use Eq. (12-11) in Eq. (12-12) to find that

$$L_{ix2} = \frac{L_o}{L_o \tan u_1 + 1}.\qquad(12\text{-}14)$$

Also

$$M_x = 1 - \tan u_1 \left(\frac{L_1 + 2\tan\theta}{L_1 \tan\theta - 2}\right),\qquad(12\text{-}15)$$

$$M_z = \frac{L_1 \tan\theta - 2 - \tan u_1(L_1 + 2\tan\theta)}{L_1 \tan\theta - 2 - 2\tan u_1(L_1 + 2\tan\theta)}.\qquad(12\text{-}16)$$

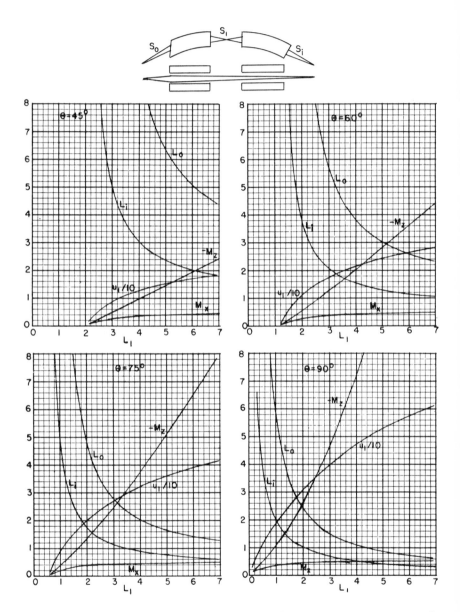

FIG. 12-4. Case B. Achromatic, double-focused image. $u_1 > 0$, $u_2 = u_3 = u_4 = 0$; $n_1 = n_2 = 0$, $\theta_1 = \theta_2$, $\rho_1 = \rho_2$.

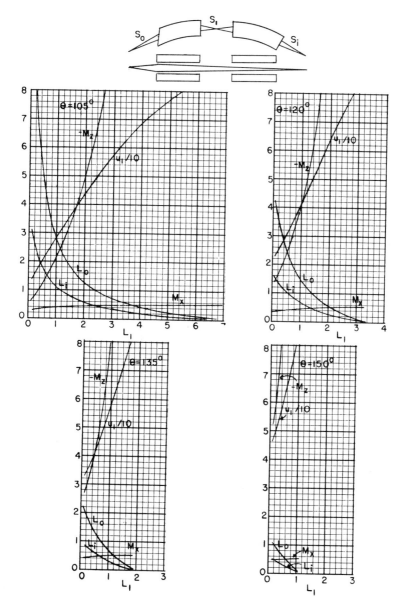

FIG. 12-5. Case B, cont'd. Achromatic double-focused image. $u_1 > 0$, $u_2 = u_3 = u_4 = 0$, $n_1 = n_2 = 0$, $\theta_1 = \theta_2$, $\rho_1 = \rho_2$.

Up to this point, both L_1 and u_1 are unrestricted. But for double focusing we must have

$$L_{ix2} = L_{iz2} = L_{iz1} - \theta - L_1$$

$$= \frac{L_o(1 - \theta \tan u_1) + \theta}{L_o \tan u_1 - 1} - \theta - L_1. \qquad (12\text{-}17)$$

In this substitute for L_{ix2} and L_o the values given above (in terms of L_1) that are appropriate for an achromatic image. Solve for $\tan u_1$;

$$\tan u_1 =$$

$$\frac{L_1{}^3\sigma^2 + L_1{}^2(2\theta\sigma^2 - 2\sigma\kappa) + L_1(4\sigma^2 - 8\theta\sigma\kappa) + 8\theta\kappa^2 - 8\sigma\kappa}{L_1{}^3 2\sigma\kappa + L_1{}^2(4\theta\sigma\kappa + 4\sigma^2 - 2\kappa^2) + L_1(8\theta\sigma^2 - 8\theta\kappa^2) + 8\sigma^2 - 16\theta\sigma\kappa},$$
$$(12\text{-}18)$$

where $\sigma = \sin \theta$ and $\kappa = \cos \theta$. Thus u_1 is determined when L_1 is chosen.

Alternatively, we may express L_o as a function of L_{ix2} by use of Eq. (12-14), and by using the result in Eq. (12-11), we may find L_1 as a function of L_{ix2}. When these values of L_o and of L_1 are employed in Eq. (12-17), we find

$$\tan u_1 = \frac{\sin \theta(L_{ix2}^2 + L_{ix2}\theta + 1) - \theta \cos \theta}{\sin \theta(L_{ix2}^3 + 2L_{ix2}^2\theta + 2L_{ix2}) + \cos \theta(L_{ix2}^2 - L_{ix2}\theta)}, \qquad (12\text{-}19)$$

where $L_{ix2} = L_{iz2} = L_i$ is the double-focused image distance.

Graphs of L_o, L_i, u_1, M_x, and M_z as functions of L_1, at eight different values of θ are displayed in Figs. 12-4 and 12-5.

CASE C. $u_4 > 0$, $u_1 = u_2 = u_3 = 0$, $n_1 = n_2 = 0$, $\theta_1 = \theta_2$, $\rho_1 = \rho_2$ (Fig. 12-6)

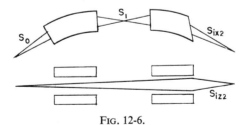

FIG. 12-6.

To obtain an achromatic image, we need

$$L_o = \frac{L_1 + 2 \tan \theta}{L_1 \tan \theta - 2}, \qquad (12\text{-}20)$$

whence

$$L_1 = 2L_{ix1} = 2L_{ox2} = \frac{2(L_o + \tan \theta)}{L_o \tan \theta - 1}. \qquad (12\text{-}21)$$

Also

$$L_{ix2} = \frac{L_1 + 2 \tan \theta}{L_1 \tan \theta - 2 - \tan u_4(L_1 + 2 \tan \theta)}, \qquad (12\text{-}22)$$

whence

$$L_1 = \frac{2[L_{ix2}(1 + \tan u_4 \tan \theta) + \tan \theta]}{L_{ix2}(\tan \theta - \tan u_4) - 1}. \qquad (12\text{-}23)$$

Use Eq. (12-21) in Eq. (12-22) to find that

$$L_o = \frac{L_{ix2}}{L_{ix2} \tan u_4 + 1}. \qquad (12\text{-}24)$$

Also

$$M_x = \frac{1}{1 - [\tan u_4(L_1 + 2 \tan \theta)]/(L_1 \tan \theta - 2)}, \qquad (12\text{-}25)$$

$$M_z = \frac{L_1 \tan \theta - 2 - 2 \tan u_4(L_1 + 2 \tan \theta)}{L_1 \tan \theta - 2 - \tan u_4(L_1 + 2 \tan \theta)}. \qquad (12\text{-}26)$$

For double focusing: ($\sigma = \sin \theta$, $\kappa = \cos \theta$)

$$\tan u_4 = \frac{L_1^3 \sigma^2 + L_1^2(2\theta\sigma^2 - 2\sigma\kappa) + L_1(4\sigma^2 - 8\theta\sigma\kappa) + 8\theta\kappa^2 - 8\sigma\kappa}{L_1^3 2\sigma\kappa + L_1^2(4\theta\sigma\kappa + 4\sigma^2 - 2\kappa^2) + L_1(8\theta\sigma^2 - 8\theta\kappa^2) + 8\sigma^2 - 16\theta\sigma\kappa}$$

$$(12\text{-}27)$$

or

$$\tan u_4 = \frac{\sin \theta(L_o^2 + L_o\theta + 1) - \theta \cos \theta}{\sin \theta(L_o^3 + 2L_o^2\theta + 2L_o) + \cos \theta(L_o^2 - L_o\theta)}. \qquad (12\text{-}28)$$

Case C is simply Case B with the particle direction reversed. We interchange u_1 and u_4, L_o and L_i; M_x for one case is $1/M_x$ for the other, and similarly for M_z.

Typical behavior is shown in Figs. 12-7 and 12-8.

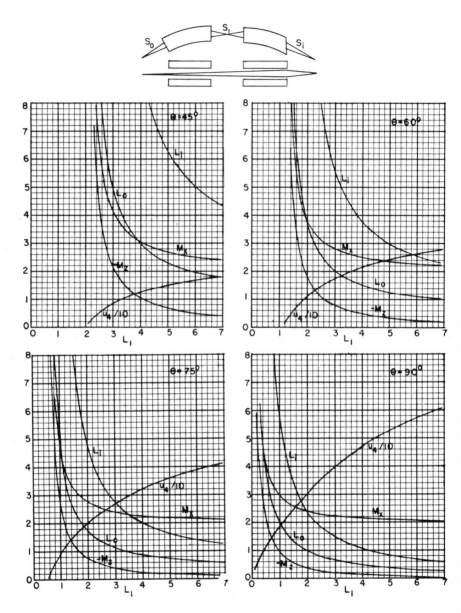

FIG. 12-7. Case C. Achromatic double-focused image. $u_4 > 0$, $u_1 = u_2 = u_3 = 0$; $n_1 = n_2 = 0$, $\theta_1 = \theta_2$, $\rho_1 = \rho_2$.

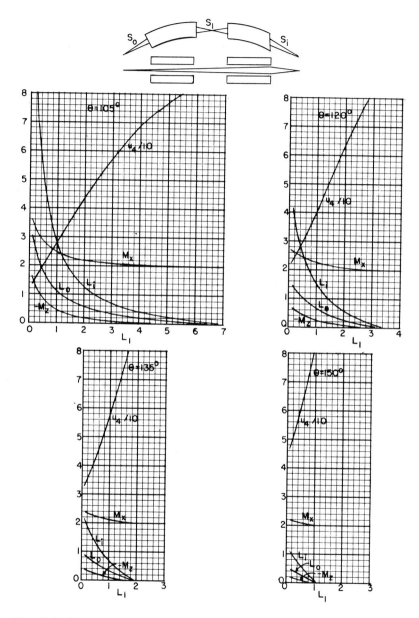

FIG. 12-8. Case C, cont'd. Achromatic double-focused image. $u_4 > 0, u_1 = u_2 = u_3 = 0,$
$n_1 = n_2 = 0, \theta_1 = \theta_2, \rho_1 = \rho_2.$

CASE D. $u_1 = u_4 = u > 0$ with $\tan u = 1/L_o$, $u_2 = u_3 = 0$, $n_1 = n_2 = 0$, $\theta_1 = \theta_2$, $\rho_1 = \rho_2$ (Fig. 12-9)

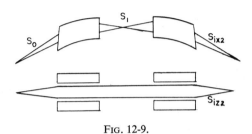

FIG. 12-9.

The system is symmetric, so to form an achromatic image we let $b^* = b_6 = 0$, wherein L_1 is replaced by $L_1/2$ and $u_2 = 0$ in Eq. (6-26). This gives

$$L_1 = 2L_{ix1} = 2L_{ox2} = \frac{2[L_o(1 + \tan u \tan \theta) + \tan \theta]}{L_o(\tan \theta - \tan u) - 1}. \qquad (12\text{-}29)$$

With $\tan u = 1/L_o$ this becomes

$$L_1 = \frac{2L_o + 4 \tan \theta}{L_o \tan \theta - 2}. \qquad (12\text{-}30)$$

From symmetry it is clear that

$$L_{ix2} = L_o = 1/\tan u. \qquad (12\text{-}31)$$

Now Eq. (3-10), modified to refer to the second magnet, gives its axial downstream focal length as $L_{iz2} = 1/\tan u_4 = 1/\tan u$. Therefore $L_{iz2} = L_{ix2}$, so that the system is double focusing. Also, obviously,

$$M_x = +1, \qquad (12\text{-}32)$$

$$M_z = -1. \qquad (12\text{-}33)$$

Figures 12-10 and 12-11 give typical parameters.

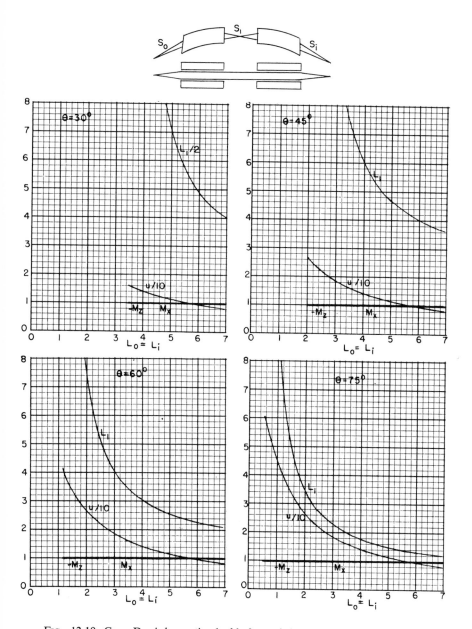

Fig. 12-10. Case D. Achromatic double-focused image. $\tan u_1 = \tan u_4 = 1/L_o$, $u_2 = u_3 = 0$, $n_1 = n_2 = 0$, $\theta_1 = \theta_2$, $\rho_1 = \rho_2$.

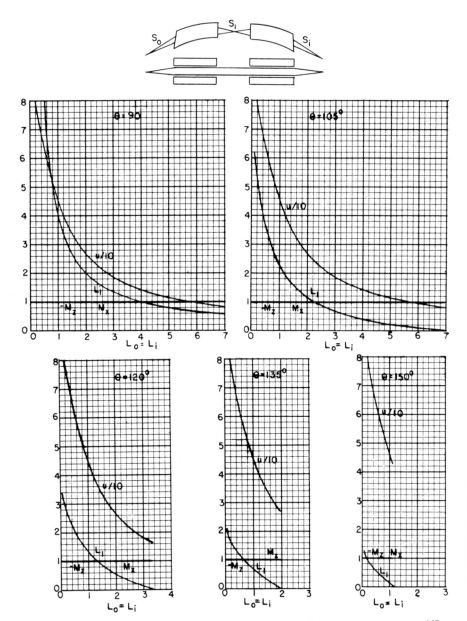

FIG. 12-11. Case D, cont'd. Achromatic double-focused image, $\tan u_1 = \tan u_2 = 1/L_o$, $u_2 = u_3 = 0$, $n_1 = n_2 = 0$, $\theta_1 = \theta_2$, $\rho_1 = \rho_2$.

CASE E. $u_1 = u_4 = u > 0$, $u_2 = u_3 = 0$, $n_1 = n_2 = 0$, $\theta_1 = \theta_2$, $\rho_1 = \rho_2$ (Fig. 12-12)

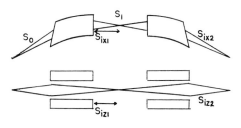

FIG. 12-12.

The condition for an achromatic final image is identical with that of Case D:

$$L_1 = 2L_{ix1} = 2L_{ox2} = \frac{2[L_o(1 + \tan u \tan \theta) + \tan \theta]}{L_o(\tan \theta - \tan u) - 1}. \tag{12-34}$$

But u in this case is not yet determined. It becomes so when we demand double focusing. By symmetry we see that if $L_{ix2} = L_{iz2}$, then we will also have

$$L_{ix1} = L_{iz1}. \tag{12-35}$$

We express these in terms of L_o, using Eqs. (2-18) and (3-6), with $u_2 = 0$, and solve for $u_1 = u$;

$$\tan u = \frac{\theta \sin \theta + 2 \cos \theta}{2(\theta \cos \theta - \sin \theta)}$$

$$\pm \left[\left(\frac{\theta \sin \theta + 2 \cos \theta}{2(\theta \cos \theta - \sin \theta)} \right)^2 - \frac{\sin \theta(L_o^2 + L_o\theta + 1) - \theta \cos \theta}{L_o^2(\theta \cos \theta - \sin \theta)} \right]^{1/2}. \tag{12-36}$$

(Note that this is the same as Eq. (4-56), where double focusing was required after a single magnet with $u_1 > 0$ and $u_2 = 0$.)

$$M_x = 1, \tag{12-37}$$

$$M_z = 1. \tag{12-38}$$

(See Figs. 12-13 and 12-14.)

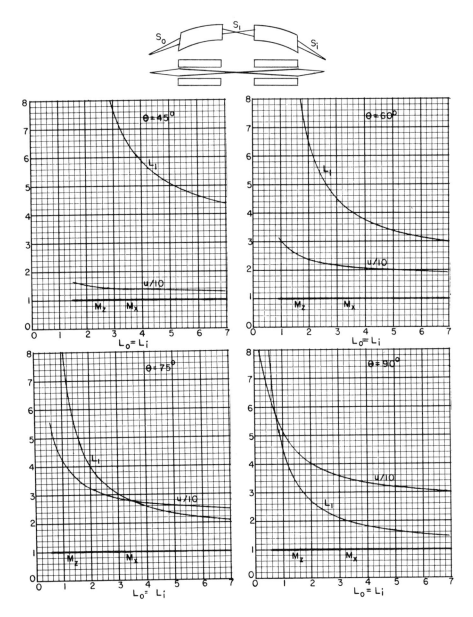

FIG. 12-13. Case E. Achromatic double-focused image. $u_1 = u_4 = u > 0$, $u_2 = u_3 = 0$, $n_1 = n_2 = 0$, $\theta_1 = \theta_2$, $\rho_1 = \rho_2$.

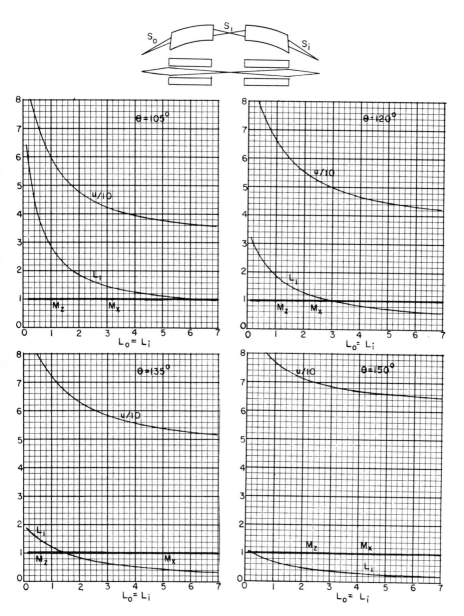

FIG. 12-14. Case E cont'd. Achromatic double-focused image. $u_1 = u_4 = u > 0$ $u_2 = u_3 = 0$, $n_1 = n_2 = 0$, $\theta_1 = \theta_2$, $\rho_1 = \rho_2$.

CASE F. $u_1 = u_2 = u_3 = u_4 = u$, with $\tan u = 1/L_o$, $n_1 = n_2 = 0$, $\theta_1 = \theta_2$, $\rho_1 = \rho_2$ (Fig. 12-15)

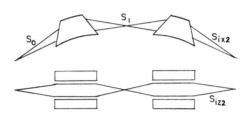

FIG. 12-15.

To obtain an achromatic image it is required that

$$L_1 = \frac{L_o + 2\tan\theta}{\left[\dfrac{L_0}{2} - \dfrac{1}{L_0}\right]\tan\theta - \tfrac{3}{2}} \tag{12-39}$$

and from symmetry we see that $L_{ix2} = L_o$.

With parallel axial paths inside the second magnet, as indicated, its exit edge must cause the final axial image to be at the down-stream focal point; we re-express Eq. (3-10) in terms of the second magnet, setting $t_1 = 0$ and $t_2 = 1/L_o$, whence we find that $L_{iz2} = L_o$. Hence $L_{iz2} = L_{ix2}$, so the system is double focusing.

It is obvious that we have

$$M_x = 1, \tag{12-40}$$

$$M_z = 1. \tag{12-41}$$

(See Figs. 12-16 and 12-17.)

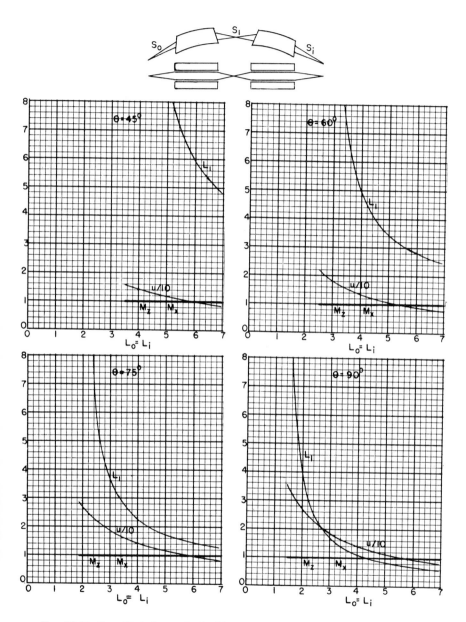

FIG. 12-16. Case F. Achromatic double-focused image. All u equal; tan $u = 1/L_o$, $n_1 = n_2 = 0$, $\theta_1 = \theta_2$, $\rho_1 = \rho_2$.

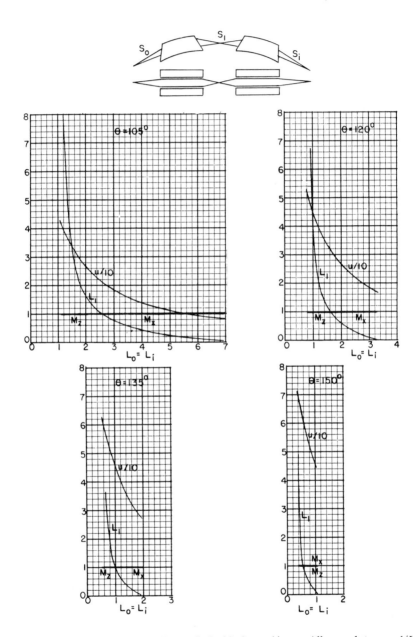

FIG. 12-17. Case F, cont'd. Achromatic double-focused image. All u equal; $\tan u = 1/L_0$, $n_1 = n_2 = 0$, $\theta_1 = \theta_2$, $\rho_1 = \rho_2$.

CASE G. $u_1 = u_2 = u_3 = u_4 = 0, n_1 = n_2 = 0.5, \theta_1 = \theta_2, \rho_1 = \rho_2$ (Fig. 12-18)

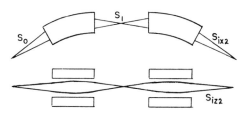

FIG. 12-18.

For an achromatic image,

$$L_o = L_{ix2}$$

$$= L_{iz2}$$

$$= L_i$$

$$= \frac{\sqrt{2}L_1 + 4\tan(\theta/\sqrt{2})}{L_1\tan(\theta/\sqrt{2}) - 2\sqrt{2}}, \tag{12-42}$$

whence

$$L_1 = 2L_{ix1}$$

$$= 2L_{iz1}$$

$$= \frac{2[\sqrt{2}L_o + 2\tan(\theta/\sqrt{2})]}{L_o\tan(\theta/\sqrt{2}) - \sqrt{2}}, \tag{12-43}$$

$$M_x = M_z = 1. \tag{12-44}$$

For $L_o = L_i = \infty$, we have

$$L_1 = 2\sqrt{2}\cot(\theta/\sqrt{2}). \tag{12-45}$$

(See Fig. 12-19.)

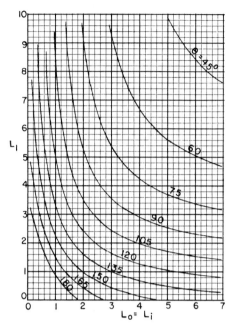

FIG. 12-19. Case G. Achromatic double-focused image. All $u = 0$, $n_1 = n_2 = 0.5$, $\theta_1 = \theta_2$, $\rho_1 = \rho_2$.

CASE H. $u_1 = u_2 = u_3 = u_4 = 0, n_1 = n_2 < 0.5, \theta_1 = \theta_2, \rho_1 = \rho_2$ (Fig. 12-20)

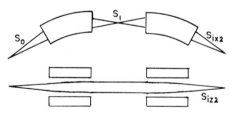

FIG. 12-20.

No intermagnet axial image.

In this more general case, wherein n is not specified, the analog of Eq. (12-42), giving the condition for an achromatic radial image, is

$$L_o = L_{ix2} = \frac{(L_1/\delta) + (2 \tan \phi)/\delta^2}{L_1 \tan \phi - 2/\delta}, \qquad (12\text{-}46)$$

where $\phi = \delta\theta = (1 - n)^{1/2} \, \theta$.

Considering axial motion, we see that the first magnet, alone, gives an image at infinity; on setting $L_{iz1} = \infty$ in Eq. (3-5), we obtain

$$L_o = \frac{1}{\varepsilon} \cot \psi, \tag{12-47}$$

where $\psi = \varepsilon\theta = n^{1/2}\theta$. By symmetry, we see that $L_{iz2} = L_o$, whence $L_{iz2} = L_{ix2}$, so the system is double focusing and achromatic, provided that L_1, θ, and n are so chosen that Eqs. (12-46) and (12-47) are satisfied, i.e., if we have

$$\frac{1}{\varepsilon} \cot \psi = \frac{(L_1/\delta) + (2 \tan \phi)/\delta^2}{L_1 \tan \phi - 2/\delta}. \tag{12-48}$$

We now note that if the two magnets are in contact, so that $L_1 = 0$, then Eq. (12-48) becomes

$$\frac{1}{\varepsilon} \cot(\varepsilon\theta) = -\frac{1}{\delta} \tan(\delta\theta). \tag{12-49}$$

Since there is then only a single magnet of angle $\Theta = 2\theta$, this may be written as

$$\frac{1}{\varepsilon} \cot\left(\frac{\varepsilon\Theta}{2}\right) = -\frac{1}{\delta} \tan\left(\frac{\delta\Theta}{2}\right). \tag{12-50}$$

Now this is the same expression as Eq. (4-109) of Case 17 for a single magnet with a radial, dispersed image at its center and an achromatic double-focused image beyond it. Hence Case 17 is a special instance (wherein the magnets' separation L_1 is zero) of the present Case H. Since in Case 17 we saw that a solution was possible for $n < 0.5$ and $\theta > 180°$, it should not be surprising that somewhat the same conditions hold in the present instance.

Alvarez et al.* have examined the situation and have given curves showing the angle θ of each of the two magnets (with θ ranging between 60° and 150°) as a function of L_o for various values of n (lying between 0.23 and 0.315), and they also display curves giving the values of L_1 as a function of L_o for these same values of n and with θ having particular values between 105° and 115°. The parameters chosen for the spectrograph at Stanford are:

$$n_1 = n_2 = 0.27, \; \theta_1 = \theta_2 = 110°, \; L_o = L_{ix2} = L_{iz2} = 1.25, \text{ and } L_1 = 1.90,$$

with $\rho_1 = \rho_2 = 30$ in.

In all the two-magnet systems with an achromatic final image that we have described, the first radial image is dispersed, so a narrow band of momenta may be selected by a slit midway between the magnets (rather than in the magnet, as in Case 17); the particles that are transmitted then form an achromatic double-focused image beyond the second magnet.

* 210, Alvarez et al.

13 Beam Bending by One Magnet and Two Quadruples, with Achromatic Image

Radially focusing quadrupoles Q_1 and Q_2 are placed symmetrically on each side of a single magnet of bending angle 2θ, bending radius ρ, index $n = 0$, and edge angles $u_1 = u_2 = 0$. We treat this magnet as though it were two, m_1 and m_2, that are in contact at the plane of symmetry s. Q_1 is adjusted so that it and m_1 together form a dispersed image at s. (If $\Delta p/p$ is small, the image distances of all momenta are essentially the same, see Chapter 17.) Because of symmetry, we expect that the images at s will act as objects for m_2 and Q_2, so that a final achromatic image will be formed. (See Fig. 13-1.)

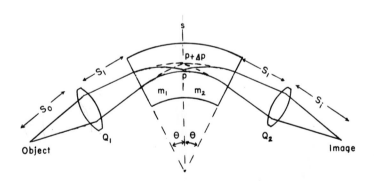

FIG. 13-1. System to give an achromatic final image.

The system is symmetric, so to employ the short-cut method of Eq. (11-13) we must find the matrix coefficients a^*, b^*, ... at the plane of symmetry. We write the matrices for passage through S_0, Q_1, S_1, and m_1 as follows:

188

$$
\begin{pmatrix} x^* \\ x'^* \\ \dfrac{\Delta p}{p} \end{pmatrix} =
\begin{pmatrix} \kappa & \rho\sigma & \rho(1-\kappa) \\[2mm] -\dfrac{\sigma}{\rho} & \kappa & \sigma \\[2mm] 0 & 0 & 1 \end{pmatrix}
\begin{pmatrix} 1 & S_1 & 0 \\ 0 & 1 & 0 \\ 0 & 0 & 1 \end{pmatrix}
$$

$$
\times
\begin{pmatrix} \cos\tau & \dfrac{1}{K}\sin\tau & 1 \\[2mm] -K\sin\tau & \cos\tau & 0 \\[2mm] 0 & 0 & 1 \end{pmatrix}
\begin{pmatrix} 1 & S_0 & 0 \\ 0 & 1 & 0 \\ 0 & 0 & 1 \end{pmatrix}
\begin{pmatrix} x_1 \\ x_1' \\ \dfrac{\Delta p}{p} \end{pmatrix}
\qquad (13\text{-}1).
$$

Here, for the magnet we write $\sigma = \sin\theta$ and $\kappa = \cos\theta$, while for the quadrupole we have $\tau = KQ$, where Q is its length, and $K^2 = dB/(dxB_0\,\rho_0)$, the ion's momentum being proportional to $B_0\,\rho_0$. Multiplication yields the coefficients:

$$
a^* = \kappa\cos\tau - (S_1\kappa + \rho\sigma)K\sin\tau, \qquad (13\text{-}2)
$$

$$
b^* = (S_0\kappa + S_1\kappa + \rho\sigma)\cos\tau + \left(\frac{\kappa}{K} - S_0 S_1 K\kappa - S_0\rho K\right)\sin\tau, \qquad (13\text{-}3)
$$

$$
c^* = \rho(1-\kappa), \qquad (13\text{-}4)
$$

$$
d^* = \left(\frac{S_1}{\rho}\sigma - \kappa\right)K\sin\tau - \frac{\sigma}{\rho}\cos\tau, \qquad (13\text{-}5)
$$

$$
e^* = \left(\kappa - \frac{S_0}{\rho}\sigma - \frac{S_1}{\rho}\sigma\right)\cos\tau + \left(S_0\frac{S_1}{\rho}K\sigma - S_0 K\kappa - \frac{\sigma}{\rho K}\right)\sin\tau, \qquad (13\text{-}6)
$$

$$
f^* = \sigma. \qquad (13\text{-}7)
$$

By Eq. (11-13), the three coefficients of interest at some distance beyond the second quadrupole are

$$
B = 2e^* b^*, \qquad C = 2b^* f^*, \qquad F = 2a^* f^*.
$$

The system would be doubly achromatic, if $C = F = 0$, which would occur if $f^* = 0$. But we see that $f^* = \sigma = \sin\theta$, and this can vanish only if the bending angle of both m_1 and m_2 is 0 or 180°. Hence the system cannot be doubly achromatic.

Nevertheless, a final image will exist if $B = 0$, and it will be achromatic if $C = 0$. Both of these conditions are met if $b* = 0$, and this also causes a dispersed image at the midpoint of the system. Setting $b* = 0$ leads to

$$\tan \tau = \frac{L_o + L_1 + \tan \theta}{(L_o \rho K / \cos \theta) + \rho L_o L_1 K - 1/(\rho K)}, \tag{13-8}$$

where, be it recalled, θ is the half-angle of the magnet. This expression gives the requisite strength of each of the quadrupoles. Since $\tan \tau = \tan KQ \approx KQ$, we may find that

$$K^2 = \frac{L_o + L_1 + \tan \theta + Q/\rho}{Q \rho L_o (L_1 + 1/\cos \theta)}. \tag{13-9}$$

In the simplified description given above, the two quadrupoles defocus the beam axially. In practice, each is replaced by a quadrupole pair in which the polarity of one is rotated 90° to that of the other. It is then possible to obtain the radial focusing required above and at the same time to get adequate axial focusing.

This system has been used since 1956 with the switch magnets that follow the cyclotron, and more recently, those associated with the electron linear accelerator, at Argonne National Laboratory.* It has also been described, independently, by Draper.†

* 208, Ramler.
† 222, Draper.

14 Achromatic Single Magnets

$270°$ MAGNET, $n = 0$, $u_1 = 45°$, $u_2 = 32.4°$

For this particular bending angle the analysis is very simple. Setting $c_6 = 0$ in Eq (6-27), we find that there is no dispersion at the distance

$$S_1 = \rho/(1 - \tan u_2). \tag{14-1}$$

Setting $b_6 = 0$ in Eq. (6-26), we determine that the radial image distance is

$$S_{ix} = \frac{S_0 \tan u_1 + \rho}{(S_0/\rho)(1 - \tan u_1 \tan u_2) - \tan u_2}. \tag{14-2}$$

Equating these gives the condition for an achromatic image:

$$S_0 = \rho/(1 - \tan u_1). \tag{14-3}$$

Since the edge angles are fixed, this condition can be made independent of p (and hence of ρ) if we choose $u_1 = 45°$ so that $\tan u_1 = 1$ and $S_0 = \infty$.

For double focusing, Eq. (3-19) shows that $\tan u_2 = 0.6347$ so that $u_2 = 32.4°$. The common radial and axial image distances, $S_{ix} = S_{iz} = 2.74 \, \rho$, are found from Eqs. (2-21) and (3-10), these being appropriate for $S_0 = \infty$.

It is interesting to note that the point axial image is erect, since Eq. (1-10) shows that the axial focal length of the input edge is $f = \rho/\tan u_1$. Thus there is an inverted axial image inside the magnet at a distance ρ from the entrance.

This system has been described briefly by Enge.* It will be profitable to consider it in somewhat greater detail to see to what extent the image will be achromatic for particles with a considerable spread in momentum, for we see from Fig. 14-1 that the p particle with radius ρ_0 is deflected $270°$ and experiences the designed exit edge angle (which we now call u_0), while a less

* 22a, Enge.

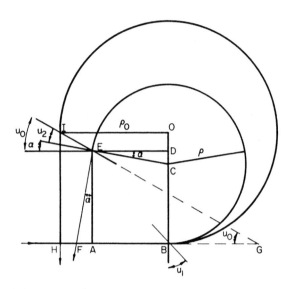

FIG. 14-1. Paths of central and lower energy in the 270° magnet.

energetic ion with a smaller radius ρ is bent through $\theta = 270 - \alpha$ and traverses a different exit edge angle u_2.

We first find how ρ is related to the bending angle. We have $\tan u_0 = AE/AG$. But $AE = BC + CD = \rho\,(1 + \sin \alpha)$. Hence $AG = \rho(1 + \sin \alpha)/\tan u_0$. Also $HA = HB - AB = IO - ED = \rho_0 - \rho \cos \alpha$. Further, $HG = HA + AG$. Now also

$$\tan u_0 = HI/HG = \rho_0/[\rho_0 - \rho \cos \alpha + \rho(1 + \sin \alpha)\cot u_0].$$

We solve this for ρ, realizing that $\alpha = 270 - \theta$, to find

$$\rho = \frac{\rho_0(1 - \tan u_0)}{1 + \sin(270 - \theta) - \tan u_0 \cos(270 - \theta)}. \tag{14-4}$$

This expression is valid both when $\alpha = 270 - \theta$ and when $\alpha = \theta - 270$.

The edge angle presented to the orbit is

$$u_2 = u_0 - \alpha = u_0 - 270 + \theta$$

so that

$$\tan u_2 = \tan(u_0 - 270 + \theta). \tag{14-5}$$

By Eq. (2-21), valid when $S_0 = \infty$, the radial image distance is

$$\frac{S_{ix}}{\rho} = \frac{\cos \theta + \sin \theta}{\sin \theta - \cos \theta - \tan(u_0 + \theta - 270)(\cos \theta + \sin \theta)}. \tag{14-6}$$

The axial image distance comes from Eq. (3-10):

$$\frac{S_{iz}}{\rho} = \frac{\theta - 1}{(\theta - 1)\tan u_2 - 1}. \tag{14-7}$$

Finally, to determine the dispersion we evaluate Eq. (6-27) wherein S_1 is replaced by S_{ix}, as given above:

$$c_6 = \rho(1 - \cos \theta) + S_{ix}[\tan(u_0 + \theta - 270)(1 - \cos \theta) + \sin \theta]. \tag{14-8}$$

In these last three expressions, ρ should be computed in terms of ρ_0, using Eq. (14-4), in order to obtain all quantities in the same units.

The lateral separation of the p and $p - \Delta p$ images is $c_6 \Delta p/p$. For relativistic particles this may be written as $c_6 \Delta E/E$. Equations (14-4), (14-6), (14-7), and (14-8) are plotted in Fig. 14-2.

For example, we will now compute the dispersion of a beam of electrons with energy centered at 22.5 MeV and extending to 20 and 25 MeV, with $B = 10$ kG.

Using the values of ρ/ρ_0 shown in Table 14-1, we refer to Fig. 14-2 to find

TABLE 14-1

E(MeV)	B(kG-cm)	ρ(cm)	ρ/ρ_0	$\Delta E/E$	c_6/ρ_0	$c_6\Delta E/E$ (cm)	S_{ix}/ρ_0	S_{iz}/ρ_0
25	85.08	8.51	1.108	0.111	0.1	0.085	2.85	2.65
22.5	76.74	7.67(ρ_0)	1.000	0	0	0	2.74	2.74
20	68.40	6.84	0.891	−0.111	−0.1	−0.085	2.62	2.91

that the bending angles of the high, central and low energies are 272°, 270°, and 267.7°; thereupon we may read the other quantities that are recorded in the sixth, eighth, and ninth columns of the table. For a point source, the total width of the image is 0.17 cm, which is indeed a good approximation to achromatism. The extent by which the images fail to coincide along the flight path in the laboratory frame of reference is somewhat less than the difference in the values of S_{ix}, since these are measured from the sloping edge of the magnet. Thus, if R is the difference between the image distance of the central energy (S_c) and that of either extreme energy (S), then it is not difficult to show that

$$R/\rho_0 = S_c/\rho_0 - S/\rho_0 - (1 - \rho/\rho_0) \tan u_0,$$

wherein, since α is small, we have set $\cos \alpha = 1$. Note that double focusing occurs only at 270°.

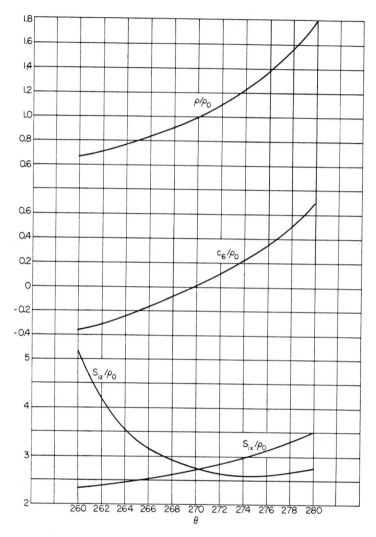

FIG. 14-2. Parameters of the 270° magnet with $n = 0$, $u_1 = 45°$, and $u_2 = 32.4°$.

An unfortunate characteristic of this magnet is the large gap that is required. For parallel input rays, an axial image is formed at the focal distance of the entrance edge; $f = \rho/\tan u_1 = \rho$, since $u_1 = 45°$. The length of the 270° path is 4.7124ρ, so the remaining length of magnet beyond the focus is 3.7124ρ. Hence at the exit the height of the beam is 3.7 times its height at entry.

Since by Eq. (6-30) we have $f_6 = \tan u_2(1 - \cos \theta) + \sin \theta = 0.6347 - 1 = -0.3653$, the magnet is not doubly achromatic, for such would require that $f_6 = 0$, in addition to having $c_6 = 0$.

270° MAGNET, $n \approx -1$, $u_1 = u_2 = 45°$

A doubly achromatic 270° magnet has been suggested by Enge,* as sketched in Fig. 14-3. A particle enters through the straight edge (which lies along the

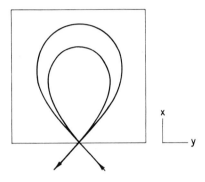

FIG. 14-3. The field increases along x as $B = k/x^n$, with $n = -1$ near the edge and -0.8 elsewhere.

y axis) with an incidence angle such that $u_1 = 45°$; hence the edge is axially focusing. As the particle penetrates deeper into the field, along x, the field strength increases according to $B = k/x^n$, where k is a constant and the field index is $n = -1$ for a short distance near the edge and then keeps the value $n = -0.8$ for the remaining radial extent of the gap. With an infinitely narrow input beam, ions of different momenta describe loops of different size and all emerge at the entrance point and along the same path, with $u_2 = 45°$ for all.

In addition to the vertical focusing supplied by the input and exit edges, the body of the magnet is axially converging in the first and last portions of the loops, since there the field is decreasing in the direction of increasing radius; opposite conditions exist over the remainder of the curved path. The net result is axial convergence.

A complete analysis is too involved for a brief summary.

540° ACHROMATIC REFLECTOR, $n = 0$, $u_1 = u_2 = u_3 = u_4 = 45°$

Consider a uniform field magnet in which a 90° notch exists, as shown in Fig. 14-4. It is obvious that particles of different momentum all will be bent through 270° in each traversal, and that all four edge angles are 45°.

* 215, Enge.

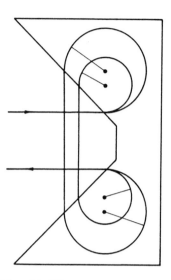

FIG. 14-4. Paths of particles with different momenta in the 540° magnet. The use of half of this arrangement yields a parallel beam of small dispersion bent through 90° net. In either case, the same patterns are formed if the input beam is composed of parallel rays with finite width.

For an object at infinity, Eq. (2-21) applied to the first magnet gives $S_{ix1} = \infty$. Hence for the second magnet we have $S_{0x2} = \infty$ and therefore $S_{ix2} = \infty$. A radially parallel input beam of mixed energies is returned as a radially parallel beam, with no dispersion at all.

Axially, the situation is somewhat less favorable. By Eq. (3-10) we find for the first magnet that

$$S_{iz1} = \frac{\rho(\theta - 1)}{\theta - 2} = 1.369\rho. \tag{14-9}$$

To obtain an output beam that is axially parallel, S_{iz1} should lie halfway between the incident and reflected paths, in order to supply symmetry. But since S_{iz1} varies with ρ, this condition can be met by ions of only one value of momentum; the rest of the particles will be axially diverging on the return path. The gap of the first magnet is as large as in the first case of this chapter, while that of the second magnet may be even larger.

The system is symmetric, with $\theta = 270°$. Hence we have $f^* = f_6 = \tan u_2(1 - \cos \theta) + \sin \theta = 1 - 1 = 0$, so the arrangement is doubly achromatic. The input beam may be of finite width, provided all the paths are parallel to each other.

540° ACHROMATIC REFLECTOR, $n = 0, u_1 = u_4 = 0, u_2 = u_3 = 45°$

A variation of the preceding scheme, for use in a proposed* back-and-forth traversal of a linear accelerator, is shown in Fig. 14-5. An input beam of mixed energy is returned directly along the incident path; again we have $f^* = f_6 = 0$, so there is double achromatism. Since $S_{01} = \infty$ and $\tan u_1 = 0$,

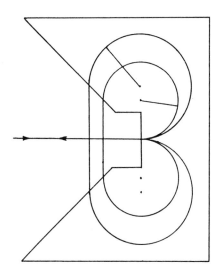

FIG. 14-5. Achromatic reflection with no radial divergence is obtained in this magnet only if the input beam is of vanishing width.

there is no internal axial image, and Eq. (3-10) shows that $S_{iz1} = \rho$; i.e., the first axial image lies on the input-output path. Hence $S_{0z2} = \rho$ and Eq. (3-6), adjusted to describe the second magnet, shows that $S_{iz2} = \infty$.

For radial motion, Eq. (2-21) gives $S_{ix1} = 0$, so the first radial image is at the exit edge of the first magnet. Then $S_{0x2} = S_1 = 2\rho$ (the separation), so by use of Eq. (2-18), rewritten for the second magnet, we find that $S_{ix2} = \rho/2$. Radial divergence is introduced if the beam has finite radial width, as may be seen from a geometrical construction.

Note that in these 540° magnets the straight-line intermediate paths lie between the *effective* edges. Hence the iron edges must be sufficiently separated so that this condition does indeed exist.

* 222b, Kolomensky.

270° MAGNET, $n = 0$, $u_1 = u_2 = 45°$. ACHROMATIC SLOPE AND DISPERSED IMAGE

A uniform field with one straight edge (such as one half of the structure of Fig. 14-4) gives a net deflection of 90°. As before, we find that $f_6 = 0$, so the slope in the image space is achromatic. But since station 6 is not now at the symmetry plane, we see that $f_6 \neq f^*$, so there is no automatic assurance that $c_6 = 0$. On the contrary, Eq. (6-27) shows that $c_6 = \rho$, so the images of different momenta are dispersed.

For each momentum of a particular ρ, Eq. (2-18) gives $S_{ix} = S_0 - \rho$, so $M_x = -1$, and Eq. (3-6) shows that $S_{iz} = [3.7 S_0 - 4.7 \rho]/[(2.7 S_0 / \rho) - 3.7]$. The lateral separation of the images is $c_6 \Delta p / p = e \Delta \rho / \rho = \Delta \rho$. Double focusing for each component occurs for $S_0 = 2.49 \rho$, for which $S_{ix} = S_{iz} = 1.49 \rho$. When S_0 is infinite, then $S_{ix} = \infty$ and $S_{iz} = 1.37 \rho$.

270° MAGNET, $n = 0$, $u_1 = 0$, $u_2 = 45°$. ACHROMATIC SLOPE AND DISPERSED IMAGE

This magnet is half of that shown in Fig. 14-5. Again we find that $f_6 = 0$ and $c_6 = \rho$. The radial images lie at $S_{ix} = \rho / [(S_0 / \rho) - 1]$ and the axial images at $S_{iz} = [S_0 + 4.7 \rho]/[(S_0 / \rho) + 3.7]$. There is double focusing for $S_0 = 1.85 \rho$ and then $S_{ix} = S_{iz} = 1.18 \rho$. When S_0 is infinite, then $S_{ix} = 0$ and $S_{iz} = \rho$.

Recall also the doubly focused achromatic image of Case 17, p. 81, where $n < 0.5$ and θ exceeds 180°, its size depending on the value of n.

360° PARTICLE SEPARATOR

There are occasions when it is desirable to separate the different species of ions produced by an ion source (e.g., H^+ and HH^+) without introducing any deflection in the path of the wanted particles, say protons. The 360° magnet described by Perry,† Fig. 14-6, employs two immediately adjacent uniform fields of different strengths. The protons are turned through 360° but HH^+ ions that have fallen through the same potential in the source have a radius that is $\sqrt{2}$ times that of the protons and so are deflected through a smaller angle and may be intercepted at a barrier.

It is interesting to calculate the radial divergence produced in the proton beam because of the deflection and the inevitable energy spread from the source. This spread is so small that, to first order, all radii and angles (bending

---

* 215, Enge.
† 222a, Perry.

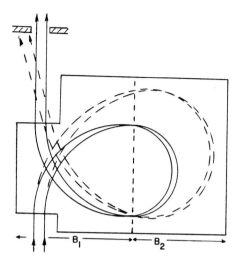

FIG. 14-6. Paths of proton (solid line) and that of HH^+ ion (dashed line), both having fallen through the same potential in the ion source. $B_2 = 2B_1$.

and edge) are constant. The system may be considered as composed of three magnets; the deflection angles are $\theta_1 = \theta_3 = 90°$ and $\theta_2 = 180°$; the radii are $\rho_1 = \rho_3$ and ρ_2; all $u = 0$ and the intermagnet separations are $S_1 = S_2 = 0$. From the expressions of Chapter 6 we readily find that the momentum-dependent contribution to the radial slope at any distance past the third magnet is $f_{14} \Delta p/p = 2(1 - \rho_2/\rho_1)\Delta p/p$. This divergence is therefore reduced as ρ_2 approaches ρ_1, but the limit of $\rho_2 = \rho_1$ cannot be reached, for then the particles would describe only a semicircle.

We may compare this divergence with that produced by a single-field magnet, for which $f_6 = \sin \theta$. For $\theta = 90°$, we have $f_6 = 1$, so to attain a slope less than this with the 360° magnet we must have $\rho_2/\rho_1 > 0.5$; for $\theta = 30°$, we need $\rho_2/\rho_1 > 0.75$, etc.

The dispersion is found to be $c_{14} \Delta p/p = 2S_3(1 - \rho_2/\rho_1) \Delta p/p$. Hence at the exit edge, where $S_3 = 0$, the radial displacement is independent of momentum even if ρ_2/ρ_1 is not unity. Further downstream, however, dispersion becomes apparent.

15 Beam Translation by Two Magnets with Achromatic Image

INTRODUCTION

Translation here means that the beam is shifted laterally by two oppositely bending magnets of equal angles. The radial half-width and maximum slope at distance S_2 beyond the second magnet are given by

$$x_{10\,max} = (\gamma_9 - 2\beta_9 S_2 + \alpha_9 S_2^2)^{1/2} x_0 x_0' + c_{10}^{+-} \Delta p/p, \qquad (15\text{-}1)$$

$$x'_{10\,max} = \alpha_9^{1/2} x_0 x_0' + f_{10}^{+-} \Delta p/p, \qquad (15\text{-}2)$$

where

$$c_{10}^{+-} = c_9^{+-} + f_9^{+-} S_2, \qquad (15\text{-}3)$$

$$f_{10}^{+-} = f_9^{+-}. \qquad (15\text{-}4)$$

It does not appear practical to make both $x_{10\,max}$ and $x'_{10\,max}$ independent of Δp. This would require that both $c_{10}^{+-} = 0$ and $f_{10}^{+-} = 0$. Although a general nonexistence proof of this is lacking, in the cases here investigated the necessary condition is that each magnet should bend through more than $180°$.

Therefore we now consider the circumstances which will produce only an achromatic image, the radial slope in the image space being momentum dependent. Since the magnets bend in opposite directions, an analysis based on mirror symmetry is not valid, and we appeal, first, to Eq. (5-15) for magnets of opposite polarity that have a radial image between them:

$$R_p^{+-} = \frac{\Delta p}{p} = \frac{-w_o}{-\rho_1 F_1 + \rho_2 F_2/M_{x1}}. \qquad (15\text{-}5)$$

Since M_{x1} is negative (for $\theta_1 < 180°$), it is impossible for such an arrangement to be nondispersive, because the denominator cannot vanish.

We therefore realize that an achromatic final image cannot be obtained

200

if there is an intermagnet image. The conditions for the goal must be found by a basic procedure that can be very tedious. In the interest of simplicity we assume, in what follows, that $n_1 = n_2$, although this is not necessary in principle.

The distance of no dispersion is found by setting $c_{10}^{+-} = 0$, using Eqs. (6-88)–(6-90). (This means that we will find a specific value $S_2 = -c_9^{+-}/f_9^{+-}$.) Now c_{10}^{+-} is a function of S_1 and S_2, and it is found that c_{10}^{+-} will vanish if S_2 is the downstream focal length of the second magnet and if $\theta_1 = \theta_2$; it is not necessary that $\rho_1 = \rho_2$.

The object for the second magnet is therefore at infinity, which implies that the object of the first magnet must be at its upstream focal distance.

The radial image distance for the second magnet is found by setting $b_{10} = 0$, using Eq. (6-87). We let $\theta_1 = \theta_2$, replace S_2 by S_{ix2}, substitute the upstream focal distance of the first magnet for S_0, and solve for S_{ix2}. It is found to equal the distance of no dispersion usually only if $\rho_1 = \rho_2$ (although there are several cases where this equality is not necessary). Thus far, the separation S_1 between magnets is irrelevant.

However, when double focusing is required, S_1 becomes prescribed. The analysis depends on which of the edge angles are finite.

The magnifications are usually best obtained from the relations $M_x = a_{10}$ and $M_z = \bar{a}_{10}$. These coefficients are functions of S_1 and S_2; for each of these, the expressions that are appropriate for the achromatic image should be used. In certain cases, M_x and M_z can be found by inspection.

We now present six systems with uniform-field magnets and one in which both magnets have $n = 0.5$.

CASE I.   All $u = 0$, $n_1 = n_2 = 0$, $\theta_1 = \theta_2$ (Fig. 15-1)

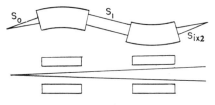

FIG. 15-1.

To make $c_{10}^{+-} = b_{10} = 0$, we must have

$$L_o = L_{ix2} = \cot \theta. \tag{15-6}$$

Setting $L_2 = L_{ix2} = \cot \theta$ in Eq. (6-79) for a_{10} ($= M_x$), we find that terms in L_1 cancel out and that

$$M_x = -\rho_1/\rho_2. \tag{15-7}$$

There is no axial focusing, the separation S_1 may have any value, and ρ_1 need not equal ρ_2.

CASE II. $u_1 > 0$, $u_2 = u_3 = u_4 = 0$, $n_1 = n_2 = 0$, $\theta_1 = \theta_2$ (Fig. 15-2)

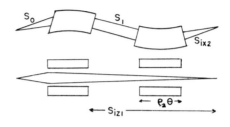

FIG. 15-2.

To make $c_{10}^{+-} = b_{10} = 0$, L_o must be given by Eq. (2-20):

$$S_0/\rho_1 = L_o = 1/(\tan \theta - \tan u_1), \qquad (15\text{-}8)$$

whence

$$\tan u_1 = \tan \theta - (\rho_1/S_0). \qquad (15\text{-}9)$$

The radial image's location is given by Eq. (2-21) (adjusted for the second magnet):

$$S_{ix2}/\rho_2 = L_{ix2} = \cot \theta. \qquad (15\text{-}10)$$

For double focusing, we need

$$S_1 + \rho_2 \theta + S_{ix2} = S_{iz1}. \qquad (15\text{-}11)$$

Substitute for S_{ix2} as given above, and for S_{iz1} use Eq. (3-6). Solve for S_1:

$$S_1 = \frac{2\theta(\rho_1 + \rho_2) + 2\rho_2 \cot \theta + S_0(1 - \rho_2/\rho_1) - S_0 \theta \tan \theta(1 + \rho_2/\rho_1)}{(S_0/\rho_1) \tan \theta - 2}.$$

$$(15\text{-}12)$$

The radial magnification depends on both magnets. We have $M_x = a_{10}$ (Eq. 6-79) with $S_2 = S_{ix2} = \rho_2 \cot \theta$ as shown above. All terms in S_1 cancel and we find

$$M_x = -(\rho_1/\rho_2) + (\rho_2/\rho_1)\tan u_1 \cot \theta. \qquad (15\text{-}13)$$

Substitution for $\tan u_1$ as in Eq. (15-9) gives

$$M_x = -(\rho_1/\rho_2) + (\rho_2/\rho_1)[1 - \rho_1/(S_0 \tan \theta)]. \qquad (15\text{-}14)$$

The axial magnification is governed only by the first magnet. By Eq. (3-4):

$$M_z = -1/[(S_0/\rho_1)\tan u_1 - 1]. \qquad (15\text{-}15)$$

Using Eq. (15-9), this becomes

$$M_z = -1/[(S_0/\rho_1)\tan\theta - 2].\qquad(15\text{-}16)$$

Note that it is not necessary that $\rho_1 = \rho_2$ in order to obtain an achromatic image.

Typical behavior is shown in the following Fig. 15-3, where for simplicity we assume $\rho_1 = \rho_2$. For example, if $\theta_1 = \theta_2 = 45°$ and double focusing is *not* required, an achromatic radial image can be formed only at $L_{ix2} = 1$; it can be obtained for any object distance between $L_0 = 1$ and infinity, provided that u_1 is suitably chosen; u_1 will lie between $0°$ and $45°$. The separation L_1 is immaterial.

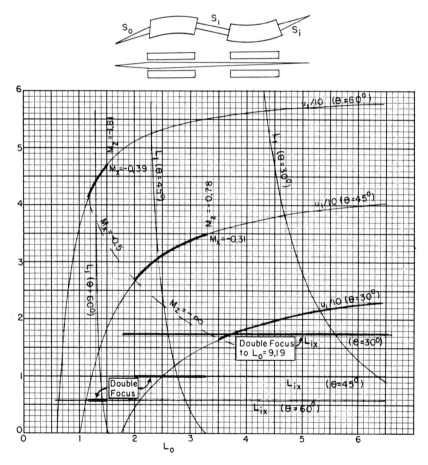

FIG. 15-3. Case II. Achromatic image. $u_1 > 0$, $u_2 = u_3 = u_4 = 0$, $n_1 = n_2 = 0, \theta_1 = \theta_2$, $\rho_1 = \rho_2$.

If double focusing is wanted, we have $L_{ix2} = L_{iz2} = 1$, but L_o is restricted to the range 2 to 3.27. The corresponding value of u_1 lies between 27.4° and 34.9°. The separation $S_1 = \rho L_1$ must have an appropriate value in the span infinity to zero. M_x ranges from -0.500 to -0.305, while M_z lies between $-\infty$ and -0.78.

CASE III. $u_4 > 0$, $u_1 = u_2 = u_3 = 0$, $n_1 = n_2 = 0$, $\theta_1 = \theta_2$ (Fig. 15-4)

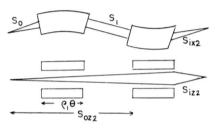

FIG. 15-4.

Although this case may be worked out in detail, it is simpler to realize that it is Case II with the particles going backwards. We interchange L_o with L_{ix2}, u_1 with u_4, and ρ_1 with ρ_2. The magnifications are the reciprocals of those in Case II, including the above changes.

$$L_{ix2} = \frac{S_{ix2}}{\rho_2}$$

$$= \frac{1}{\tan\theta - \tan u_4}, \tag{15-17}$$

$$\tan u_4 = \tan\theta - \frac{\rho_2}{S_{ix2}}, \tag{15-18}$$

$$L_o = \frac{S_0}{\rho_1}$$

$$= \cot\theta, \tag{15-19}$$

$$M_x = \frac{1}{-(\rho_2/\rho_1) + (\rho_1/\rho_2)[1 - \rho_2/(S_{ix2}\tan\theta)]} \tag{15-20}$$

$$M_z = -\left[\frac{S_{ix2}}{\rho_2}\tan\theta - 2\right]. \tag{15-21}$$

For double focusing, we must have

$$S_1 = \frac{2\theta(\rho_1 + \rho_2) + 2\rho_1 \cot \theta + S_i(1 - \rho_1/\rho_2) - S_i\theta \tan \theta(1 + \rho_1/\rho_2)}{(S_i/\rho_2)\tan \theta - 2}.$$

$$(15\text{-}22)$$

This case has been discussed by Panofsky and McIntyre* for the special case where $\rho_1 = \rho_2$ and $S_0 = \infty$. The gap must be larger than in Case II, since axial focusing does not occur until the ions leave the second magnet.

In Fig. 15-5, we assume that $\rho_1 = \rho_2$.

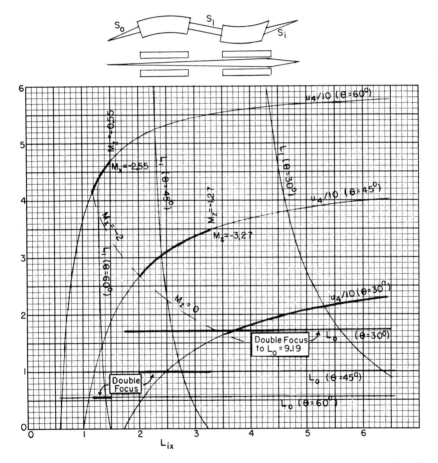

FIG. 15-5. Case III. Achromatic image. $u_4 > 0$, $u_1 = u_2 = u_3 = 0$, $n_1 = n_2 = 0$, $\theta_1 = \theta_2$, $\rho_1 = \rho_2$.

* 205, Panofsky and McIntyre.

Case IV. $u_1 = u_4 = u$, $\tan u = 1/L_0$, $u_2 = u_3 = 0$, $n_1 = n_2 = 0$, $\theta_1 = \theta_2$, $\rho_1 = \rho_2$ (Fig. 15-6)

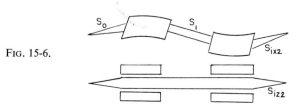

Fig. 15-6.

For an achromatic image, the object and image distances are the radial focal distances (Eqs. (2-20) and (2-21), the latter adjusted to the second magnet):

$$L_o = L_{ix2} = 1/(\tan \theta - \tan u). \tag{15-23}$$

For double focusing, the object and image distances are the axial focal lengths (Eqs. (3-9) and (3-10)) for the paths indicated in Fig. 15-6:

$$L_o = L_{iz2} = 1/\tan u. \tag{15-24}$$

Equating these gives

$$\tan u = 0.5 \tan \theta. \tag{15-25}$$

Therefore

$$L_o = L_i = 2 \cot \theta. \tag{15-26}$$

Typical data are given in Table 15-1 and the following two equations:

TABLE 15-1

θ (deg)	15	30	45	60	75
u (deg)	7.6	16.1	26.6	40.9	61.8
$L_o = L_i$	7.46	3.46	2.0	1.15	0.54

$$M_x = -1, \tag{15-27}$$
$$M_z = -1. \tag{15-28}$$

The separation S_1 is irrelevant, except that an object of finite size will require a larger gap in the second magnet as S_1 increases.

Case V. $u_1 = u_4 = u > 0$, $u_2 = u_3 = 0$, $n_1 = n_2 = 0$, $\theta_1 = \theta_2$, $\rho_1 = \rho_2$ (Fig. 15-7)

From $c_{10}^{+-} = b_{10} = 0$, we get

$$L_o = L_{ix2} = 1/(\tan \theta - \tan u), \tag{15-29}$$

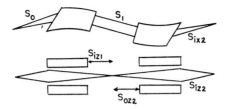

FIG. 15-7.

whence

$$\tan u = \tan \theta - 1/L_o. \tag{15-30}$$

For double focusing, $L_{iz2} = L_{ix2}$. For the former, use Eq. (3-6) (adapted for the second magnet) and for L_{ix2} use the expression in Eq. (15-29). We find

$$L_{oz2} = \frac{1 + \theta \tan \theta - 2\theta \tan u}{2 \tan u - \tan \theta}. \tag{15-31}$$

Use this and the expression for L_{iz1} given by Eq. (3-6) in the relation

$$L_1 = L_{iz1} + L_{oz2}, \tag{15-32}$$

substituting for $\tan u$ as shown above. The result is

$$L_1 = \frac{L_o(1 - \theta \tan \theta) + 2\theta}{0.5 \, L_o \tan \theta - 1}. \tag{15-33}$$

In this, substitute Eq. (15-29) for L_o and then solve for $\tan u$:

$$\tan u = \frac{(0.5 \, L_1 + \theta)\tan \theta + 1}{L_1 + 2\theta}. \tag{15-34}$$

From symmetry it is clear that

$$M_x = -1, \tag{15-35}$$

$$M_z = 1. \tag{15-36}$$

Examples are shown in Fig. 15-8.
    This case has been discussed by Brown.*

* 206, Brown.

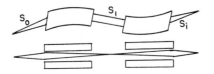

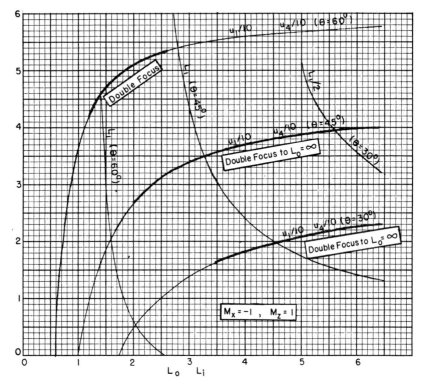

FIG. 15-8. Case V. Achromatic image. $u_1 = u_4 = u > 0$, $u_2 = u_3 = 0$, $n_1 = n_2 = 0$, $\theta_1 = \theta_2$, $\rho_1 = \rho_2$.

CASE VI. $u_1 = u_2 = u_3 = u_4 = u$, $\tan u = 1/L_o$, $n_1 = n_2 = 0$, $\theta_1 = \theta_2$, $\rho_1 = \rho_2$ (Fig. 15-9)

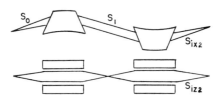

FIG. 15-9.

To obtain an achromatic image, the radial object and image distances are the radial focal lengths. By Eqs. (2-20) and (2-21), we find

$$L_o = L_{ix2} = \frac{1 + \tan u \tan \theta}{\tan \theta - 2 \tan u + \tan^2 u \tan \theta}. \qquad (15\text{-}37)$$

From this we obtain a quadratic in $\tan u$:

$$L_o \tan \theta \tan^2 u + (2L_o + \tan \theta)\tan u + 1 - L_o \tan \theta = 0. \qquad (15\text{-}38)$$

For axial motion with paths parallel to the midplane inside the magnets (for ions starting on the axis as shown in Fig. 15-9), the object distance must be the focal length as given by Eq. (3-9) with u_2 taken as zero; thus

$$\tan u = 1/L_o. \qquad (15\text{-}39)$$

From the last two expressions, we find

$$L_o = L_i = \tfrac{3}{2} \cot \theta \pm (\tfrac{9}{4} \cot^2 \theta + 2)^{1/2}. \qquad (15\text{-}40)$$

From symmetry it is clear that the system is double focusing. The separation of the magnets must be

$$L_1 = 2L_o. \qquad (15\text{-}41)$$

Also

$$M_x = -1, \qquad (15\text{-}42)$$

$$M_z = 1. \qquad (15\text{-}43)$$

Typical data are given in Table 15-2.

TABLE 15-2

θ (deg)	30	45	60	75	90	105	120	150
u (deg)	10.2	15.7	21.6	28.1	35.3	43.2	51.6	70.2
$L_o = L_i$	5.56	3.56	2.53	1.87	1.41	1.07	0.79	0.36
L_1	11.12	7.12	5.06	3.74	2.82	2.14	1.58	0.72

CASE VII. $u_1 = u_2 = u_3 = u_4 = 0$, $n_1 = n_2 = 0.5$, $\theta_1 = \theta_2$ (Fig. 15-10)

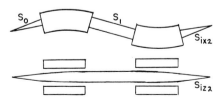

FIG. 15-10.

The image is achromatic for

$$L_o = S_0/\rho_1 = \sqrt{2}\cot(\theta/\sqrt{2}), \tag{15-44}$$

$$L_i = S_{ix2}/\rho_2 = S_{iz2}/\rho_2 = \sqrt{2}\cot(\theta/\sqrt{2}), \tag{15-45}$$

$$M_x = M_z = -\left[\cos^2(\theta/\sqrt{2}) + \frac{\rho_2}{\rho_1}\sin^2(\theta/\sqrt{2})\right] \tag{15-46}$$

$$= -1 \quad \text{if} \quad \rho_1 = \rho_2.$$

The system is double focusing no matter what the separation S_1. See data given in Table 15-3.

TABLE 15-3

$(\rho_1 = \rho_2)$

θ (deg)	15	30	45	60	90	120	127.5
$L_o = L_i$	7.55	3.65	2.28	1.55	0.702	0.129	0

THE TRANSLATION DISTANCE

When one of the preceding schemes is used to produce an achromatic image by shifting the beam laterally with two magnets, it is often desirable to know the translation distance (see Fig. 15-11); floor space may not be available.

$$q_1 = \rho_1 \tan(\theta/2), \qquad q_2 = \rho_2 \tan(\theta/2),$$

$$K = (q_1 + q_2 + S_1)\cos\theta, \tag{15-47}$$

$$T = K\tan\theta = [(\rho_1 + \rho_2)\tan(\theta/2) + S_1]\sin\theta.$$

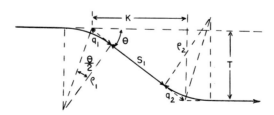

FIG. 15-11. The geometry of the translation distance T.

16 Dispersed or Achromatic Image with Two Magnets

Two magnets, deflecting in opposite directions, are often used to produce a highly dispersed image, as discussed earlier. Yet there are occasions when the experimenter desires the maximum intensity at the final slit without regard to homogeneity of energy.

One way to accomplish this is to open wide the final slit, and the inter-magnet slit if one is used, but the resulting dispersed image may be too wide for the purpose.

A better solution is to produce an achromatic final image. A happy situation exists if both magnets have $n = 0.5$, for, as shown in Eq. (4-94), if the object and image distances are equal, with the value

$$S_0 = S_i = \sqrt{2}\rho \cot \frac{\theta}{2\sqrt{2}}, \qquad (16\text{-}1)$$

and if the magnets are separated by $S_1 = 2S_0$, then the resolution function of each is $F = 4$, so that a highly dispersed and double-focused image is produced.

Now, as we have just seen in Eq. (15-44), such a pair of magnets will give an achromatic double-focused image, irrespective of their separation, if the object slit and final image slit are relocated so that

$$S_0 = S_i = \sqrt{2}\rho \cot \frac{\theta}{\sqrt{2}}. \qquad (16\text{-}2)$$

Such a procedure* involves adjusting the upstream quadrupole so as to concentrate the beam on the "achromatic" input slit rather than on the "dispersive" one. (The unused input, output, and intermagnet slits must be opened wide.)

* 214, Blosser and Butler.

The situation is not quite so favorable if both magnets have $n = 0$. The edge angles supply double focusing in the dispersive case, when there are specified values not only for S_0 and S_i, but also for the separation S_1. To obtain an achromatic image, the object and image slits may be repositioned, but since the value of S_1 for double focusing is often fixed, at a magnitude different from that needed for dispersion, the achromatic image is not double focused.* (It is impractical to change the value of S_1.) Note, however, that S_1 is not specified for an achromatic image in the previous double focused case IV and in the single focused case I.

When such a shift from a dispersed to an achromatic image is contemplated (with either value of n), the change in object distance can be substantial, so there can be appreciable differences in the required height and width of the magnets' gaps. Preliminary calculations of these dimensions are advisable, for both the dispersed and achromatic arrangements.

If the object distance is altered, as required above, by simply changing the currents in the quadrupoles that illuminate the object slit, there will be a change in the object's dimensions x_0 and z_0, and in the maximum slopes x_0' and z_0'. Since x_0/x_0' and z_0/z_0' play a role in the envelopes' size, these changes must be investigated. Let x_{00} and x_{00}' define the beam leaving the accelerator. In the dispersive arrangement, the quadrupoles produce an image (actually, a waist) with coordinates x_{0d} and x_{0d}'. By the usual arguments of optics, we have

$$\frac{\text{Image size}}{\text{Object size}} = \frac{\text{Image distance}}{\text{Object distance}}$$

or

$$\frac{x_{0d}}{x_{00}} = \frac{Q_d}{P} \tag{16-3}$$

as shown in Fig. 16-1. (This argument is valid only when distances are measured from the principal planes. But the usual quadrupole is "thin," so that these planes are almost coincident at its center. See Chapter 19.) In the achromatic configuration, we see that

$$\frac{x_{0a}}{x_{00}} = \frac{Q_a}{P}. \tag{16-4}$$

On dividing this by the expression just above, we find

$$x_{0a} = \frac{Q_a}{Q_d} x_{0d}. \tag{16-5}$$

* 221, Ramler *et al.*

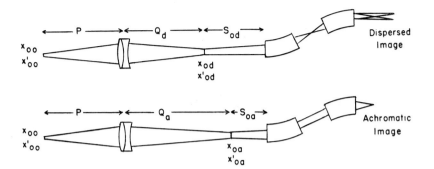

FIG. 16-1. Changes in the object's parameters when its position is altered.

Now by Eq. (7-106), (area of phase-space ellipse)$/\pi = x_{0a} x'_{0a} = x_{0d} x'_{0d}$, so that

$$x_{0a} = \frac{x_{0d} x'_{0d}}{x'_{0a}}. \qquad (16\text{-}6)$$

Equating these two relations gives

$$x'_{0a} = \frac{Q_d x'_{0d}}{Q_a}. \qquad (16\text{-}7)$$

Expressions similar to Eqs. (16-5) and (16-7) hold for the axial parameters.

17 Chromatic Aberrations

INTRODUCTION

Chromatic aberrations in magnets represent departures from an "ideal" situation in that certain parameters depend on the energy of the projectile. Some of these aberrations are often negligible, while others are not; in fact, magnets used for momentum analysis are designed to exploit and augment the aberration that produces a radial displacement of images with different momenta. This aspect has been considered already; we will now discuss some of the others, very briefly, to show that their neglect in earlier chapters is justified.

CHROMATIC ABERRATIONS IN MAGNIFICATION

We repeat Eq. (2-24) for the radial magnification (where $\sigma \equiv \sin \phi$ and $\kappa \equiv \cos \phi$),

$$M_x = - \frac{1}{(S_0/\rho)[\delta\sigma - (t_1 + t_2)\kappa - (t_1 t_2 \sigma/\delta)] - \kappa - t_2\sigma/\delta}. \quad (17\text{-}1)$$

If the momentum p increases, then so does ρ, and hence also M_x. For small changes, we proceed as follows. Since $dp/p = d\rho/\rho$, then $dM/dp = \rho dM/(p d\rho)$. Using Δ to denote a finite increment, to first order we have

$$M_{p+\Delta p} = M_p + \Delta p \frac{dM}{dp},$$

so

$$\Delta M = M_{p+\Delta p} - M_p = \Delta p \frac{dM}{dp} = \frac{\Delta p}{p} \rho \frac{dM}{d\rho}. \quad (17\text{-}2)$$

By differentiation of Eq. (17-1), we find that $dM/d\rho = -S_0 M^2 H/\rho^2$, where H is the expression in square brackets in Eq. (17-1). Hence Eq. (17-2) becomes

$$\Delta M_x = -\frac{\Delta p}{p}\frac{S_0}{\rho} M_x^2 \left[\delta\sigma - (t_1 + t_2)\kappa - \frac{t_1 t_2}{\delta}\sigma\right]. \qquad (17\text{-}3)$$

This is negative, and since M_x is also negative, the $p + \Delta p$ ion has a larger (negative) magnification, and hence a larger image than the p particle. The change is generally negligible, however; an example will be given later.

An identical argument may be applied to the expression for the axial magnification M_z, but the same result may be obtained more quickly by converting the last expression to the axial form by the procedure given earlier. We obtain

$$\Delta M_z = -\frac{\Delta p}{p}\frac{S_0}{\rho} M_z^2 \left[\varepsilon \sin\psi + (t_1 + t_2)\cos\psi - t_1 t_2 \frac{\sin\psi}{\varepsilon}\right]. \qquad (17\text{-}4)$$

where $\varepsilon = \sqrt{n}$ and $\psi = \varepsilon\theta$. Thus the $p + \Delta p$ image is larger than the p image, but by only a very small amount.

CHROMATIC ABERRATION IN IMAGE DISTANCE

Eq. (2-18) has shown that

$$S_{ix} = \frac{S_0[\kappa + (t_1\sigma/\delta)] + (\rho\sigma/\delta)}{(S_0/\rho)[\delta\sigma - (t_1 + t_2)\kappa - (t_1 t_2\sigma/\delta)] - \kappa - t_2\sigma/\delta}. \qquad (17\text{-}5)$$

Arguing as before, we have

$$\Delta S_{ix} = \frac{\Delta p}{p}\rho\frac{dS_{ix}}{d\rho}, \qquad (17\text{-}6)$$

so by differentiation we obtain

$$\Delta S_{ix} = \frac{\Delta p}{p} M_x^2 \left\{\left[\delta\sigma - (t_1 + t_2)\kappa - t_1 t_2 \frac{\sigma}{\delta}\right]\right.$$
$$\left. \times \left[\frac{2S_0}{\rho}\frac{\sigma}{\delta} + \frac{S_0^2}{\rho^2}\left(\kappa + t_1\frac{\sigma}{\delta}\right)\right] - \frac{\sigma}{\delta}\left(t_2\frac{\sigma}{\delta} + \kappa\right)\right\}. \qquad (17\text{-}7)$$

The images of increasing momentum straddle a line that is slanted with respect to the optic axis, those with greater momentum having the larger image distance. The tilt of this line can be considerable in a mass spectrometer where the changes in momenta are large, but for a magnet used to take a small momentum bite out of the continuous distribution from an accelerator, all those portions of the images of different momenta that pass through the image slit may be considered to lie at the same distance from the magnet, for most practical purposes. (When second-order effects are included, the images straddle a curved line.)

The corresponding expression for the change in the axial image distance is

$$\Delta S_{iz} = \frac{\Delta p}{p} M_z^2 \left\{ \left[\varepsilon \sin \psi + (t_1 + t_2) \cos \psi - t_1 t_2 \frac{\sin \psi}{\varepsilon} \right] \right.$$
$$\left. \times \left[\frac{2S_0}{\rho} \frac{\sin \psi}{\varepsilon} + \frac{S_0^2}{\rho^2} \left(\cos \psi - t_1 \frac{\sin \psi}{\varepsilon} \right) \right] - \frac{\sin \psi}{\varepsilon} \left(\cos \psi - t_2 \frac{\sin \psi}{\varepsilon} \right) \right\}.$$

$$(17\text{-}8)$$

For the usual case, where the output slit is one image wide, we have $\Delta p/p = w_0/\rho F$ by Eq. (2-34), where w_0 is the object's width, and F is the resolution function. Hence the expressions for the various aberrations can be written in terms of F and w_0 instead of $\Delta p/p$. To obtain an idea of the magnitude of the chromatic aberrations that have been discussed, we consider the example of a magnet with $n = 0$, $\tan u_1 = \tan u_2 = 1/L_0$, with L_0 so chosen for every θ that $M_x = M_z = -1$ and $F = 4$. It is then found from the expressions given above that ΔS_{ix}, ΔS_{iz}, ΔM_x, and ΔM_z are of order $-w_0/\rho$ for the particles that pass through the image slit. Such aberrations are negligible.

18 Correction of Certain Aberrations

INTRODUCTION

As has been emphasized by Penner, aberrations in magnetic systems fall into two general categories; physical aberrations caused by faulty construction (e.g., misaligned apparatus, field not exactly as specified, fluctuating current to the coils, etc.) and mathematical aberrations, arising from a theory that does not take into account all the factors involved.

Only meticulous care can eliminate the first class. Understanding the second is a continuing effort on the part of the theoreticians, whose recommendations must be followed during manufacture, if indeed a simultaneous alleviation of the various effects can be carried out, even in principle.

Although the study of aberrations is beyond the scope of this book, we will quote, without proof, certain methods used to eliminate some of the more serious ones.

When second-order effects are taken into account, the expression for the radial half-width at any distance beyond a magnet is of the form

$$w_i/2 = a_6 x_0 + b_6 x_0' + c_6 \, dp/p + g_6 x_0{}^2 + h_6 x_0'^2 + j_6 (dp/p)^2$$
$$+ k_6 x_0 x_0' + m_6 x_0 \, dp/p + n_6 x_0' \, dp/p + q_6 z_0{}^2 + r_6 z_0 z_0'$$
$$+ s_6 z_0'^2 + \cdots. \tag{18-1}$$

The first three terms are the familiar first-order terms of Eq. (2-12). The effect of the remainder is to increase the displacement, so that at the image plane, where $b_6 = 0$, the image is wider than when computed by first-order theory only. Hence a larger increase in momentum is needed to shift the $p + dp$ image to a region behind the jaws of the slit, and the resolution is therefore poorer.

Fortunately, the coefficient h_6 can be made zero by properly shaping the edge faces of the magnet. The physical reason why this should be effective

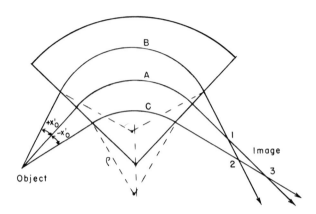

FIG. 18-1. A flat-faced $n = 0$ magnet gives an imperfect image.

may be seen in a special case, shown in Fig. 18-1. With a flat-faced, uniform-field, 90° magnet, it is clear that the intersection of path B with path A (point 1) would move further away from the magnet if path B were deflected less, and that the crossing of path C with path A (point 3) would come closer to the magnet if path C also did not bend so much. To accomplish these aims, paths B and C should lie in the field for shorter distances. This is done in Fig. 18-2, where, for $\theta = 90°$ and $M_x = -1$, we see that if the edges are cylindrical with radii $R = \rho$, then all three intersection points merge into one.

We will now discuss some of the methods employed in more general configurations.

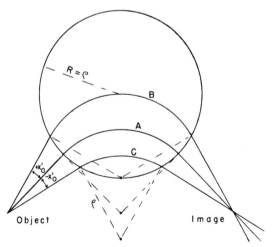

FIG. 18-2. When the faces have radii $R = \rho$, there is no aberration due to x_0' if $\theta = 90°$ and $M_x = -1$.

UNIFORM FIELDS—CURVED EDGES

The problem and methods of solution have been treated in a number of papers.* A particularly useful approach is that of Hintenberger,† who gives

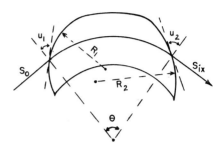

FIG. 18-3. Cylindrical faces of a magnet can eliminate the $x_0'^2$ aberration.

an expression to eliminate $h_6 x_0'^2$ by the use of cylindrical faces with radii R_1 and R_2 (Fig. 18-3). It is:

$$\rho\left(\frac{K_1}{R_1} + \frac{K_2}{R_2}\right) = C_1 + C_2, \tag{18-2}$$

where

$$\frac{1}{K_{1,2}} = \cos^3 u_{1,2}\left\{\left[1 + \left(\frac{\rho}{S_{1,2}} + \tan u_{1,2}\right)^2\right]^3\right\}^{1/2} \tag{18-3}$$

and

$$C_{1,2} = \frac{\rho^2[(\rho/S_{1,2}) + 3 \tan u_{1,2}]}{S_{1,2}^2(\{1 + [(\rho/S_{1,2}) + \tan u_{1,2}]^2\}^3)^{1/2}}. \tag{18-4}$$

Here S_1 and S_2 are the object and image distances, respectively, related through Eq. (2-18).

In the symmetrical case where $S_1 = S_2 = S$ and $u_1 = u_2 = u$, we have $K_1 = K_2$ and $C_1 = C_2$. Then it follows that

$$\frac{1}{R_1} + \frac{1}{R_2} = \frac{2\rho}{S^2}\left(\frac{\rho}{S} + 3 \tan u\right)\cos^3 u. \tag{18-5}$$

If we choose $R_1 = R_2 = R$, and if $u = 0$, this gives

$$R = \frac{S^3}{\rho^2} = L^3\rho. \tag{18-6}$$

* 61, Kerwin; 62, Kerwin and Geoffrion; 76, Walton; 122, Crewe.
† 64, Hintenberger; 60, Hintenberger.

For a magnet with circular poles. $R = r_e$, so that we may write

$$\frac{r_e}{\rho} = \frac{S^3}{\rho^3}.$$

(18-7)

From Fig. 18-4 we see, by Barber's rule, that $2A + \theta = 180°$ so $A = 90° - \theta/2$.

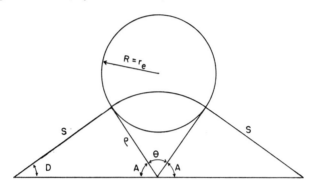

FIG.18-4. Barber's rule when $S_0 = S_{1x} = S$.

Also from the figure we see that $D + A = 90°$, so that $D = \theta/2$. It is also evident that

$$\tan D = \tan(\theta/2) = \rho/S.$$

(18-8)

Now use Eq. (18-8) in Eq. (18-7) to find that

$$r_e/\rho = 1/\tan^3(\theta/2).$$

(18-9)

But by Eq. (4-5), for a circular pole we always have

$$r_e/\rho = \tan(\theta/2).$$

(18-10)

Equating these last two expressions gives

$$\tan^4(\theta/2) = 1 \qquad \text{so} \qquad \theta = 90°.$$

Thus a uniform-field circular magnet used at $90°$ and at $M_x = -1$ will automatically eliminate the $x_0'^2$ aberration, as was also shown by a graphical argument in Fig. 18-2.

For other special cases, see Hintenberger's papers.

A very complete analysis of second-order effects in uniform-field magnets has been given by Brown et al.* The coefficients a, b, ... are designated, for example, in the form $(x \mid x_0^2)$, which indicates the coefficient of x_0^2 in the expression for x. The coefficients that are given are associated with the

* 84, Brown et al.; 86, Brown.

entrance and exit faces of the magnet, so that further manipulation is re-quired to include the object and image distances. When this is done, the expressions defining the face radii R_1 and R_2 which will bring to zero the $x_0'^2$ aberration are in the form:

$$K_1 S_0^2 + K_2 S_0^2 S_1 + K_3 S_0 S_1 + K_4 S_0 + K_5 S_1 + K_6 = 0, \quad (18\text{-}11)$$

where S_0 and S_1 are the object and image distances, respectively. Writing $\sigma = \sin \theta$, $\kappa = \cos \theta$ and $t = \tan u$, we have

$$K_1 = -\frac{1}{2\rho}(\sigma - \kappa t_1)^2 + \frac{t_2^2}{2\rho}(\kappa + \sigma t_1)^2 + \frac{\sigma}{2R_1 \cos^3 u_1}, \quad (18\text{-}12)$$

$$K_2 = -\frac{t_2}{2\rho^2}[-\sigma + \kappa(t_1 + t_2) + \sigma t_1 t_2]^2 + \frac{\kappa + \sigma t_2}{2R_1 \rho \cos^3 u_1} + \frac{(\kappa + \sigma t_1)^2}{2R_2 \rho \cos^3 u_2}, \quad (18\text{-}13)$$

$$K_3 = \frac{1}{\rho}[-\sigma + \kappa(t_1 + t_2) + \sigma t_1 t_2][t_1 - t_2(\kappa + \sigma t_2)] + \frac{\sigma(\kappa + \sigma t_1)}{R_2 \cos^3 u_2}, \quad (18\text{-}14)$$

$$K_4 = \tfrac{1}{2} \sin 2\theta + t_1[\kappa(1 - \kappa) + \sigma t_1] + \sigma t_2^2(\kappa + \sigma t_1), \quad (18\text{-}15)$$

$$K_5 = -\frac{\sigma}{2} + \frac{\kappa t_2}{2} - \frac{t_2}{2}(\kappa + \sigma t_2)^2 + \frac{\rho \sigma^2}{2R_2 \cos^3 u_2}, \quad (18\text{-}16)$$

$$K_6 = \frac{\rho}{2}[\kappa(1 - \kappa) + \sigma^2 t_2^2]. \quad (18\text{-}17)$$

This gives a result close to that of Hintenberger.

UNIFORM FIELDS—SHIMMING THE MAGNET

Returning to Fig. 18-1, we may note that improvement in the size of the image could be accomplished, even if the magnet's edge faces remained flat, by weakening the fields traversed by B and C or by strengthening the field over path A, or by a little of both. This may be done by slipping properly shaped sheets of iron between the vacuum chamber and the upper and lower pole tips, a procedure known as "shimming the magnet." It is often done empirically, but an analysis to compute the shape of the shim has been reported by Balestrini and White,[*] and Anderson[†] has given computations for loops of current-carrying wires attached to the pole tips to accomplish the same end.

[*] 230, Balestrini and White.
[†] 231, Anderson.

NONUNIFORM FIELDS—CONTROL OF THE β FACTOR

As described in Chapter 2, some magnets have a field with a radial dependence of the form

$$B = K/r^n, \qquad (18\text{-}18)$$

where both K and n are constant and $1 > n > 0$. For a small displacement x from a fixed radius r_0, where $B = B_0$, we write $r = r_0 + x$, so that the field may be expressed in a series:

$$B = B_0 \left(\frac{r_0}{r_0 + x}\right)^n = \frac{B_0 r_0^n}{[r_0(1 + x/r_0)]^n} = B_0 \left(1 + \frac{x}{r_0}\right)^{-n}$$

$$= B_0 \left[1 - n\frac{x}{r_0} + \frac{n}{2}(n+1)\left(\frac{x}{r_0}\right)^2 - \frac{n}{6}(n+1)(n+2)\left(\frac{x}{r_0}\right)^3 + \cdots\right].$$

$$(18\text{-}19)$$

This we may write as

$$B = B_0 \left[1 - \alpha\frac{x}{r_0} + \beta\left(\frac{x}{r_0}\right)^2\right], \qquad (18\text{-}20)$$

where $\alpha = n$, $\beta = \frac{1}{2}n(n+1)$, and we have dropped the small terms in $(x/r_0)^3$ and higher powers. If we assume that $n = \frac{1}{2}$, Eq. (18-20) shows that we have

$$B = B_0 \left[1 - \frac{1}{2}\frac{x}{r_0} + \frac{3}{8}\left(\frac{x}{r_0}\right)^2\right], \qquad (18\text{-}21)$$

so that $\alpha = \frac{1}{2}$ and $\beta = \frac{3}{8}$.

If we are willing to slightly distort the field, so that it is not quite represented by Eq. (18-18), then we may treat α and β as independent; α is set at the value $\frac{1}{2}$, but β is arbitrary. This has interesting consequences.

As has been seen earlier, first-order theory shows that ions which start from a point in this field and with finite slopes x_0' and z_0' will experience only focusing forces; they execute betatron oscillations and come to a point focus (also in the field) at $\theta = \pi\sqrt{2}$, provided $n = \frac{1}{2}$ and $u_1 = u_2 = 0$. More exact calculations of the paths in a field expressed as in Eq. (18-20) show that there are, in fact, certain defocusing forces present. The image is broadened by amounts that depend on the initial parameters. For a source of half-width x_0, half-height z_0, and with maximum radial and axial slopes x_0' and z_0', the radial half-width of the image is*

* 135, Shull and Dennison.

$$\frac{w_i}{2} = M_x x_0 + \frac{2}{3\rho}(1 - 2\beta)x_0^2 + \frac{2}{3\rho}\left(2\beta - \frac{3}{2}\right)z_0^2 + \frac{2}{3}(1 - 8\beta)\rho x_0'^2$$

$$+ \frac{2}{3}(8\beta - 3)\rho z_0'^2. \quad (18\text{-}22)$$

The second term vanishes if $\beta = \frac{1}{2}$, the third if $\beta = \frac{3}{4}$, the fourth if $\beta = \frac{1}{8}$ and the fifth if $\beta = \frac{3}{8}$. A frequent compromise is $\beta = \frac{1}{4}$. If $x_0' = z_0'$, the contribution to the width due to divergence is independent of β.

The half-height of the axial image, for the $\pi\sqrt{2}$ magnet, is given by

$$\frac{h_i}{2} = M_z z_0 + \frac{8\beta}{3\rho} x_0 z_0 + \frac{4}{3}(8\beta - 3)\rho x_0' z_0'. \quad (18\text{-}23)$$

This is independent of the initial slopes when $\beta = \frac{3}{8}$.

Alterations in β are brought about by contouring the poles until the field shows a radial dependence as given by Eq. (18-21), and it is apparent that it is impossible to eliminate all of the aberrations simultaneously.

NONUNIFORM FIELDS—CURVED EDGES

The aberration due to $x_0'^2$ also can be removed in an inhomogeneous field by making the end faces of the magnet cylindrical. This has been described in an article by Bretscher.* The coefficient (his A_{11}) of $x_0'^2$ is given by his Eq. (66), which in the present notation is

$$A_{11} = \frac{-\rho}{2\delta^2}\left\{\left(\frac{1 + L_i^2\delta^2}{1 + L_o^2\delta^2}\right)^{1/2}\left[1 - \frac{2(n - \beta)}{3\delta^2}(2 + 3L_o^2\delta^2) - \frac{L_o^3\delta^2}{R_1/\rho}\right]\right.$$

$$\left. + \frac{1 + L_o^2\delta^2}{1 + L_i^2\delta^2}\left[1 - \frac{2(n - \beta)}{3\delta^2}(2 + 3L_i^2\delta^2) - \frac{L_i^3\delta^2}{R_2/\rho}\right]\right\}. \quad (18\text{-}24)$$

This is applicable for normal entry and exit ($u_1 = u_2 = 0$). As usual, the object and image distances are $S_0 = \rho L_o$ and $S_i = \rho L_i$, with $\delta = (1 - n)^{1/2}$. R_1 and R_2 are the radii of the input and output faces (positive for faces convex when seen from the outside), while β occurs in the series expression for the field, Eq. (18-20).

In the symmetric case where $L_o = L_i = L$ and $R_1 = R_2 = R$, the condition for $A_{11} = 0$ (no aberration due to $x_0'^2$) is:

$$R = \frac{3\delta^4 L^3 \rho}{3\delta^2 - 2(n - \beta)(2 + 3\delta^2 L^2)}. \quad (18\text{-}25)$$

* 149, Bretscher; 147, Ikegami.

For a uniform field ($n = 0$, so that also $\beta = 0$) this becomes

$$R = \frac{S^3}{\rho^2} = L^3 \rho, \tag{18-26}$$

which is in agreement with Hintenberger's result for the same conditions, Eq. (18-6).

When $n = \frac{1}{2}$ and $\beta = \frac{1}{4}$, and when the magnet has flat ends, so that $R_1 = R_2 = \infty$, Eq. (18-25) shows that the $x_0'^2$ aberration disappears when

$$L = L_o = L_i = 0.8165. \tag{18-27}$$

This equality of the object and image distances means that the radial magnification is $M_x = -1$. (More precisely, the arguments of the following Chapter 19 may be used to show that the principal planes of the magnet are equidistant from its edges. Therefore the object and image distances, measured from these planes, are equal, whereby we have $M_x = -1$.) Using this value of L_o in Eq. (4-88), viz:

$$\frac{-1}{M_x} = \frac{L_o}{\sqrt{2}} \sin\left(\frac{\theta}{\sqrt{2}}\right) - \cos\left(\frac{\theta}{\sqrt{2}}\right), \tag{18-28}$$

we find that the bending angle must be

$$\theta = 169.7° = 2\sqrt{2}\,\pi/3. \tag{18-29}$$

In practice, a value of θ in this neighborhood is adequate; the layout of apparatus has dictated $\theta = 153°$ for the analyzing magnet used with the Oak Ridge isochronous cyclotron ORIC.*

---

* 188, Hudson *et al.*

19 Principal Planes

GENERAL RELATIONS

It is possible, though by no means necessary, to describe certain properties of magnets (for ions of a single momentum) in terms of distances measured from the magnet's principal planes, these being defined as in ordinary optics.

Consider radial motion. Rays approaching from an object at infinity on the left (Fig. 19-1) may be imagined to continue moving parallel to the axis

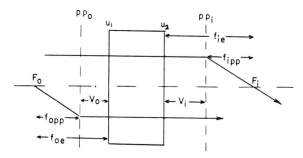

FIG. 19-1. Principal planes and associated parameters.

until they reach the image space principal plane pp_i (distant by V_i from the effective exit edge). Here they are abruptly deflected and then pass through the image space focal point F_i which is distant by f_{ipp} from pp_i and by f_{ie} from the effective edge of the magnet.

Similarly, rays originating at the object space focal point F_o may be considered as being deflected at the object space principal plane pp_o, which is distant by V_o from the input effective edge. Thereafter they travel parallel to the axis. F_o is distant from pp_o by f_{opp} and from the effective edge by f_{oe}.

In accord with the convention embodied in Fig. 19-1, V_o and V_i are positive if the principal planes lie outside the magnet.

It should be evident that f_{oe} and f_{ie} are respectively identical with what were called the upstream and downstream focal distances of Eqs. (2-20) and (2-21) (radial) and Eqs. (3-9) and (3-10) (axial).

For ions of a single momentum, Eq. (2-11) becomes

$$\begin{pmatrix} x_6 \\ x_6' \end{pmatrix} = \begin{pmatrix} 1 & S_1 \\ 0 & 1 \end{pmatrix} \begin{pmatrix} 1 & 0 \\ \dfrac{t_2}{\rho} & 1 \end{pmatrix} \begin{pmatrix} \kappa & \dfrac{\rho\sigma}{\delta} \\ -\dfrac{\delta\sigma}{\rho} & \kappa \end{pmatrix} \begin{pmatrix} 1 & 0 \\ \dfrac{t_1}{\rho} & 1 \end{pmatrix} \begin{pmatrix} 1 & S_0 \\ 0 & 1 \end{pmatrix} \begin{pmatrix} x_1 \\ x_1' \end{pmatrix}, \qquad (19\text{-}1)$$

where, as usual, $\sigma = \sin\phi$, $\kappa = \cos\phi$, $\phi = \delta\theta$, $\delta = (1 - n)^{1/2}$, $t_1 = \tan u_1$, $t_2 = \tan u_2$. We may rewrite this as

$$\begin{pmatrix} x_6 \\ x_6' \end{pmatrix} = \begin{pmatrix} 1 & S_1 \\ 0 & 1 \end{pmatrix} \begin{pmatrix} A & B \\ D & E \end{pmatrix} \begin{pmatrix} 1 & S_0 \\ 0 & 1 \end{pmatrix} \begin{pmatrix} x_1 \\ x_1' \end{pmatrix}, \qquad (19\text{-}2)$$

where the matrix with elements A, B, D, E represents traversal of the body of the magnet and its two edges. These elements may be evaluated by the indicated multiplication, but it is simpler to recognize that they are the already-tabulated coefficients a_6, b_6, d_6, e_6 (of Chapter 6) in which S_0 and S_1 have been set equal to zero. Thus we have

$$A = \frac{t_1\sigma}{\delta} + \kappa, \qquad (19\text{-}3)$$

$$B = \frac{\rho\sigma}{\delta}, \qquad (19\text{-}4)$$

$$D = -\frac{1}{\rho}\left[\delta\sigma - (t_1 + t_2)\kappa - \frac{t_1 t_2 \sigma}{\delta}\right], \qquad (19\text{-}5)$$

$$E = \frac{t_2\sigma}{\delta} + \kappa. \qquad (19\text{-}6)$$

Inspection of Eqs. (2-20) and (2-21) shows that

$$f_{oe} = -\frac{E}{D}, \qquad (19\text{-}7)$$

$$f_{ie} = -\frac{A}{D}. \qquad (19\text{-}8)$$

Consider a particle starting at $x_1 > 0$ and $x_1' = 0$, as in Fig. 19-2. The general expression for radial displacement in the image space is given by Eq. (2-12) (here with $\Delta p/p = 0$);

$$x_6 = a_6 x_1 + b_6 x_1', \qquad (19\text{-}9)$$

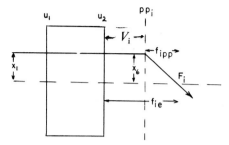

FIG. 19-2. Relations determining the downstream focal length.

where by Eq. (6-25)

$$a_6 = -\frac{S_1}{\rho}\left[\delta\sigma - (t_1 + t_2)\kappa - t_1 t_2 \frac{\sigma}{\delta}\right] + \left(t_1 \frac{\sigma}{\delta} + \kappa\right).$$

In terms of the magnet's elements given in Eqs. (19-5) and (19-3), this is

$$a_6 = S_1 D + A. \tag{19-10}$$

Now in Fig. 19-2, we have $x_1' = 0$, and at $S_1 = V_i$ we have $x_6 = x_1$. Hence in Eq. (19-9) we see that $a_6 = 1$, so from Eq. (19-10) it follows that

$$V_i = \frac{1 - A}{D}. \tag{19-11}$$

Also from Fig. 19-2 it can be seen that, using Eq. (19-7),

$$f_{ipp} = f_{ie} - V_i = -\frac{A}{D} - \frac{1 - A}{D}, \tag{19-12}$$

so

$$f_{ipp} = -\frac{1}{D}. \tag{19-13}$$

To find f_{opp}, assume a source on the axis at F_o, and let x_2 be the displacement at pp_o of a ray that started with slope x_1', as in Fig. 19-3. Once

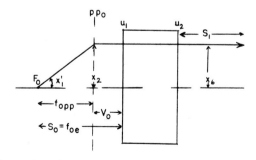

FIG. 19-3. Relations determining the upstream focal length.

again $x_6 = a_6 x_1 + b_6 x_1'$, but now $x_1 = 0$, and $x_6 = x_2$, so

$$x_2 = b_6 x_1'. \tag{19-14}$$

But by geometry we have

$$x_1' = x_2/f_{opp}. \tag{19-15}$$

Hence

$$f_{opp} = b_6. \tag{19-16}$$

Now b_6, given in Eq. (6-26), may be re-expressed in terms of Eqs. (19-3)–(19-6) as

$$b_6 = S_0 A + S_1 E + S_0 S_1 D + B. \tag{19-17}$$

Since the ray beyond the magnet is parallel to the axis, the distance S_1 is unspecified, so we may set $S_1 = 0$. Since in Fig. 19-3 we have $S_0 = f_{oe}$, then it follows that Eq. (19-16) becomes (using Eqs. (19-17) and (19-7))

$$f_{opp} = b_6 = f_{oe} A + B = -\frac{E}{D} A + B = \frac{-AE + BD}{D}. \tag{19-18}$$

But $AE - BD = 1$. Therefore, recalling Eq. (19-13), we have

$$f_{opp} = f_{ipp} = f_{pp} = -\frac{1}{D}. \tag{19-19}$$

From Fig. (19-3), we see that

$$V_o = f_{oe} - f_{pp} = -\frac{E}{D} + \frac{1}{D} \tag{19-20}$$

or

$$V_o = \frac{1 - E}{D}. \tag{19-21}$$

Thus the upstream and downstream focal lengths, when measured from the principal planes, are identical (Eqs. (19-13) and (19-19)), but the principal planes are at unequal distances V_o and V_i from the magnet's effective edges (Eqs. (19-11) and (19-21)), unless $t_1 = t_2$, as shown in Eqs. (19-3) and (19-6).

Similar expressions hold for axial motion, provided A, B, D, and E are converted by the means shown in Eq. (3-1).

When a magnet is described in terms of its principal planes, the object and image distances P and Q are measured from these planes, as indicated in Fig. (19-4).

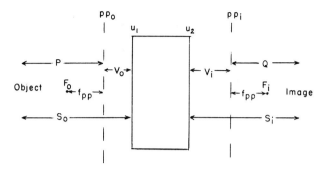

FIG. 19-4. Object and image distances P and Q are measured from the principal planes.

Equation (2-18) for the radial image distance may be written as

$$S_{ix} = \frac{S_0 A + B}{-S_0 D - E}.$$

(19-22)

But from Fig. 19-4,

$$S_0 = P + V_o = P + [(1 - E)/D]$$

(19-23)

and

$$S_{ix} = Q + V_i = Q + [(1 - A)/D].$$

(19-24)

On substituting these in Eq. (19-22) and recalling that $AE - BD = 1$ and that $D = -1/f_{pp}$, we find that

$$\frac{1}{P} + \frac{1}{Q} = \frac{1}{f_{pp}}.$$

(19-25)

With the above conventions as to the signs of distances, we must express the magnification, when given in terms of P and Q, in the form

$$M_x = -\frac{Q}{P}.$$

(19-26)

CIRCULAR MAGNET WITH $n = u_1 = u_2 = 0$

With this magnet, as shown by Eq. (4-6), we have

$$\rho = \frac{r_e}{\tan(\theta/2)} = \frac{r_e \sin \theta}{1 - \cos \theta}.$$

(19-27)

Using Eqs. (19-19, -5, -21, -6, -11, -3), we obtain

$$f_{pp} = -\frac{1}{D} = \frac{\rho}{\sin\theta} = \frac{r_e}{1 - \cos\theta},$$ (19-28)

$$V_o = \frac{1 - E}{D} = -\frac{\rho}{\sin\theta}(1 - \cos\theta) = -\rho\frac{r_e}{\rho} = -r_e,$$ (19-29)

$$V_i = \frac{1 - A}{D} = -\frac{\rho}{\sin\theta}(1 - \cos\theta) = -r_e.$$ (19-30)

Hence both principal planes pass through the magnet's center. See Fig. 19-5.

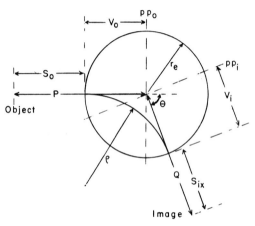

FIG. 19-5. Principal planes in a circular magnet.

By Eq. (19-25),

$$\frac{1}{P} + \frac{1}{Q} = \frac{1}{f_{pp}}.$$ (19-31)

This will revert to the form of Eq. (4-2) (which shows S_{ix} as a function of S_0) on substitution of

$$P = S_0 + r_e,$$ (19-32)

$$Q = S_{ix} + r_e.$$ (19-33)

There is no axial focusing.

SEMICIRCULAR MAGNET WITH $n = u_1 = 0, u_2 > 0$

As shown by Eqs. (4-39) and (4-42),

$$u_2 = \theta/2$$ (19-34)

and

$$\rho = \frac{r_e}{2\sin(\theta/2)}. \tag{19-35}$$

Hence

$$t_2 = \tan u_2 = \tan(\theta/2) = \frac{1 - \cos\theta}{\sin\theta}. \tag{19-36}$$

Now consider radial motion: ($\sigma = \sin\theta$, $\kappa = \cos\theta$)

$$f_{ppx} = -\frac{1}{D} = \frac{\rho}{\sigma - t_2\kappa} = \frac{\rho}{\sigma - [(1-\kappa)/\sigma]\kappa}$$

$$= \frac{\rho\sin\theta}{1 - \cos\theta} = \rho\cot(\theta/2) = \frac{r_e\cos(\theta/2)}{1 - \cos\theta}. \tag{19-37}$$

$$V_{ox} = \frac{1-E}{D} = \frac{-\rho}{\sigma - t_2\kappa}(1 - t_2\sigma - \kappa) = -\frac{\rho}{\sigma - t_2\kappa}\left[1 - \frac{(1-\kappa)\sigma}{\sigma} - \kappa\right] = 0. \tag{19-38}$$

$$V_{ix} = \frac{1-A}{D} = -\frac{\rho}{\sigma - t_2\kappa}(1 - \kappa) = -\frac{\rho(1-\kappa)}{\sigma - [(1-\kappa)/\sigma]\kappa}$$

$$= -\rho\sin\theta = -\frac{r_e\sin\theta}{2\sin(\theta/2)}. \tag{19-39}$$

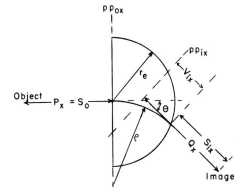

Fig. 19-6. Radial principal planes in a semicircular magnet.

We see that pp_{ox} is at the effective entrance edge and that pp_{ix} lies inside the magnet. The expression

$$\frac{1}{P_x} + \frac{1}{Q_x} = \frac{1}{f_{ppx}} \tag{19-40}$$

can be shown to reduce to Eq. (4-34) (giving S_{ix} in terms of S_0) if we make the substitutions

$$P_x = S_0 \tag{19-41}$$

$$Q_x = S_{ix} + \frac{r_e \sin \theta}{2 \sin(\theta/2)}. \tag{19-42}$$

Axial motion is treated as follows. By converting A, D, and E of Eqs. (19-3), (19-5), and (19-6) into their axial counterparts (see Eq. (3-1)), we obtain

$$f_{ppz} = -\frac{1}{D} = \frac{\rho}{\varepsilon \sin \psi + t_2 \cos \psi} = \frac{\rho}{t_2} = \frac{\rho \sin \theta}{1 - \cos \theta} = \rho \cot(\theta/2) = \frac{r_e \cos(\theta/2)}{1 - \cos \theta}. \tag{19-43}$$

This is the same as Eq. (19-37), so the radial and axial focal lengths are identical.

$$V_{oz} = \frac{1 - E}{D} = -\frac{\rho}{t_2} \left[1 - \left(-t_2 \frac{\sin \psi}{\varepsilon} + \cos \psi \right) \right]$$

$$= -\frac{\rho}{t_2} [1 - ((t_2\theta + 1)] = -\rho\theta. \tag{19-44}$$

$$V_{iz} = \frac{1 - A}{D} = -\frac{\rho}{t_2} (1 - \cos \psi) = -\frac{\rho}{t_2} (1 - 1) = 0. \tag{19-45}$$

Hence both pp_{oz} and pp_{iz} cut the optic axis at the effective exit edge.

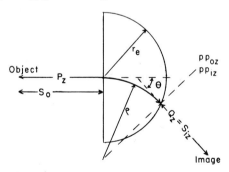

FIG. 19-7. Axial principal planes in a semicircular magnet.

The general expression

$$\frac{1}{P_z} + \frac{1}{Q_z} = \frac{1}{f_{pp}} \tag{19-46}$$

can be manipulated into Eq. (4-35) (which gives S_{iz} as a function of S_0) by setting

$$P_z = S_0 + \rho\theta = S_0 + \frac{r_e \theta}{2 \sin(\theta/2)}, \qquad (19\text{-}47)$$

$$Q_z = S_{iz}. \qquad (19\text{-}48)$$

CONVERGING QUADRUPOLE

The matrix that describes traversal of a converging quadrupole of effective length Q can be shown* to be

$$\begin{pmatrix} A & B \\ D & E \end{pmatrix}, \qquad (19\text{-}49)$$

where

$$A = \cos \tau, \qquad (19\text{-}50)$$

$$B = (1/K)\sin \tau, \qquad (19\text{-}51)$$

$$D = -K \sin \tau, \qquad (19\text{-}52)$$

$$E = \cos \tau, \qquad (19\text{-}53)$$

with

$$K^2 = G/B_0 \rho_0 \qquad (19\text{-}54)$$

and

$$\tau = KQ. \qquad (19\text{-}55)$$

Here G is the gradient $dB_x/dz = dB_z/dx$, and $B_0 \rho_0$ measures the momentum. Eqs. (19-50)–(19-53) are the analogs of Eqs. (19-3)–(19-6) that applied to a bending magnet. Since $A = E$, we may use either Eq. (19-11) or (19-21) to find that the locations of the principal planes of the converging lens are

$$V_c = V_o = V_i = \frac{1 - A}{D} = \frac{1 - E}{D} = \frac{1 - \cos \tau}{-K \sin \tau}. \qquad (19\text{-}56)$$

This expression being negative indicates that the principal planes lie inside the magnet and are symmetrically disposed. For a "thin" lens (short Q, small

* 13, Livingood; 33, Penner.

gradient G, and large particle momentum $B_0\,\rho_0$, such that τ is small), we may write

$$V_c = \frac{1 - \cos \tau}{-K \sin \tau} \approx \frac{1 - (1 - \tau^2/2)}{-K\tau} = \frac{\tau}{-2K} = \frac{KQ}{-2K} = -\frac{Q}{2}. \quad (19\text{-}57)$$

Hence for Q approaching zero, the two planes approach coincidence at the midpoint. See Fig. 19-8.

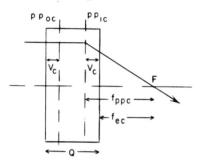

FIG. 19-8. Parameters of a converging quadrupole.

By Eqs. (19-19) and (19-52), the converging focal length measured from a principal plane is

$$f_{\text{ppc}} = -\frac{1}{D} = \frac{1}{K \sin \tau}. \quad (19\text{-}58)$$

The converging focal length measured from an effective edge may be found from Fig. (19-8) to be

$$f_{\text{ec}} + (-V_c) = f_{\text{ppc}},$$

so

$$f_{\text{ec}} = \frac{1}{K \sin \tau} + \frac{1 - \cos \tau}{-K \sin \tau} = \frac{1}{K} \cot \tau. \quad (19\text{-}59)$$

DIVERGING QUADRUPOLE

Here the matrix elements are

$$A = \cosh \tau, \quad (19\text{-}60)$$

$$B = (1/K)\sinh \tau, \quad (19\text{-}61)$$

$$D = K \sinh \tau, \quad (19\text{-}62)$$

$$E = \cosh \tau. \quad (19\text{-}63)$$

Hence

$$V_d = V_o = V_i = \frac{1 - A}{D} = \frac{1 - E}{D} = \frac{1 - \cosh \tau}{K \sinh \tau}. \qquad (19\text{-}64)$$

Since $\cosh \tau$ always exceeds unity, V_d is negative, and both principal planes lie inside the lens and are close to its center if it is thin, as may be seen by expansion. Notice that V_c (Eq. (19-56)) can be appreciably different from V_d (Eq. (19-64)) if the lens is thick. From Eq. (19-19) we have

$$f_{ppd} = -\frac{1}{D} = \frac{-1}{K \sinh \tau}. \qquad (19\text{-}65)$$

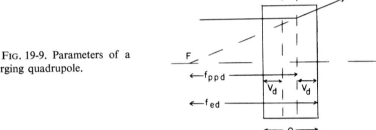

FIG. 19-9. Parameters of a diverging quadrupole.

From Fig. 19-9 we see that the focal length measured from an effective edge is

$$f_{ed} + (-V_d) = f_{pp}, \qquad (19\text{-}66)$$

so

$$f_{ed} = \frac{-1}{K \sinh \tau} + \frac{1 - \cosh \tau}{K \sinh \tau} = -\frac{1}{K} \coth \tau. \qquad (19\text{-}67)$$

BIBLIOGRAPHY

REVIEWS AND BOOKS

1. F. W. Aston, "Isotopes," 2nd ed. Longmans, Green, New York, 1924. A classic, with references to the early work of Aston and others at the turn of the century.
2. E. B. Jordan and L. B. Young, A Short History of Isotopes and the Measurement of Their Abundance. *J. Appl. Phys.* **13**, 526–538 (1942).
3. E. Persico and C. Geoffrion, Beta-Ray Spectroscopes. *Rev. Sci. Instr.* **21**, 945–970 (1950). Excellent treatment of theory; $n = 0$ and $n = 0.5$; aberrations. Solenoidal and special types.
4. K. I. Mayne, Mass Spectroscopy. *Rept. Progr. Phys.* **15**, 24–48 (1952).
5. N. F. Verster, The Electron Optical Properties of Magnetic Beta Ray Spectrometers. *Progr. Nucl. Phys.* **2**, 1–20 (1952). Various types.
6. K. T. Bainbridge, Charged Particle Dynamics and Optics. *In* "Experimental Nuclear Physics" (E. Segré, ed.), Vol. I, pp. 559–614. Wiley, New York, 1953.
7. M. G. Inghram and R. J. Hayden, A Handbook on Mass Spectroscopy. Nucl. Sci. Ser., Rept. No. 14, Natl. Acad. Sci.–Natl. Res. Council (1954).
8. K. Siegbahn, "Beta- and Gamma-Ray Spectroscopy." Wiley (Interscience), New York, 1955.
9. W. W. Buechner, The Determination of Nuclear Reaction Energies by Deflection Measurements. *Progr. Nucl. Phys.* **5**, 1–35 (1956). Brief review of magnet types.
10. H. Hintenberger and L. A. König, *Advan. Mass Spectrometry, Proc. Conf. Univ. London 1958* (E. Waldron, ed.), pp. 16–35. Pergamon Press, Oxford, 1959.
11. O. Chamberlain, Optics of High Energy Beams. *Ann. Rev. Nucl. Sci.* **10**, 161–192 (1960).
12. M. Mladjenovic, Recent Developments in Beta Spectrometers. *Nucl. Instr. Methods* **7**, 11–21 (1960). Emphasis on $n = 0.5$ type, especially iron-free; current loops and sheets.
13. J. J. Livingood, "Principles of Cyclic Particle Accelerators." Van Nostrand, Princeton, New Jersey, 1961. Introduction to matrix methods, edge focusing and quadrupoles.
14. H. Hintenberger, High Sensitivity Mass Spectroscopy in Nuclear Studies. *Ann. Rev. Nucl. Sci.* **12**, 435–506 (1962). Mostly on results, with brief review of magnetic and electric focusing devices.
15. R. R. Kepple, Beam Transport—A Selected Annotated Bibliography. ANL-6602. Argonne Natl. Lab., Argonne, Illinois, August 1962. Covers 891 abstracts, from 1949 to 1961, on electric and magnetic devices for focusing, bending and separating particle beams; 289 pages.
16. B. Milman, Aimants Spectromètres et Appareillages de Détection Utilisés. *L'Onde Élec.* **42**, 310–329 (1962). Excellent review of the matrix description of magnets, with examples from the equipment used with the 1.3 GeV electron linear accelerator at Orsay.
17. R. M. Sternheimer, Beam Bending and Focusing Systems. *In* "Methods of Experimental Physics" (L. Marton, ed.-in-chief), Vol. 5B, Nuclear Physics (L. C. L. Yuan and C.-S.Wu, eds.), pp. 691–747. Academic Press, New York, 1963
18. H. A. Enge, Magnetic Spectrographs and Beam Analyzers. *Nucl. Instr. Methods* **28**, 119–130 (1964).
19. N. M. King, Theoretical Techniques of High Energy Beam Design. *Progr. Nucl. Phys.* **9**, 71–116 (1964). Largely on quadrupoles and beam transport.

20. K. G. Steffen, "High Energy Beam Optics." Wiley (Interscience), New York, 1965. Magnets, quadrupoles and transport, with emphasis on the latter two. Aberrations.
21. A. P. Banford, "The Transport of Charged Particles." Spon, London, 1966. A wide range of subjects well covered; magnets, quadrupoles, electric fields, etc.
22. H. A. Enge, Magnetic Spectrographs. *Phys. Today* **20**, 65–75 (1967). Good qualitative discussions.
22a. H. A. Enge, Deflecting Magnets. *In* "Focusing of Charged Particles" (A. Septier, ed.), Vol. 2, Chapter 4.2. Academic Press, New York, 1967. This monumental opus, by 27 authors, contains 979 pages in the two volumes. It should be in the library of every serious student of the subject.

SPECIALIZED REPORTS

23. *Proc. Intern. Symp. Magnet Technol., Stanford, 1965.* Clearinghouse for Federal and Tech. Inform., Natl. Bur. of Std., U.S. Dept. of Comm., Springfield, Virginia. 842 pages of detailed data on construction of magnets and their coils, superconductivity included. A few theoretical papers on ion paths in magnets. $8.50.
24. *Proc. 2nd Intern. Conf. Magnet Technol., Oxford, 1967.* The same subject matter as above, but with two years' more data. 768 pages. Rutherford Lab., Chilton, Didcot, Berkshire, England. £5.

GENERAL THEORY

25. D. W. Kerst and R. Serber, Electronic Orbits in the Induction Accelerator. *Phys. Rev.* **60**, 53–58 (1941). The theory of axial and radial "betatron oscillations" about the central orbit.
26. P. A. Sturrock, The Imaging Properties of Electron Beams in Arbitrary Static Electromagnetic Fields. *Phil. Trans. Roy. Soc. London Ser. A.* **245**, 155–187 (1952).
27. R. M. Sternheimer, Double Focusing of Charged Particles with a Wedge-Shaped Non-Uniform Magnetic Field. *Rev. Sci. Instr.* **23**, 629–634 (1952). Very general conditions, including $n < 0$.
28. R. M. Sternheimer, Double Focusing of Charged Particles by a System of Two Magnets with Non-Uniform Fields. *Rev. Sci. Instr.* **24**, 573–585 (1953). Includes cases with $n > 0$ in first and $n < 0$ in second.
29. B. L. Cohen, Resolution of Accelerator Magnetic Analyzing Systems. *Rev. Sci. Instr.* **30**, 415–418 (1959).
30. B. Sjögren, Combination of Magnetic Analyzers in Nuclear Reaction Experiments. *Nucl. Instr. Methods* **7**, 76–88 (1960). Includes study of analyzers with coincident and perpendicular bending planes.
31. H. Daniel, Theory of a High Resolution Beta-Ray Spectrometer of High Luminosity. *Rev. Sci. Instr.* **31**, 249–252 (1960). $\theta > 360°$.
32. H. Daniel and L. J. Laslett, Theory of a High Dispersion Double Focusing Beta-Ray Spectrometer. *Rev. Sci. Instr.* **31**, 1225–1228 (1960).
33. S. Penner, Calculations of Properties of Magnetic Deflection Systems. *Rev. Sci. Instr.* **32**, 150–160 (1961); Errata 1068–1069 (1961). Matrix methods for magnets with $n = 0$, $n \neq 0$, u_1 and u_2 zero or finite, and for quadrupoles.
34. B. L. Cohen, Limitations on Accelerator Magnetic Analyzing Systems. *Rev. Sci. Instr.* **33**, 85–92 (1962).

35. K. Kosaka, First Order Study of Some Beam Analyzing Systems for a Medium Energy Cyclotron. MSUCP-13. Michigan State Univ., East Lansing, Michigan, September 1962. $n = 0$ or $n = 0.5$, $\theta = 90°$, $u_1 = u_2 = 0$; one or two magnets with and without quadrupoles. In some cases the bending planes are orthogonal.

36. S. A. Shestopalova, Twofold Focusing $2 \times \pi\sqrt{2}$ Angle Beta-Spectrometer. *Nucl. Instr. Methods* 17, 94–96 (1962). $\theta > 360°$.

37. A. M. Sessler, Beta Ray Spectrometer with Reduced Spherical Aberration. *Nucl. Instr. Methods* 23, 165–168 (1963). Use of azimuthally varying field.

38. H. B. Knowles, A Graphical First Order Treatment of Dispersive Magnetic Particle Optics Problems. *Nucl. Instr. Methods* 25, 29–39 (1963).

39. C. M. Braams, Edge Effect in Charged-Particle Analyzing Magnets. *Nucl. Instr. Methods* 26, 83–89 (1964).

40. H. Wollnik and H. Ewald, The Influence of Magnetic and Electric Fringing Fields on the Trajectories of Charged Particles. *Nucl. Instr. Methods* 36, 93–104 (1965).

41. H. Wollnik, Image Aberrations of Second Order for Magnetic and Electrostatic Sector Fields Including All Fringing Field Effects. *Nucl. Instr. Methods* 56–58 38, (1965).

42. H. A. Enge, Converting an Ion-Optical Layout into the Design of a Practical Magnet System. *Proc. Intern. Symp. Magnet Technol.*, Stanford, 1965, pp. 84–87.

43. K. L. Brown, A General First and Second Order Theory of Beam Transport Magnets. *Proc. Intern. Symp. Magnet Technol.*, Stanford, 1965, pp. 141–143.

44. K. E. Bergkvist and A. M. Sessler, A High Resolution High Luminosity Beta-Ray Spectrometer Design Employing Azimuthally Varying Magnetic Field. *Nucl. Instr. Methods* 46, 317–324 (1967).

45. H. Wollnik, Second Order Transfer Matrices of Real Magnetic and Electrostatic Sector Fields. *Nucl. Instr. Methods* 52, 250–272 (1967).

46. P. Bounin, Application of Fermat's Principle to Magnetic Spectrometers. *Rev. Sci. Instr.* 38, 1305–1312 (1967).

47. H. Wollnik, The Correction of Image Aberrations of Second Order for Mass or Energy Separators Consisting of One Single Magnetic Sector Field. *Nucl. Instr. Methods* 53, 197–215 (1967).

48. H. F. Mahlein, Ein Doppelfokussierendes Betaspektrometer mit hoher Dispersion und Zwischenbild zur Messung von Konversionselektronen nach Neutroneneinfang. *Nucl. Instr. Methods* 53, 229–248 (1967). Combinations of $n = 0$ and $n \neq 0$ magnets. See also Refs. 274 and 275 on page 252.

UNIFORM FIELDS. THEORY

49. N. F. Barber, Note on the Shape of an Electron Beam Bent in a Magnetic Field. *Proc. Leeds Phil. Lit. Soc. Sci. Sect.* 2, 427–434 (1933). Barber's rule.

50. W. E. Stephens, Magnetic Refocusing of Electron Paths. *Phys. Rev.* 45, 513–518 (1934). $n = 0$, $u_1 = u_2 = 0$, $\theta < 180°$.

51. L. Cartan, Sur La Focalisation des Faiseaux de Particules Chargées Par Deviation Circulaire en Champ Magnetic Transversal. *J. Phys. Radium* 8, 453–470 (1937).

52. M. Cotte, Recherches Sur L'Optique Électronique. *Ann. Physique* 10, 333–405 (1938). Analogies between geometrical and electron optics. See below for errata.

53. L. Cartan, L'Optique des Rayons Positifs et Ses Applications à le Spectrographie de Mass. *Ann. Physique* 10, 426–501 (1938).

54. M. Cotte, Les Aberrations des Systemes Orthogonaux de l'Optique Électronique à l'Approximation Relativiste. *Ann. Phys.* (*Paris*) 11, 351–352 (1939). Includes errata for the 1938 paper.

55. K. Siegbahn, Studies in β-Spectroscopy. *Arkiv. Mat. Astron. Fys.* 30A (20), 1–82 (1944).

56. H. Marschall, Grundlegung der Elektronenoptischen Theorie eines Massenspektrographen. *Physik. Z.* **45**, 1–37 (1944).

57. R. G. E. Hutter, The Electron Optics of Mass Spectrographs and Velocity Focusing Devices. *Phys. Rev.* **67**, 248–253 (1945). Basic analysis of electric and magnetic fields; second order and chromatic aberrations.

58. N. G. Coggeshall, Fringing Field Corrections for Magnetic Focusing Devices. *J. Appl. Phys.* **18**, 855–861 (1947). Effect of thickness of poles and of gap height.

59. H. Hintenberger, Über magnetische Zylinderlinsen mit korrigiertem Bildfehler. *Z. Naturforsch.* **3a**, 125–127 (1948). Curved edges.

60. H. Hintenberger, Richtungsfokussierung zweiter Ordnung geladener Teilchen in homogenen Magnetfeldern. *Z. Naturforsch.* **3a**, 669–670 (1948). More on curved edges to eliminate $x_0'^2$ aberration.

61. L. Kerwin, Improved Magnetic Focusing of Charged Particles. *Rev. Sci. Instr.* **20**, 36–41 (1949). Curved edges.

62. L. Kerwin and C. Geoffrion, Further Improvements in Magnetic Focusing. *Rev. Sci. Instr.* **20**, 381–384 (1949). More on curved edges.

63. C. Geoffrion, Optimum Conditions for a 180° Beta-Ray Spectrometer. *Rev. Sci. Instr.* **20**, 638–640 (1949). Interrelations of source size, beam divergence, intensity and resolution.

64. H. Hintenberger, Improved Magnetic Focusing of Charged Particles. *Rev. Sci. Instr.* **20**, 748–750 (1949). Condensed version of author's two earlier papers, above, in English.

65. G. E. Owen, Design Curves for 180° Magnetic Spectrometer. *Rev. Sci. Instr.* **20**, 916–923 (1949).

66. K. T. Bainbridge, Fringing Field Corrections for Magnetic Sector Lenses and Prisms. *Phys. Rev.* **75**, 216 (1949).

67. C. M. Fowler, R. G. Shreffler, and J. M. Cork, Focusing in a Semi-Circular Magnetic Spectrometer. *Rev. Sci. Instr.* **20**, 966–967 (1949). Line shape.

68. L. Musumeci, Dispersione e Aberrazione Nello Spettrografo di Massa a Campo Magnetico. *Nuovo Cimento* **7**, 351–363 (1950). First and second order theory.

69. W. Ploch and W. Walcher, Die Abbildungseigenschaften magnetischer Sektorfelder unter Berücksichtigung des Streufeldes. *Z. Physik* **127**, 274–288 (1950). Fringe fields.

70. H. Hintenberger, Der Öffnungsfehler bei der ionenoptischen Abbildung eines Punktes mit Hilfe eines beliebig begrenzten homogenen Magnetfeldes. *Z. Naturforsch.* **6a**, 275–276 (1951).

71. M. Camac, Double Focusing with Wedge-Shaped Magnetic Fields. *Rev. Sci. Instr.* **22**, 197–204 (1951). $n = 0$, $u_1 \neq 0$, $u_2 \neq 0$.

72. W. G. Cross, Two-Directional Focusing of Charged Particles with a Sector-Shaped, Uniform Magnetic Field. *Rev. Sci. Instr.* **22**, 717–722 (1951). $n = 0$, $u_1 \neq 0$, $u_2 \neq 0$.

73. L. Musumeci, Sull 'Aberrazione Negli Spettrometri di Massa a Settore Magnetico. *Nuovo Cimento* **9**, 429–435 (1952). Third order calculations.

74. C. Reuterswärd, Fringing Field Effects on First-Order Focusing in Magnetic Spectrographs. *Arkiv. Fysik* **3**, 53–62 (1952). $n = 0$, $u_1 \neq 0$, $u_2 \neq 0$.

75. R. Persson, Notes on the Focusing Properties of Homogeneous Magnetic Sector Fields. *Arkiv Fysik* **3**, 455–469 (1952). Curved edges. Construction details.

76. E. T. S. Walton, High Order Focusing by a Uniform Magnetic Field with Straight Line Boundaries. *Nature* **173**, 1147–1148 (1954); *Proc. Roy. Irish Acad.* **A57**, 1–13 (1954–1955).

77. D. F. Dempsey, Third Order Aberration and Focusing with Sector-Shaped Magnetic Fields. *Rev. Sci. Instr.* **26**, 1141–1145 (1955). Elimination of $x_0'^3$ term.

78. R. J. Walen, Transformation d'une Focalisation de Premier Ordre en Focalisation de

Deuxième Ordre en Spectrographie Magnetique a Champ Homogene. *Nucl. Instr. Methods* **1**, 242–250 (1957).

79. L. A. König and H. Hintenberger, Über die Abbildungsfehler von beliebig begrenzten homogenen magnetischen Sektoren Feldern. *Z. Naturforsch.* **12a**, 377–384 (1957). Second order coefficients.

80. H. Hintenberger and L. A. König, Massenspektrographen mit Doppelfokussierung erster Ordnung für alle Massen, die geringe Bildfehler in einem grossen Massenbereich entlang der Photoplatte aufweisen. *Nucl. Instr. Methods* **3**, 250–259 (1958).

81. R. L. Burman and A. I. Yavin, Multi-Purpose Magnetic Particle Analyzer. *Nucl. Instr. Methods* **7**, 101–112 (1960). Theory of quadrupole in front of Browne-Buechner magnet.

82. R. P. Haddock, Applications of the Matrix Method to the Browne-Buechner Spectrograph. *Rev. Sci. Instr.* **34**, 745–754 (1963). Excellent.

83. H. A. Enge, Effect of Extended Fringing Fields on Ion Focusing Properties of Deflecting Magnets. *Rev. Sci. Instr.* **35**, 278–287 (1964). Locations of radial and axial images; importance of coil position, etc.

84. K. L. Brown, R. Belbeoch, and P. Bounin, First and Second Order Magnetic Optics Matrix Equations for the Midplane of Uniform Field Wedge Magnets. *Rev. Sci. Instr.* **35**, 481–485 (1964).

85. K. Yagi, A New Broad Range Spectrometer with a Uniform-Field Sectorial Magnet and a Preceding Quadrupole-Magnet Doublet. *Nucl. Instr. Methods* **31**, 173–188 (1964). Matrix method. $u_1 = 15°$, $u_2 = 0$, $\theta = 80°$, $\rho = 170$ cm. 200 proportional counters on image plane.

86. K. L. Brown, First and Second Order Magnetic Optics of a Circular-Pole Uniform Field Magnet. *Rev. Sci. Instr.* **36**, 271–274 (1965).

87. T. F. Godlove and W. L. Bendel, Simplified Wedge Magnet Design Including Fringe Effects. *Rev. Sci. Instr.* **36**, 909–914 (1965); also in *IEEE Trans. Nucl. Sci.* **12**, 383–386 (1965).

88. P. Shapiro, S. Podgor, and R. B. Theus, Calculations on the Uniform-Field Bending Magnet. NRL Rept. 6248, Cyclotron Rept. 1. Naval Res. Lab., Washington, D.C., May 1965. Tabular data for double-focusing values of u_1, u_2, L_0, L_1, M_x, and M_z for $\theta = 20$, 22.5, 35, 40, and 45 degrees.

89. K. Yagi, The Third Order Aberrations in a Broad Range Spectrometer with a Uniform-Field Sectorial Magnet and a Preceding Quadrupole Doublet. *Nucl. Instr. Methods* **34**, 146–154 (1965).

90. K. Yagi, A Method for Calculations of the Reduction of the Resolution in a Uniform-Field Magnetic Analyzer System due to Inhomogeneity of the Magnetic Field. *Nucl. Instr. Methods* **39**, 88–92 (1966).

91. H. Ezoe, Two Directional Beam Convergence by Sector-Shaped Uniform Magnetic Field. *Rev. Sci. Instr.* **38**, 390–394 (1967); Errata **38**, 1547 (1967).

92. M. N. Viswesvariah and N. Sarma, The Ion-Optics of a Split Pole Magnetic Spectrograph. *Nucl. Instr. Methods* **54**, 181–189 (1967).

$n = 0$, No Edge Focusing. Chiefly on Apparatus

93. A. J. Dempster, A New Method of Positive Ray Analysis. *Phys. Rev.* **11**, 316–325 (1918). $\theta = 180°$.

94. J. D. Cockcroft, A Magnet for α-Ray Spectroscopy. *J. Sci. Instr.* **10**, 71–75 (1933). $\theta = 180°$ in 360° annular magnet.

95. W. R. Smythe, L. H. Rumbaugh, and S. S. West, A High Intensity Mass Spectrometer. *Phys. Rev.* **45**, 724–727 (1934). Convex entrance and convex exit faces. $\theta = 90°$.

96. A. O. Nier, A New Mass Spectrometer for Routine Isotope Abundance Measurements. *Rev. Sci. Instr.* **11**, 212–213 (1940). $\theta = 60°$. Details of construction.

97. A. O. Nier, A Mass Spectrometer for Isotope and Gas Analysis. *Rev. Sci. Instr.* **18**, 398–411 (1947). $\theta = 60°$.

98. W. W. Buechner, R. J. Van de Graaff, E. N. Strait, C. G. Stergiopoulos, and A. Sperduto, Magnetic Analysis of Disintegration Products. *Phys. Rev.* **74**, 1226, 1569–1574 (1948). $\theta = 180°$.

99. W. G. Wadey, The Alpha Ray Spectrum of Polonium. *Phys. Rev.* **74**, 1846–1853 (1948). $\theta = 180°$.

100. R. S. Bender, E. M. Reilley, A. J. Allen, R. Ely, J. S. Arthur, and H. J. Hausman, The University of Pittsburg Scattering Project. *Rev. Sci. Instr.* **23**, 542–547 (1952). $\theta = 60°$; magnet shimming.

101. C. P. Browne and W. W. Buechner, A Broad Range Magnetic Spectrograph. *Rev. Sci. Instr.* **27**, 899–907 (1956). $\theta = 85°$–$110°$.

102. J. H. Reynolds, High Sensitivity Mass Spectrometer for Noble Gas Analysis. *Rev. Sci. Instr.* **27**, 928–934 (1956). $\theta = 60°$; ultra high vacuum.

103. I. F. Ševarac, B. D. Perović, B. V. Dunjić, and R. M. Protić, 60° Sector Type Electromagnetic Isotope Separator in the Institute of Nuclear Sciences, Belgrade. *Nucl. Instr. Methods* **3**, 245–249 (1958). $n = u_1 = u_2 = 0$, $\rho = 75$ cm.

104. H. A. Enge, Combined Magnetic Spectrograph and Spectrometer. *Rev. Sci. Instr.* **29**, 885–888 (1958). Axially focusing quadrupole precedes Browne-Buechner magnet.

105. E. Karlsson and K. Siegbahn, A New Design for a Beta-Ray Spectrograph for Relative Measurements. *Nucl. Instr. Methods* **7**, 113–123 (1960). $\theta = 180°$. Construction details.

106. L. S. Goodman, Achievement of Extremely Homogeneous Magnetic Fields. *Rev. Sci. Instr.* **31**, 1351–1352 (1960).

107. H. W. Wilson, R. Monro, R. W. D. Hardy, and N. R. Daly, Two Stage Mass Spectrometer. *Nucl. Instr. Methods* **13**, 269–281 (1961). Opposed magnets, $\theta_1 = \theta_2 = 90°$, $\rho_1 = \rho_2 = 15$ inches.

108. D. K. McDaniels, W. Brandenberg, G. W. Farwell, and D. C. Hendrie, Magnetic Analysis of 42-MeV Cyclotron Alpha Particles. *Nucl. Instr. Methods* **14**, 263–271 (1961). Construction details of Browne-Buechner magnet; analysis of kinematic broadening of image.

109. S. E. Hunt and E. C. Fellows, A Van de Graaff Beam Deflecting System Employing Two 45° Deflecting Magnets. *Nucl. Instr. Methods* **16**, 326–334 (1962). Bends are in same direction.

110. H. A. Enge and W. W. Buechner, Multiple-Gap Magnetic Spectrograph for Charged Particle Studies. *Rev. Sci. Instr.* **34**, 155–162 (1963). 48 Browne-Buechner magnets in a circular array with a single source and 48 photoplates at image planes.

111. J. V. Allaby and D. M. Ritson, Design and Performance of a High Momentum, High Luminosity Spectrometer for Particle Analysis. *Rev. Sci. Instr.* **36**, 607–610 (1965). $\theta = 90°$, curved edges.

112. A. Huber and H. Primas, On the Design of Wide Range Electromagnets of High Homogeneity. *Nucl. Instr. Methods* **33**, 125–130 (1965).

113. R. N. Hansford, A Rotatable Switching Magnet for the Harwell Variable Energy Cyclotron. *At. Energy Res. Estab. (Gt. Brit.) Memo.* M1558 (1965).

114. D. L. Smith and H. A. Enge, A High Resolution Charged Particle Spectrometer with

Doppler Correction. *Nucl. Instr. Methods* **51**, 169–171 (1967). Axially focusing quadrupole precedes multiple-gap Browne-Buechner magnet array.

115. G. H. Mackenzie, E. Kashy, M. M. Gordon, and H. G. Blosser, The Beam Transport System of the Michigan State University Cyclotron. *IEEE Trans. Nucl. Sci.* **14**, 450–455 (1967).

116. T. F. Moran and L. Friedman, Tandem Isotope Separator-Mass Spectrometer for the Study of Ionic Collision Processes. *Rev. Sci. Instr.* **38**, 668–676 (1967). Separator: $\theta = 90°$, $\rho = 160$ cm. Spectrometer: $\theta = 60°$, $\rho = 15$ cm.

$n = 0$, WITH EDGE FOCUSING. CHIEFLY ON APPARATUS

117. E. M. Hafner, W. F. Donoghue, and H. Snyder, A New Proton Spectrometer. *Phys. Rev.* **75**, 331 (1949). $u_1 = u_2 < 0$. Fowler-Hafner magnet.

118. D. R. Inglis, Scarcity of States of Li^7 from Magnetic Observation of $Be^9(d, \alpha)Li^7$. *Phys. Rev.* **78**, 104–109 (1950). $u_1 = u_2 < 0$. Fowler-Hafner magnet.

119. T. Kitagaki, Higher Order Focusing Pair Spectrometers. *J. Phys. Soc. Japan* **9**, 4–5 (1954). Right and left bending Fowler-Hafner magnets with a common source of electron-positron pairs at edge of field. Theory and apparatus.

120. D. J. Prowse and W. M. Gibson, A Magnetic Spectrometer. *J. Sci. Instr.* **33**, 129–132 (1956). $u_1 = u_2 < 0$. Fowler-Hafner magnet, with analysis of operation.

121. A. Lovati and H. Tyrén, A Magnetic Analyser for High Energy Particles. *J. Sci. Instr.* **33**, 151–154 (1956). $u_1 = 55.1°$, $u_2 = 30.1°$, $\theta = 90°$.

122. A. V. Crewe, Magnetic Spectrometer for 450 MeV Protons. *Rev. Sci. Instr.* **29**, 880–884 (1958). $u_1 > 0$, $u_2 < 0$, $\theta = 60°$. Curved edges. Analysis and construction.

123. O. Meier, Jr., N. R. Fletcher, W. R. Wisseman, and R. M. Williamson, A Magnetic Analyzer for Nuclear Reaction Products. *Rev. Sci. Instr.* **29**, 1004–1008 (1958). $u_1 = 46.6°$, $u_2 = -18.4°$, $\theta = 60°$, curved faces.

124. V. M. Rout, W. M. Jones, K. Firth, D. P. R. Petrie, and A. C. L. Barnard, A Magnetic Spectrograph for Angular Distribution Measurements. *Nucl. Instr. Methods* **11**, 347–354 (1961). $u_1 = u_2 < 0$. Fowler-Hafner magnet analysis and construction details.

125. J. Borggreen, B. Elbek, and L. P. Nielson, A Proposed Spectrograph for Heavy Particles. *Nucl. Instr. Methods* **24**, 1–12 (1963). $u_1 = 35°$, $u_2 = -36.3°$, $\theta = 108°$.

126. P. G. Sona, A Magnetic Analyzer for Van de Graaff Accelerator. *Nucl. Instr. Methods* **24**, 245–246 (1963). $u_1 = u_2 = 26.5°$, $\theta = 90°$.

127. V. M. Kelman, B. P. Peregood, and V. I. Skopina, High Precision Beta Spectrometer. *Nucl. Instr. Methods* **27**, 190–210 (1964). $u_1 = u_2 = 58°$. Input and output solenoidal lenses. A radial image also occurs at center of magnet.

128. N. I. Tarantin, A. V. Demyanov, Yu. A. Dyachikin, and A. P. Kabachenko, The Electromagnetic Isotope Separator of the Laboratory of Nuclear Reactions, J.I.N.R. *Nucl. Instr. Methods* **38**, 103–108 (1965). $u_1 = 0$, $u_2 = 45°$, $\theta = 90°$.

129. A. E. S. Green, R. J. Berkley, C. E. Watson, and C. F. Moore, Astigmatic Magnetic Analyzer. *Rev. Sci. Instr.* **37**, 415–422 (1966). $u_1 = 35.3°$, $u_2 \approx 0$.

130. V. N. Barkovsky, Yu. G. Basargin, R. N. Litunovsky, O. A. Minjaev, A. V. Popov, and A. V. Stepanov, Ion Optical Studies of Extraction, Transport and Analysis System for 240 cm Cyclotron. *IEEE Trans. Nucl. Sci.* **13**, 344–348 (1966). $u_1 = u_2 < 0$. Fowler-Hafner magnet, with preceding axially focusing quadrupole.

131. F. Feldl, C. Fetrow, and C. F. Moore, A Broad Range Magnetic Spectrograph

System for Routine Angular Distribution Determinations. *Nucl. Instr. Methods* **44**, 98–102 (1966). Construction details of magnet by Green *et al.* (129, Green *et al.*).

132. H. Tyrén, S. Kullander, O. Sundberg, R. Ramachanran, P. Isacsson, and T. Berggren, Quasi-Free Proton-Proton Scattering in Light Nuclei. *Nucl. Phys.* **79**, 321–373 (1966). $u_1 = u_2 = 48°$, $\theta = 135°$, $\rho = 135$ cm.

133. J. E. Spencer and H. A. Enge, Split-Pole Magnetic Spectrograph for Precision Nuclear Spectroscopy. *Nucl. Instr. Methods* **49**, 181–193 (1967). $u_1 > 0$, $u_2 > 0$, $u_3 > 0$, $u_4 < 0$.

134. K. Yagi, H. Ogawa, Y. Ishizaki, T. Ishimatsu, J. Kokame, and K. Matsuda, A Magnetic Analyzer System for the INS Tokyo Synchrocyclotron. *Nucl. Instr. Methods* **52**, 29–47 (1967). $u_1 = 28.7°$, $u_2 = 22°$, $\theta = 90°$.

$n \approx 0.5$. THEORY

135. F. B. Shull and D. M. Dennison, The Double Focusing Beta-Ray Spectrometer. *Phys. Rev.* **71**, 681–687 (1947); Errata **72**, 256 (1947). The second paper is crucial. Expansion of field in a series; $x_0'^2$ or $z_0'^2$ aberrations vanish if $\beta = 1/8$ or 3/8 respectively. $\theta = \pi\sqrt{2}$.

136. N. Svartholm, The Resolving Power of a Ring-Shaped Inhomogeneous Magnetic Field for Two-Directional Focusing of Charged Particles. *Arkiv. Mat. Astron. Fys.* **33A** (24), 1–10 (1947).

137. E. S. Rosenblum, On the Double Focusing Beta-Ray Spectrometer. *Phys. Rev.* **72**, 731 (1947). Minimum width image when $\beta = 1/4$.

138. F. Beiduk and E. Konopinski, Focusing Field for a 180° Type Spectrometer. *Rev. Sci. Instr.* **19**, 594–598 (1948). Different expansion of field.

139. F. B. Shull, The Beta-Ray Spectra of Europium and Tungsten. *Phys. Rev.* **74**, 917–932 (1948). $\theta = \pi\sqrt{2}$; choice of β; line shapes.

140. N. F. Verster, Spherical Aberration in a Double Focusing Beta Ray Spectrometer. *Physica* **16**, 815–816 (1950). Other expansions of field.

141. D. L. Judd, Focusing Properties of a Generalized Magnetic Spectrometer. *Rev. Sci. Instr.* **21**, 213–216 (1950). $n = 0.5$, $u_1 = u_2 = 0$, any θ.

142. E. S. Rosenblum, A Sector-Type Double-Focusing Magnetic Spectrometer. *Rev. Sci. Instr.* **21**, 586–592 (1950). $n = 0.5$, $u_1 = u_2 = 0$, any θ. Second order effects.

143. N. Svartholm, The Focusing Properties of Inhomogeneous Magnetic Sector Fields. *Arkiv. Fysik.* **2**, 115–118 (1950).

144. S. B. Karmohapatro, On Two Directional Focusing Magnetic Analysers. *Indian J. Phys.* **29**, 393–397 (1955).

145. D. L. Judd and S. A. Bludman, Aberrations and Fringing Effects in the 180° Double Focusing Magnetic Spectrometer. *Nucl. Instr.* **1**, 46–52 (1957). $n = 0.5$.

146. G. E. Lee-Whiting and E. A. Taylor, Higher Order Focusing in the $\pi\sqrt{2}$ β-Spectrometer. *Can. J. Phys.* **35**, 1–15 (1957). Aberrations calculated to 6th order in iron-free field.

147. H. Ikegami, Second Order Properties of Double-Focusing Spectrometer with Non-uniform Magnetic Field. *Rev. Sci. Instr.* **29**, 943–948 (1958).

148. H. A. Tasman and A. J. H. Boerboom, Calculation of the Ion Optical Properties of Inhomogeneous Magnetic Sector Fields, Including the Second Order Aberrations in the Median Plane. *Z. Naturforsch.* **14a**, 121–129 (1959).

149. M. M. Bretscher, Focusing Properties of Inhomogeneous Magnetic Sector Fields. ORNL-2884, UC-34, Phys. and Math. TID-4500. Oak Ridge Natl. Lab., Oak Ridge, Tennessee, April 1960. Aberrations.

150. M. Sakai, Optimum Conditions for Double Focusing Beta Ray Spectrometers. *Nucl. Instr. Methods* **8**, 61–69 (1960).
151. F. Rüdenauer and F. P. Viehböck, On Inhomogeneous Magnetic Fields for Mass Separators. *Nucl. Instr. Methods* **38**, 140–143 (1965).
152. G. E. Lee-Whiting, Improved Beta-Spectrometers. *Nucl. Instr. Methods* **43**, 182–193 (1966). $\theta = \pi \sqrt{2}$.
153. G. E. Lee-Whiting, Proposed Electrostatic Correction of the Chalk River $\pi \sqrt{2}$ Beta-Spectrometer. *Nucl. Instr. Methods* **43**, 194–198 (1966).
154. F. Rüdenauer and F. P. Viehböck, A Numerical Method for the Calculation of Image Aberrations in Inhomogeneous Magnetic Sector Fields between Conical Pole Faces. *Z. Naturforsch.* **21a**, 2–8 (1966).

$n \approx 0.5$, No Edge Focusing. Chiefly on Apparatus

155. C. D. Bock, A Wide Angle Magnetic Spectrometer. *Rev. Sci. Instr.* **4**, 575–580 (1933). Tapered gap; field expressed as a series expansion.
156. K. Siegbahn and N. Svartholm, Focusing of Electrons in Two Dimensions by an Inhomogeneous Magnetic Field. *Nature* **157**, 872–873 (1946). $n = 0.5$, $\theta = \pi \sqrt{2}$.
157. N. Svartholm and K. Siegbahn, An Inhomogeneous Ring-Shaped Magnetic Field for Two Dimensional Focusing of Electrons and its Application to β-Spectroscopy. *Arkiv. Mat. Astron. Fys.* **33A** (21), 1–28 (1947). $\theta = \pi \sqrt{2}$. (Most bibliographies give the date as 1946, but Vol. 33A is dated 1947.)
158. L. M. Langer and C. S. Cook, A High Resolution Nuclear Spectrometer. *Rev. Sci. Instr.* **19**, 257–262 (1948). $\alpha = 0$, $\beta = 3/4$, $\gamma = 7/8$. $\theta = 180°$.
159. F. N. D. Kurie, J. S. Osoba, and L. Slack, The Design and Construction of a Double Focusing Beta-Ray Spectrometer. *Rev. Sci. Instr.* **19**, 771–776 (1948). $n = 0.5$, $\beta \approx 1/8$, $\theta = \pi \sqrt{2}$.
160. A. Hedgran, K. Siegbahn, and N. Svartholm, A Large β-Spectrometer with Two Directional Focusing for Precise Measurements of Nuclear Radiation. *Proc. Phys. Soc. (London)* **A63**, 960–986 (1950). $\theta = \pi \sqrt{2}$. Good discussion.
161. J. A. Bruner and F. R. Scott, A High Resolution Beta-Ray Spectrometer. *Rev. Sci. Instr.* **21**, 545–547 (1950). $n = 0.5$, $\theta = 180°$, $\rho = 15$ cm. Details of construction and pole-shaping to obtain the Beiduk-Konopinski contour (138, Beiduk and Konopinski).
162. C. W. Snyder, S. Rubin, W. A. Fowler, and C. C. Lauritsen, A Magnetic Analyzer for Charged Particles from Nuclear Reactions. *Rev. Sci. Instr.* **21**, 852–866 (1950). $\theta = 180°$.
163. A. A. Bartlett and K. T. Bainbridge, A High Resolution Two-Directional Focusing Beta Ray Spectrometer. *Rev. Sci. Instr.* **22**, 517–523 (1951). $\beta = 3/8$, $\theta = \pi \sqrt{2}$.
164. C. Mileikowsky, A Nuclear Spectrometer for Heavy Particles, Part I. Design and Construction of the Instrument. *Arkiv Fysik* **4**, 337–346 (1952). $n = 0.5$, $\theta = 180°$.
165. C. Mileikowsky, A Nuclear Spectrometer for Heavy Particles, Part II. Performance and Focusing Properties. *Arkiv Fysik* **4**, 33–46 (1953). $n = 0.5$, $\theta = 180°$.
166. C. Mileikowsky, A Nuclear Spectrometer for Heavy Particles, Part III. Astigmatic Two-Directional Focusing in a Nuclear Spectrometer as a Means of Eliminating Line Broadening Due to Angular Energy Spread of Transmutation Particles. *Arkiv Fysik* **7**, 57–68 (1954). $n = 0.57$, $\theta = 180°$. Tipped line images.
167. M. W. Johns, H. Waterman, D. MacAskill, and C. D. Cox, A Description of a Large

Double Focusing Beta Spectrometer and its Applications to a Study of the Decay of In^{114}. *Can. J. Phys.* **31**, 225–234 (1953). $\beta = 5/8$, $\theta = \pi \sqrt{2}$. Construction details.

168. P. H. Stoker, O. P. Hok, E. F. DeHaan, and G. J. Sizoo, A 30-cm Double Focusing Magnetic Spectrometer with an Annular Iron Yoke. *Physica* **20**, 337–349 (1954). $\beta = 1/8$. $\theta = \pi \sqrt{2}$. Construction details.

169. A. Moussa and J. Bellicard, Description D'un Spectrograph β A Plan De Symétrie et Double Focalisation Réalisé Au Moyen De Bobines Sans Fer. *J. Phys. Radium* **15**, 85A–93A (1954). $n = 0.5$, $\beta = 3/8$, $\theta = \pi \sqrt{2}$. Iron-free. Field produced by loops of current.

170. S. Rubin and D. C. Sachs, A High-Resolution Magnetic Spectrometer. *Rev. Sci. Instr.* **26**, 1029–1034 (1955). $n = 0.52$, $\beta = 1/8$, $\theta = 180°$. Variable gap.

171. E. Arbman and N. Svartholm, A High Transmission Beta-Ray Spectrometer of the Double-Focusing Type. *Arkiv Fysik* **10**, 1–18 (1956). $n = 0.5$, $\beta = 1/4$, $\theta = \pi \sqrt{2}$. Good discussion.

172. R. Pauli, Investigation of the Focusing Properties of a Double Directional Focusing Magnetic Spectrometer with Conical Pole Surfaces. *Arkiv Fysik* **10**, 175–185 (1956).

173. D. R. Bach, W. J. Childs, R. W. Hockney, P. V. C. Hough, and W. C. Parkinson, Cyclotron Instrumentation for Nuclear Spectroscopy at Medium Resolution in Energy. *Rev. Sci. Instr.* **27**, 516–526 (1956). $n = 0.2$, $\theta = 55°$ and $n = 0.45$, $\theta = 90°$.

174. A. Moussa and J. Bellicard, Recherches Sur Les Electrons De Faible Energie Emis Par Les Substances Radioactives. *J. Phys. Radium* **17**, 532–533 (1956). Improvements and compensation of earth's field, for apparatus of same authors above (169, Moussa and Bellicard).

175. E. E. Chambers and R. Hofstadter, Structure of the Proton. *Phys. Rev.* **103**, 1454–1463 (1956). Two pages of data on magnet. $n = 0.5$.

176. K. Siegbahn and K. Edvarson, β-Ray Spectroscopy in the Precision Range $1:10^5$. *Nucl. Phys.* **1**, 137–159 (1956). $n = 0.5$, $\beta = 3/8$, $\theta = \pi \sqrt{2}$. Iron free. Field in space between two coaxial cylindrical current sheets.

177. H. Wild and O. Huber, Hochauflösendes Beta-Spektrometer neuer Bauart. *Helv. Phys. Acta* **30**, 3–32 (1957). $\beta = 3/8$, $\theta = \pi \sqrt{2}$.

178. L. Bianchi, E. Cotton, and C. Mileikowsky, Spectrometre pour Particules Lourdes. *Nucl. Instr.* **3**, 69–72 (1958). $n = 0.57$. Tipped line images.

179. J. Thirion and J. Saudinos, Aimants De Focalisation et D'Analyse Du Cyclotron De Saclay. *Nucl. Instr. Methods* **5**, 165–169 (1959). $n = 0.5$, $\theta = 70°$.

180. B. Sjögren, Cyclotron Instrumentation for Nuclear Reaction Studies by Magnetic Analysis. *Nucl. Instr. Methods* **7**, 274–288 (1960). $n = 0.47$, $\theta = 92.8°$.

181. C. DeVries and A. H. Wapstra, A Siegbahn-Edvarson Type Ironfree Double Focusing Beta-Ray Spectrometer. *Nucl. Instr. Methods* **8**, 121–145 (1960). $n = 0.5$, $\beta = 3/8$, $\theta = \pi \sqrt{2}$. Excellent in theory and in description of apparatus.

182. M. S. Freedman, F. Wagner, Jr., F. T. Porter, J. Terandy, and P. P. Day, Iron Free Toroidal Beta-Beta Coincidence Spectrometer. *Nucl. Instr. Methods* **8**, 255–258 (1960).

183. M. Sakai, H. Ikegami, and T. Yamazaki, Sector-Type Double-Focusing Beta-Ray Spectrometer. *Nucl. Instr. Methods* **9**, 154–164 (1960). $n = 0.5$, $\theta = 180°$.

184. R. L. Graham, G. T. Ewan, and J. S. Geiger, A One-Meter Iron-Free Double-Focusing $\pi \sqrt{2}$ Spectrometer for β-Ray Spectroscopy with Precision of $1:10^5$. *Nucl. Instr. Methods* **9**, 245–286 (1960). Field made by current loops.

185. O. Huber, L. Schellenberg, and H. Wild, Erste Messungen mit hochauflösenden Spektrometer neuer Bauart. *Helv. Phys. Acta* **33**, 536–540 (1960). $\beta = 3/8$, $\theta = \pi \sqrt{2}$.

186. A. V. Cohen, J. A. Cookson, and J. L. Wankling, A Magnetic Particle Spectrometer for Use with a 12 MeV Tandem Electrostatic Generator. *Nucl. Instr. Methods* **10**, 84–94 (1961). $n = 0.5$, $\beta = 1/8$, $\theta = 180°$. Construction details.

187. T. Westermark, A Double-Focusing Magnetic Spectrometer for Studies of Energy Loss in Matter of Electrons from a 5 MeV Betatron. *Nucl. Instr. Methods* **10**, 129–144 (1961). $n = 0.5$, $\theta = 90°$. Construction details.

188. E. D. Hudson, R. S. Lord, M. P. Fricke, and B. Duelli, The ORIC External Ion-Optics System. ORNL-TM-335. Oak Ridge Natl. Lab., Oak Ridge, Tennessee, August 1962. $n = 1/2$, $\theta = 153°$.

189. Q. L. Baird, J. C. Nall, S. K. Haynes, and J. H. Hamilton, A Moussa-Bellicard Type Iron-Free Double-Focusing Beta-Ray Spectrometer. *Nucl. Instr. Methods* **16**, 275–283 (1962). $n = 0.5$, $\beta = 3/8$ for high resolution or $\beta = 1/4$ for high intensity; $\theta = \pi \sqrt{2}$. Field by current loops.

190. A. A. Bartlett, R. A. Ristinen, and R. P. Bird, A New Double Focusing Beta Spectrometer and the Empirical Optimization of Its Performance. *Nucl. Instr. Methods* **17**, 188–224 (1962). $\alpha = 0.483$, $\beta = 0.326$, $\theta = 253.5°$. Excellent discussion of iron $\pi \sqrt{2}$ magnets, with construction details.

191. J. Bardwick, J. M. Lambert, and W. C. Parkinson, The University of Michigan 83-inch Cyclotron, Part IV, External Beam Handling System. *Nucl. Instr. Methods* **18, 19**, 105–110 (1962). For beam analysis, two opposed magnets, $n = 0.5$, $\theta = 110°$, $\rho = 200$ cm; for reaction products analysis, three magnets, $n = 0.5$, $\theta = 180°$, $\rho = 133$ cm. See page 97 of same volume for layout.

192. J. S. Geiger and R. L. Graham, Measurement of the Radial Focusing Aberration of the Chalk River Iron-Free $\pi \sqrt{2}$ Spectrometer. *Nucl. Instr. Methods* **24**, 81–92 (1963).

193. H. U. Gersch, E. Hentschel, P. Gippner, and W. Rudolf, $\pi \sqrt{2}$ β Spektrometer mit doppeltem Umlauf. *Nucl. Instr. Methods* **25**, 314–316 (1964). Electrons focused twice in orbit.

194. K. Siegbahn, C. Nordling, S.-E. Karlsson, H. Hagström, A. Fahlman, and I. Andersson, A 50-cm Double Focusing Beta Spectrometer of the Current Sheet Type. *Nucl. Instr. Methods* **27**, 173–189 (1964). $n = 0.5$, $\theta = \sqrt{2}$. Field is between two coaxial cylindrical current sheets.

195. A. A. Bartlett and J. Keith, A New Double Focusing Beta Spectrometer, Part II. *Nucl. Instr. Methods* **36**, 119–121 (1965). Continuation of paper above (190, Bartlett, *et al.*).

196. S. Penner and J. W. Lightbody, Measurement of Ion-Optical Properties of a High Resolution Spectrometer for Electron Scattering. *Proc. Intern. Symp. Magnet Technol.*, Stanford, 1956, pp. 154–163. $n = 0.5$, $\beta = 1/4$, $\theta = 169.8°$.

197. M. Liu, J. C. Jacmart, R. A. Ricci, M. Riou, and C. Ruhla, Etude des Noyaux de Mass Moyenne par Diffusion Inélastique de Protons de 155 MeV. *Nucl. Phys.* **75**, 481–514 (1966). $n = 0.5$, $\theta = 120°$. Short description of the Orsay spectrometer.

198. E. D. Hudson and T. I. Hicks, Energy Dispersion Magnification of Accelerated Ion Beam. Private communication (1966). Radially defocusing quadrupole following $n = 0.5$ magnet.

199. H. Freiesleben, D. Kamke, and T. Walcher, Die Ionenoptik eines kommerziellen $n = 1/2$ Magnetspektrometers. *Nucl. Instr. Methods* **53**, 141–152 (1967).

$n > 0.5$ OR $n < 0.5$, NO EDGE FOCUSING

200. N. E. Alekseevsky, G. P. Prudkovsky, G. I. Kosourov, and S. I. Filimonov, The Use of an Inhomogeneous Magnetic Field to Increase the Resolution of Mass Spectro-

meters. *Dokl. Akad. Nauk SSSR* **100**, 229–232 (1955); *At. Energy Res. Estab. (Gt. Brit.) Transl. Lib/Transl.* 629 (1955). Two magnets, each with $\theta = 180°$; one has $n = 0.87$, other has $n = 0.89$.

201. A. V. Dubrovin and G. V. Balabina, Application of Mass Spectrometers with In-homogeneous Magnetic Field for Determining Atomic Masses. *Dokl. Akad. Nauk SSSR* **102**, 719–721 (1955). English version. $n = 0.82$, $\theta = 180°$.

202. V. N. Barkovsky, Ju. G. Basargin, R. N. Litunovsky, O. A. Minjaev, A. V. Popov, and A. V. Stepanov, Ion Optical Studies of Extraction, Transport and Analysis System for the 240 cm Cyclotron. *IEEE Trans. Nucl. Sci.* **13**, 344–348 (1966). Double focusing 270° magnet with adjustable field index. When $n = 0.831$, there is an auxil-iary axial focus at 135° and the final image is highly dispersed with $F = 11.8$. When $n = 0.169$, there is a dispersed image at 135° and an achromatic image beyond the magnet.

$n > 0.5$, WITH EDGE FOCUSING. THEORY

203. S. B. Karmohapatro, Improved Transmission of Ions with Inhomogenous Fields. *Indian J. Phys.* **32**, 26–34 (1958). Curves for u_2 and $L_{1x} = L_{1z}$ as functions of u_1 and L_0, for $\theta = 180°$ and $n = 0.8$ or $n = 0.9$.

NONUNIFORM FIELDS; PLANE POLES WITH WEDGE GAP

204. O. W. Richardson, Magnetic Focusing between Inclined Plane Pole Faces. *Proc. Phys. Soc. (London)* **59**, 791–804 (1947).

204a. O. Kofoed-Hansen, J. Lindhard, and O. B. Nielsen, A New Type of β-Ray Spectro-graph. *Kgl. Danske Videnskab. Selskab Mat. Fys. Medd.* **25** (16), 1–27 (1950).

204b. O. B. Nielsen and O. Kofoed-Hansen, A Six Gap β-Ray Spectrometer. *Kgl. Danske Videnskab. Selskab Mat. Fys. Medd.* **29**, 1–19 (1955).

204c. C. Schuhl and C. Tzara, Monochromateur de Positrons en Secteur D'Orange. *Nucl. Instr. Methods* **10**, 217–223 (1961).

204d. J. S. O'Connell, A Simple Broad Range Magnetic Spectrometer. *Rev. Sci. Instr.* **32**, 1314–1316 (1961).

ACHROMATIC SYSTEMS

205. W. K. H. Panofsky and J. A. McIntyre, Achromatic Beam Translation System for Use with the Linear Accelerator. *Rev. Sci. Instr.* **25**, 287–290 (1954). $n_1 = n_2 = u_1 = u_2 = u_3 = 0$, $u_4 > 0$.

206. K. L. Brown, Achromatic Beam Translation Systems for Linear Accelerators. *Rev. Sci. Instr.* **27**, 959–963 (1956). $n_1 = n_2 = u_2 = u_3 = 0$, $u_1 = u_4 > 0$.

207. H. Bruck, G. Gendreau, and M. Salvat, Inflecteur D'Injection Achromatique pour le Synchrotron a Protons de Saclay. *CERN Symp. High Energy Accelerators Pion Phys., Geneva, 1956, Proc.* pp. 200–204. CERN, Geneva, 1956.

208. W. J. Ramler, Achromatic image with an $n = 0$ magnet flanked by quadrupoles. Private communication (1956).

209. V. V. Vladimirsky and D. G. Koshkarev, The Achromatic Bending Magnet System. *Instr. Exptl. Tech.* (*USSR*) (*English Transl.*) No. 6, 770 (1958). Magnet, quad, magnet. $n_1 = n_2 = 0$. All $u = 0$.

210. R. A. Alvarez, K. L. Brown, W. K. H. Panofsky, and C. T. Rockhold, Double Focusing Zero Dispersion Magnetic Spectrometer. *Rev. Sci. Instr.* **31**, 556–564 (1960). $n_1 = n_2 = 0.27$, $\theta_1 = \theta_2 = 110°$. All $u = 0$. Dispersed image after first magnet, achromatic image after second.

211. L. C. Teng, Modified Achromatic Bending Magnet System for the ZGS. L.C.T.-25. Argonne Natl. Lab., Argonne, Illinois, May 1961. Bend right, left, right. All $n = 0$. $u_1 = u_6 > 0$. All other $u = 0$.

212. L. Marshall, Magnetic Lens Systems of Unit Magnification for High Energy Charged Particles. *Rev. Sci. Instr.* **33**, 919–921 (1962).

213. H. Atterling, Beam Transport System for the Berkeley 88-inch Cyclotron. *Nucl. Instr. Methods*, **18, 19**, 589–594 (1962). Two magnets bending same way. $\theta_1 \neq \theta_2$, $\rho_1 \neq \rho_2$, $L_0 = \infty$.

214. H. G. Blosser and J. W. Butler, Experimental Facilities and Resolution Capability of the M.S.U. Cyclotron. *Proc. Intern. Conf. Sector Focused Cyclotrons Meson Factories, 1963*, p. 138–143. CERN, Geneva, 1963. Altering slit positions for two opposed magnets gives dispersed or achromatic image.

215. H. A. Enge, Achromatic Magnetic Mirror for Ion Beams. *Rev. Sci. Instr.* **34**, 385–389 (1963). $\theta \approx 270°$ for $B = K/x^n$ where $n \approx -1$.

216. B. Milman, A Three-Magnet Extraction System for the 1 GeV Orsay Linear Accelerator. *Nucl. Instr. Methods* **20**, 13–16 (1963). Bend right, left, right. All n and $u = 0$.

217. I. A. Grishaev, V. V. Kondratenko, V. V. Petrenko, A. T. Popov, and V. A. Skubko, Outlet Device for a Linear Accelerator for Electrons with Energy up to 90 MeV. *Instr. Exptl. Tech.* (*USSR*) (*English Transl.*) No. 2, 212 (1963). Achromatic translation; $n_1 = n_2 = 0$, $u_1 = n_4 > 0$, $u_2 = u_3 = 0$; three quadrupoles between magnets.

218. D. A. Swenson, Achromatic Translation System for Charged Particle Beams. *Rev. Sci. Instr.* **35**, 608–612 (1964). Four quadrupoles between two magnets, $n_1 = n_2 = 0$, $u_1 = u_4 > 0$, $u_2 = u_3 = 0$. Symmetric.

219. C. H. M. Turner, Some Notes Bearing on the Synthesis of Achromatic Beam Transport Systems. C.H.M.T.-17. Particle Accelerator Div., Argonne Natl. Lab., Argonne, Illinois, July 1965. Very general matrices.

220. D. D. Randall, An Achromatic 90° Bending System. *Proc. Intern. Symp. Magnet Technol., Stanford, 1965*, pp. 715–722. Magnet, quad, magnet; doubly achromatic.

221. W. J. Ramler, J. J. Livingood, G. W. Parker, J. Aron, and M. C. Oselka, Energy-Analyzing System for the Argonne 60-inch Cyclotron. ANL-7251. Argonne Natl. Lab., Argonne, Illinois, October 1966. Altering slit positions for two opposed magnets gives dispersed or achromatic image. $n_1 = n_2 = 0$, $u_1 = u_2 = u_3 = u_4 = 41.7°$, $\theta_1 = \theta_2 = 120°$, $\rho_1 = \rho_2 = 40$ inches.

222. J. E. Draper, Simple System for Dispersionless Deflection of Beam of Particles. *Rev. Sci. Instr.* **37**, 969–970 (1966). Quad, magnet, quad; achromatic image.

222a. R. Perry, A 360° Beam Separating Magnet, R.P.-10, Particle Accelerator Div., Argonne Natl. Lab., Argonne, Illinois, June 1967.

222b. A. A. Kolomensky, Linotron, a Proposed System for Particle Acceleration, *Proc. Sixth Intern. Conf. High Energy Accelerators*, CEAL-2000, pp. 46–48, Cambridge Electron Accelerator, Cambridge, Massachusetts, Sept. 1967. Clearinghouse for Fed. Sci. and Tech. Information, Springfield, Virginia. $9.

SYMMETRY

223. C. H. M. Turner, On Mirror-Symmetry in Beam Transport Systems. C.H.M.T.-12. Particle Accelerator Div., Argonne Natl., Lab., Argonne, Illinois, September 1962.
224. J. McL. Emmerson and N. Middlemas, Symmetry Properties in Beam Transport Systems. *Nucl. Instr. Methods* **24**, 93–102 (1963).
225. E. E. Bliamptis, Reflection Properties of Deflecting Magnet Systems. *Rev. Sci. Instr.* **35**, 1521–1522 (1964).
226. J. C. Herrera and E. E. Bliamptis, Symmetry Properties of Beam Handling Systems. *Rev. Sci. Instr.* **37**, 183–188 (1966).

SLIT SCATTERING

227. E. D. Courant, Multiple Scattering Corrections for Collimating Slits. *Rev. Sci. Instr.* **22**, 1003–1005 (1951).
228. E. J. Burge and D. A. Smith, Theoretical Study of Slit Scattering. *Rev. Sci. Instr.* **33**, 1371–1377 (1962).
229. K. Yagi, A Method for Reducing a Background Tail in Inelastic Scattering Experiments by a Magnetic Analyzer System. *Nucl. Instr. Methods* **25**, 371–372 (1964). Use of second magnet with one-jawed half slit to intercept particles degraded by scattering at image slit of first magnet.

MAGNET SHIMMING

230. S. J. Balestrini and F. A. White, Workable Magnetic Shim to Correct Second-Order Aberration in a Mass Spectrometer. *Rev. Sci. Instr.* **31**, 633–636 (1960).
231. W. A. Anderson, Electrical Current Shims for Correcting Magnetic Field. *Rev. Sci. Instr.* **32**, 241–250 (1961).
232. K. E. Bergkvist and J. M. Hollander, Definition and Realization of Critical Focusing Conditions of $\pi\sqrt{2}$ Magnetic Field at High Resolution. *Nucl. Instr. Methods* **53**, 25–28 (1967). Use of trimming coils to correct imperfections in field of iron-free spectrometer with $\beta = 3/8$.

ELECTRIC AND MAGNETIC FIELDS IN COMBINATION

233. A. L. Hughes and V. Rojansky, On the Analysis of Electronic Velocities by Electrostatic Means. *Phys. Rev.* **34**, 284–290 (1929). When an electric field varies as $1/r$, as does that between two concentric cylindrical electrodes, a point source gives an image of least width when the deflection angle is $\theta = 127.3° = \pi/\sqrt{2}$. The analysis is not as simple as might be supposed.
234. A. L. Hughes and J. H. McMillen, Re-Focusing of Electron Paths in a Radial Electrostatic Field. *Phys. Rev.* **34**, 291–295 (1929). Experimental confirmation of predictions of the previous paper above (233, Hughes and Rojansky).
235. R. Herzog, Ionen- und electronenoptische Zylinderlinsen und Prismen. *Z. Physik* **89**, 447–473 (1934).

236. J. Mattauch and R. Herzog, Über einen neuen Massenspektrographen. Z. Physik 89, 786–795 (1934). Radial electric field followed by $n = 0$ magnet bending in opposite direction. Image plane at edge of magnet.

237. K. T. Bainbridge and E. B. Jordan, Mass Spectrum Analysis. Phys. Rev. 50, 282–296 (1936). $\pi/\sqrt{2}$ electric field followed by 60° uniform magnet that bends the same way. Image plane is beyond the edge of the magnet.

238. J. Mattauch, A Double-Focusing Mass Spectrometer and the Masses of N^{15} and O^{18}. Phys. Rev. 50, 617–623 (1936). Double focusing here means radial and velocity focusing. Apparatus similar to that of Mattauch and Herzog (236, Mattauch and Herzog).

239. A. J. Dempster, Electric and Magnetic Focusing in Mass Spectroscopy. Phys. Rev. 51, 67–69 (1937); Errata 53, 64–75 (1938). 90° electric field precedes 180° uniform magnetic field that bends the same way.

240. W. Bleakney and J. A. Hipple, Jr., A New Mass Spectrometer with Improved Focusing Properties. Phys. Rev. 53, 521–529 (1938). Crossed electric and magnetic fields; the "trochotron."

241. E. M. Purcell, The Focusing of Charged Particles by a Spherical Condenser. Phys. Rev. 54, 818–826 (1938).

242. C. Reuterswärd, Ein neuer Massenspektrograph. Arkiv. Mat. Astron. Fys. 30A (7), 1–4 (1944). Similar to Mattauch-Herzog device, but image plane lies beyond edge of magnet.

243. A. E. Shaw and W. Rall, An a.c. Operated Mass Spectrograph of the Mattauch Type. Rev. Sci. Instr. 18, 278–288 (1947). Construction details.

244. W. E. Millett, The Focusing in Crossed Fields of Charged Particles at Relativistic Energies. Phys. Rev. 74, 1058–1063 (1948).

245. G. W. Monk and G. K. Werner, Trochotron Design Principles. Rev. Sci. Instr. 20, 93–96 (1949).

246. W. Walcher, Ion Optics and Mass Spectroscopy. Nucleonics 5, 42–51 (1949). Description and theory of the Mattauch-Herzog instrument.

247. N. Svartholm, Velocity and Two-Directional Focusing of Charged Particles in Crossed Electric and Magnetc Fields. Arkiv. Fysik. 2, 195–207 (1950).

248. C. R. McKinney, J. M. McCrea, S. Epstein, H. A. Allen, and H. C. Urey, Improvements in Mass Spectrometers for the Measurement of Small Differences in Isotope Abundance Ratios. Rev. Sci. Instr. 21, 724–730 (1950). Entirely on voltage stabilizers, and other electronic circuits.

249. E. G. Johnson and A. O. Nier, Angular Aberrations in Sector Shaped Electromagnetic Lenses for Focusing Beams of Charged Particles. Phys. Rev. 91, 10–17 (1953). Analysis of superposed electric and magnetic fields; application to purely one or the other, and to a series of both.

250. R. Herzog, Über einen neuen Massenspektrographen mit anastigmatischer Abbildung. Z. Naturforsch. 8a, 191–197 (1953). Electric field and magnetic field with $n = 0$ and $u_1 > 0$.

251. K. Ogata and H. Matsuda, Preliminary Report on a Large Mass Spectrograph Newly Constructed at Osaka University. Z. Naturforsch. 10a, 843–850 (1955). $\theta = \sqrt{2}\pi/3$ electric field, $\rho = 109.3$ cm, followed by $n = 0$, $\theta = \pi/3$ magnet, $\rho = 120$ cm; bending the same way.

252. H. G. Voorhies, Second Order Aberrations in Sector Shaped Electromagnetic Analyzers. Rev. Sci. Instr. 26, 716–717 (1955); Errata 27, 58 (1956). Superposed fields.

253. K. S. Quisenberry, T. T. Scolman, and A. O. Nier, Atomic Masses of H^1, D^2, C^{12}, and S^{32}. Phys. Rev. 102, 1071–1075 (1956). 90° electric field with $\rho = 20$ inches followed by 60° magnetic with $n = u_1 = u_2 = 0$, $\rho = 16$ inches.

254. C. F. Robinson, Second-Order Aberrations in a Modified Mattauch-Type Mass Spectrometer. *Rev. Sci. Instr.* **28**, 777–779 (1957). Entrance face of magnet is cylindrical.

255. E. Wald and H. Liebl, Die Bildfehler des Toriodkondensators. *Z. Naturforsch.* **12a**, 28–33 (1957).

256. H. Hintenberger and L. A. König, Massenspektrometer mit Doppelfokussierung zweiter Ordnung. *Z. Naturforsch.* **12a**, 773–785 (1957). Theory of electric and magnetic field combinations.

257. L. A. König and H. Hintenberger, Massenspektrographen mit korrigierten Bildfehlern. *Nucl. Instr. Methods* **3**, 133–148 (1958). Detailed analysis of electric and magnetic fields in series.

258. H. Hintenberger and L. A. König, Massenspektrograph mit Doppelfokussierung erster Ordnung für alle Massen, die geringe Bildfehler in einem grossen Massenbereich entlang der Photoplatte aufweisen. *Nucl. Instr. Methods* **3**, 250–259 (1958). Electric and magnetic fields.

259. C. M. Stevens, J. Terandy, G. Lobell, J. Wolfe, M. Beyer, and R. Lewis, The Argonne 100-inch Radius Double-Focusing Mass Spectrometer. *Proc. Intern. Conf. Nuclidic Masses, Hamilton, Ont., 1960*, pp. 403–417. Univ. of Toronto Press, Toronto, 1961. $75°$ electric field, $\rho = 100$ inches, followed by reversed curvature magnet with $\theta = 110°$, $n = 0$, $u_1 = 36.5°$, $u_2 = -35°$; $\rho = 100$ inches.

260. A. O. Nier, Small General Purpose Double-Focusing Mass Spectrometer. *Rev. Sci. Instr.* **31**, 1127–1132 (1960). $90°$ electric field followed by $60°$ uniform magnetic field (with $\rho = 2$ inches) bending the same way.

261. J. H. Futrell and C. D. Miller, Tandem Mass Spectrometer for Study of Ion-Molecule Reactions. *Rev. Sci. Instr.* **37**, 1521–1526 (1966).

262. I. Takeshita, Matrix Representation for Calculation of the Second Order Aberration in Ion Optics. *Z. Naturforsch.* **21a**, 9–14 (1966).

263. I. Takeshita, Mattauch-Herzog Type Mass Spectrograph with a Two Stage Electrostatic Field. *Z. Naturforsch.* **21a**, 14–25 (1966).

264. H. Matsuda, S. Fukumoto, Y. Kuroda, and M. Nojiri, A New Mass Spectrograph with Very Large Dispersion. *Z. Naturforsch.* **21a**, 25–33 (1966). Electric field bends to right; then $n = 1$ magnet bends to left with great dispersion, strong axial but no radial focusing; then $n = 0$ magnet bends to left and supplies radial focusing.

265. J. Geerk, Ein neuer hochauflösender Massenspektrograph. *Z. Naturforsch.* **21a**, 34–36 (1966). Electric then magnetic field.

266. F. A. White and L. Forman, Four Stage Mass Spectrometer of Large Radius. *Rev. Sci. Instr.* **38**, 355–359 (1967). Electric, magnetic, magnetic and electric fields in series, all of $90°$; magnets with $n = u_1 = u_2 = 0$; all radii are 50.8 cm.

267. I. Takeshita, Mattauch-Herzog Type Mass Spectrograph with Corrected β-Dependent Image Defects for all Masses. *Rev. Sci. Instr.* **38**, 1361–1367 (1967). Two stage electric field plus uniform magnetic field.

Auxiliary Instrumentation

268. W. C. Elmore, M. W. Garrett, I. E. Dayton, F. C. Shoemaker, and R. F. Mozley, Measurement of Two-Dimensional Fields. *Rev. Sci. Instr.* **25**, 480–489 (1954).

269. C. Germain, Bibliographical Review of the Methods of Measuring Magnetic Fields. *Nucl. Instr. Methods* **21**, 17–46 (1963).

270. J. Camplan and R. Meunier, Simple Method of Measurement of Magnetic Field Indices. *Nucl. Instr. Methods* **31**, 192–194 (1964).
271. P. H. Rose, R. P. Bastide, N. B. Brooks, J. Airy, and A. B. Wittkower, Description of a Device to Measure Ion Beam Emittance. *Rev. Sci. Instr.* **35**, 1283–1285 (1964).
272. A. E. S. Green and R. J. Berkley, Instrument for Designing Uniform Field Spectrometers. *Rev. Sci. Instr.* **37**, 414–415 (1966).
273. A. Van Steenberger, Evaluation of Particle Beam Phase Space Measurement Techniques. *Nucl. Instr. Methods* **51**, 245–253 (1967).
274. K. L. Brown, A First and Second Order Matrix Theory for the Design of Beam Transport Systems and Charged Particle Spectrometers. SLAC-75. Stanford Linear Accelerator Center, July 1967.
275. P. Shapiro, FORTRAN Programs for First Order Calculation of Properties of Beam Transport Systems, Cyclotron Rpt. No. 4, NRL Rpt. 6710, June 20, 1968. Naval Research Lab. Washington, D.C.

Author Index

The numbers indicate reference numbers under which the authors' works are listed in the Bibliography, pages 236–252. Italic numbers in parentheses indicate the pages on which a reference is referred to in the text.

Subject Index